CUCKOO IN THE NEST

CUCKOO IN THE NEST
Sally Sheringham

Barrie & Jenkins
London

First published in 1989 by
Barrie & Jenkins Ltd
289 Westbourne Grove
London W11 2QA

This book is a work of fiction
and any resemblance between characters portrayed and real persons,
living or dead, is purely coincidental.

British Library Cataloguing in Publication Data

Sheringham, Sally
Cuckoo in the nest
I. Title
823'.914 [F]

ISBN 0–7126–2198–9

Typeset and printed by Butler & Tanner Ltd
Frome and London

To My Parents, With Love

Sexual intercourse began
In nineteen sixty-three ...
Between the end of the Chatterley ban
And the Beatles' first LP.

Philip Larkin

ACKNOWLEDGEMENTS

'Annus Mirabilis' taken from HIGH WINDOWS by Philip Larkin, reprinted by permission of Faber & Faber Ltd.

Extract from THE LION, THE WITCH AND THE WARDROBE by permission of C. S. Lewis Pte Ltd.

THE TALE OF MRS. TITTLEMOUSE by Beatrix Potter, copyright © Frederick Warne & Co., 1910. Reproduced by permission of Penguin Books Ltd.

THE TALE OF MR. TOD by Beatrix Potter, copyright © Frederick Warne & Co., 1912. Reproduced by permission of Penguin Books Ltd.

SUMMER HOLIDAY (Welch/Bennett) © 1963, reproduced by permission of EMI Music Publishing Ltd, T/AS Elstree Music, London WC2H 0EA.

BLUE SUEDE SHOES, Carl Lee Perkins, and JAILHOUSE ROCK, Jerry Leiber and Mike Stoller, used by kind permission of Carlin Music Corporation, 14 New Burlington Street, London W1X 2LR.

SWEET LITTLE SIXTEEN, Chuck Berry, © 1958 100% Jewel Music Pub. Co. Ltd, reproduced by permission of Warner/Chappell Music.

ROUND AND AROUND, Chuck Berry, © 1958 100% Jewel Music Pub. Co. Ltd, reproduced by permission of Warner/Chappell Music.

THE NIGHT HAS A THOUSAND EYES, Victor Young, 100% Famous/Chappell.

I CAN'T STOP LOVING YOU, Don Gibson, © 1962 Acuff Rose Publications Inc., reproduced by permission of Acuff Rose and Opryland Music Ltd.

SEALED WITH A KISS, P. Udell and G. Geld, © 1960 United Artists Co. Inc., reproduced by permission of CPP/Belwin Inc. and International Music Publications.

CHAMPION THE WONDER HORSE, words and music by Marilyn Keith and Norman Luboff, © 1956 Walton Music Inc., reproduced by kind permission of MCA Music Ltd.

Part One

CHAPTER ONE

This summer, which started so brillyantly, has turned into a whole tin of worms, read my diary entry for 7 August 1963. *One is beginning to smell a rat round every corner, and I can't help wondering how it's all going to end. Let's hope not in tears!*

But to start at the 'brillyant' start.

'Blimey O'Reilly!' I yelled over the roar of a car going too fast for its own good, fields and farm animals and cottages helter-skeltering by in a green and brown blur. 'Blimey O'Reilly, Dan, your driving's worse than Mr Toad's!'

I'd been storing up 'blimey O'Reilly' for days, and what better time to give it its first airing than racing through England's green and pleasant land with your brother and sister and no parents to tell you off for swearing?

But we were going far too fast. It was one thing to be frightened, another to be *terrified,* and though you wanted to laugh and cry and scream and whoop and hold your breath and look and not look and burst with happiness and be frightened to death all at once, a bit of you wanted to scream 'But what if we don't die? I don't want to spend my life as a vegetable with tubes up my nose, thank you very much.' But you didn't want to be called a spoilsport so you simply pretended your sister's small, cold, white hand was the brake and gripped on to it for dear life.

'Poop, poop!' said Dan looking round (keep your eyes on the *road*), a happy smile on his face (and he only needed a cap, goggles and gauntleted gloves and he'd have been Mr Toad to a T), his hair fluttering and dancing in the breeze like a host of daffodils, his ears red as beetroots though he couldn't have been hot with the one-hell-of-a-breeze blustering through the open window upon which his bare elbow rested as casually as a Post Office van driver's, and if a pretty girl had appeared he'd have jammed on his brakes and *wolf-whistled,* he was in that kind of devil-may-care mood. 'One has to live dangerously now and again – good for the blood pressure,' he shouted in his new man's voice, swerving unnecessarily wide round

9

a bicycle. 'That's my motto for the summer, by the way: Live Dangerously.'

I longed to say it might be yours but it's not mine and please just go a *trifle* slower, you only passed your test a fortnight ago and aren't *used* to driving fast, and have you remembered this isn't Daddy's new Jaguar but Mummy's old Morris whose floor could cave in or a wheel fall off at any moment? But instead you just grinned and bore it.

A long lean red car with frowning bumpers began to overtake us. Its driver, in sharp black sun-glasses and matching slick-as-pitch hair, sat hunched over the wheel. A toy dog nodded in time to the pop music which blasted like a funfair through the open windows.

'I'm going to get that bugger,' said Dan. 'Hold on to your hats, girls.'

'We aren't wearing any,' said Hattie but her pale voice was whisked away on the wind.

'Come on, baby,' Dan said to the weary old Morris, rocking backwards and forwards to encourage her. 'Come on, me little beauty.' But though the little beauty showed willing it was no match for a red racing demon which vanished over the horizon in a puff of smoke.

'Ruddy maniac,' snorted Dan and said we'd better ease up or the big end would go and Hattie and I laughed because 'big end' sounded rude and I said yes, Mummy's car isn't *geared up* to go fast and we laughed again, partly at my joke but mainly because it was such a relief everything was returning to normal, to be able to see things as they really were and not as a speeded-up cartoon, to talk instead of roar. We released our grip on each other's hand and I wanted to say, though I didn't in case Dan called me soppy, that I felt the happiest I'd ever felt in my whole life.

'Never mind, Dan,' I said. 'I bet he hasn't got cricket bats and suitcases and guitars and sisters in *his* car to slow him up.'

'No, all he had was a vile nodding dog,' said Hattie, who was two years, six months younger than me and would have been much prettier if she didn't wear spectacles. They were little round pink ones that made her look wise before her time. The first time I saw them, neatly folded on her bedside table, they looked the loneliest spectacles in the world and nearly made me cry.

'Gee whizz,' said Dan who was seven years, three months older than me and, apart from one other, was the handsomest boy I knew. 'If there's one thing in this world I loathe it's a nodding dog,' and he relaxed his checked shoulders and lit a Player's.

'And big woolly dice hanging from the mirror, you said,' I said.

'Yeah and those too.'

'Same here,' I said because Dan's opinions were mine too.

'Same here,' said Hattie because she was just a copycat.

'Having said that, I know that bloke,' said Dan, his cigarette smoke whisking away on the breeze. 'He's a mate of mine. That's why I was trying to catch up with him.'

Dan had a *mate* (he'd never used that word before; friend or pal, but not mate – wasn't that what animals did?) with a nodding dog in the back of his car! All his friends up till now had been well-behaved, well-spoken boys from school, whose fathers drove Wolsleys or Rovers or Jaguars or Bentleys or Daimlers.

'Bet you don't. Bet you're just saying that.'

'Bet I'm not. His name's Rick Benton and I met him at a club in Ealing, though funnily enough he's from Norfolk. He's a mechanic at Brewsters. We dig the same sort of music.'

'How can you *dig* music?' said Hattie. 'Don't you mean flower bed instead of music?'

'It all sounds most infra *dig* to me,' I said.

'You know the trouble with you two? You just aren't hip to the latest lingo,' said Dan and started to sing loudly in an American accent about being the kind of guy who likes to roam around.

Having common friends, swearing, smoking, living dangerously, driving too fast, 'digging' music ... were these all part and parcel of becoming a man? If so, I preferred Dan as a boy.

'It's like the start of an Enid Blyton book, isn't it,' I said to shut him up.

'Are you implying I drive like Noddy?' said Dan.

'No – us. Three children setting off to spend the summer holidays with their grandmother in a big old creaky house in Norfolk. Who knew what adventures would be awaiting them?'

'Perhaps Clifford, their granny's dog, has turned into a werewolf,' said Hattie.

'Or Jack the trusty cowman has turned into a blunderbuss-wielding murderer,' said Dan. 'Or perhaps Granny herself has turned into a wicked witch. By the way, I can only count two children in this car.'

'You can't be a *man*,' I said. 'The only men in Enid Blyton books are either fathers or crooks.'

'Who have black beards and eyes too close together,' said Hattie.

'And are rough and rude and have fags dangling out of their mouths and say bloody and blimey.'

'What makes you fink I'm not going to talk common and say bloody and blimey all summer?' said Dan, squinting round at us, a

11

fag dangling out of his mouth like Andy Capp. 'Bloody, blimey, bloody, blimey ... Or maybe I'll settle for older brother. But make sure he's a dashing, handsome, witty, debonair, yummy, scrummy old brother with twinkling blue eyes and a mischievous grin.'

'Isn't he a vile bighead?' said Hattie. 'Go on then, Sarah. Let's pretend we're in an Enid Blyton story and you read it.'

'Are you sitting comfortably?'

'No, thanks to Dan's stupid fishing rod.'

'Then I'll begin. Dan, Sarah and Hattie Hillington waved goodbye to their mummy and daddy who were going to France on a second honeymoon, and set off for their granny's in a little green car with – er, wood bits round it. It was a simply spiffing July morning, the sun was, er, grinning, the clouds were ...'

'Bleating,' said Hattie. 'They look like sheep.'

'... dancing across the sky like cotton-wool ballerinas.'

'Or how about "The clouds were frilly white knickers tossed into the air by voluptuous strip-tease artists"?'

'Dan, that's rude!'

'So? I feel like being rude. Exceedingly, disgustingly rude.'

'Why, exactly?'

'Because, exactly, sisters dear, after a lifetime of being governed by middle-class rules ...'

'Mummy says we're upper middle class.'

'To misquote Mandy Rice-Davies, she would, wouldn't she ... and public school regulations, of doing what I'm told and never stepping out of line, the shackles have loosened. For the first time, you see before you a free man,' and he turned and grinned and rolled his eyes like a village idiot.

'I prefer you the way you were, as an unfree boy,' I said. 'You sound like an escaped convict.'

'And look like one,' said Hattie.

'That's because that's what I am,' shouted Dan, aiming his cigarette end at an oncoming bubble car. 'I'm like a man who's spent eighteen years behind hypothetical bars! Man was born free but is everywhere in chains. Who said that?'

'The crocodile in *Peter Pan*.'

'Spotty Dog in *The Woodentops*,' said Hattie. 'I'm not in chains, are you, Sarah?'

'Yes, you are,' said Dan. 'You can't see them, but they're there all right. You behave not how *you* want to but how this hypocritical out-of-touch class-ridden society of ours wants you to. Well, knickers to all that, I say. From now on, I do as I please. I'm in my prime and the world's my oyster.' He looked round and grinned again, and his hair had blown all over the place and made him look like the Wild Man of Borneo which made me want to die laughing.

'Is that why you're coming out with all these *pearls* of wisdom?' I said. 'You know – oyster – pearl.'

'Or perhaps Dan's hinting he's going to marry Pearl Carr.'

'He can't – Teddy Johnson got there first,' I said.

'Oh, God, you two,' said Dan. 'Can't you see what I'm driving at?'

'Yes, the hedge if you don't keep your eyes on the road!' I screeched, and Hattie and I went into hysterics and Dan shrugged and sang about a man called Johnny B. Goode.

'*Dan* be good, don't you mean,' Hattie said.

'Yes, you won't be able to be disgustingly rude at Granny's,' I said. 'You know how strict she is about manners and meal times. And you'll have to organise the cricket match because Daddy won't be there. *And* help with the harvest. *And* the Shotestead Show.'

'*And* be polite to the great aunts and be told, *You're the last of the Hillington line*,' Hattie and I said in unison, for that was what they always said, and Dan always blushed because what they were hinting at was that if he didn't have four babies to be on the safe side, at least two of them boys, the Hillington line would die out.

'Sod that for a game of soldiers,' said Dan, lighting *another* Player's. 'Anyway, I have a few wheezes of my own for this summer.'

'You'll end up with *loads* of wheezes if you keep on smoking at that rate of knots,' said Hattie.

'What wheezes, Dan?' I said, a small uncertain feeling creeping into my heart. Being in no-man's-land between school and Cambridge meant he was going through a strange phase but even so, I couldn't imagine him doing anything other than the things he always did at Granny's: helping with the harvest and the Show, going fishing and to Young Farmers' meetings with Rupert and playing games with us.

Dan shrugged. 'A man's gotta do what a man's gotta do.'

'Stop showing off, Dan. What?'

'I'm not going to tell you yet, in case it doesn't come off. A chap has to have some secrets from his sisters.'

'No, he doesn't.'

'Give us a hint,' said Hattie.

'It may bring me fame and fortune,' said Dan. 'And on the other hand it may not. I'll tell you when we arrive.'

'You'll still help with harvest, won't you?' I said.

'What's the point of earning a pittance when there's a chance of making a packet?'

'There's more to life than making money,' I said. 'And Granny will be disappointed – furious. She might even decide not to leave you the farm.'

'So? What's a few hundred acres when there's a chance I could have thousands of girls worshipping the air I breathe. Anyway, I doubt Granny will mind what I get up to. According to Pa, she's gone a bit gaga.'

'What, like that smelly man with food in his beard who wanders down the middle of the road muttering about the Germans?' cried Hattie with tears in her voice. 'Granny isn't doing *that*, is she?'

'Blast, no,' said Dan in a Norfolk accent.

'Well, what then?'

'That I don't rightly know, bor,' said Dan. 'We'll have to wait and see, won't we.'

The thought of Granny being anything other than dear, dignified, delightful Granny, made you want to cry.

'It was that there blasted old bugger of a winter what done it,' said Dan. 'Right as rain she was till then. Bugger that blasted old bugger of a winter.'

Just the thought of that blasted old bugger of a winter made you shiver, even on a summer's day. Arctic conditions, the papers had described it; the coldest for a hundred years, when you thought you'd gone colour-blind because the whole country, even London, remained snow-white for days and weeks and months and you'd forgotten what a green blade of grass or a red pillar-box looked like, when the air was so icy-raw it took your breath away, and even the teachers wore hats and coats and scarves in the classroom, and the ink iced up so we had to write in pencil, and sheep on high ground and old people in their beds died because their blood had frozen, and Mr Gaitskell the Labour party leader died because his lungs packed in, and 'When will it be over?' was on everyone's lips. It reminded you of Narnia in *The Lion, the Witch and the Wardrobe* (always winter and no Christmas) except there was no magical lion called Aslan to come along and start the thaw. But if ever we moaned, Daddy said, 'We must think of poor old Granny and count our blessings.'

Granny certainly gave us something to boast about at school. The conversation would go: 'A bottle of beer exploded all on its own in our pantry.'

'There were icicles on the inside of our windows.'

'Our milk took a whole day to thaw out.'

'When I woke up this morning my breath was like a white fog.'

And then my voice, quiet and calm because it had more impact

14

than a loud, showing-off one: 'Because there's nothing between Norfolk and the North Pole, it is fit for neither man nor beast. My grandmother has eight lorry drivers staying with her because their lorries got stuck in a drift at the end of her drive. They have no telephone, running water or electricity, and peel potatoes by candle- and firelight. When the candles and coal run out they'll have to go to bed at four o'clock like in the olden days. When the potatoes run out they'll have to eat rats or starve to death. They are cut off from the outside world and if one of them gets appendicitis they'll have to wave flags at passing helicopters. If there are no passing helicopters, the person will experience an agonising death.' And I looked round in a 'beat that' sort of way and none of them could, not even Valerie Lake.

One good thing came out of the wicked old bugger of a winter: evidence that I had magical powers. I tried them out one night and the very next morning the country awoke to the sound of drip, drip, drip.

At Granny's I'd start up my magic again, in order to rid her of any lingering effects of the old bugger of a winter. And this time I'd go the whole hog and do it properly....

We were driving through rolling Suffolk countryside now, past old thatched cottages with rabbit hutches in their gardens and new red-brick houses with gnomes or crazy paving in their gardens, and stopped for petrol in a once-pretty village that had been ruined by a red rash of council houses. Dan said to the petrol attendant, 'Fill her up, pal', and no 'please'. And the attendant, a drainpipe-trousered Teddy-boy type, just said, 'Sure, mate', without turning a hair. What was the country coming to!

'By the way,' Dan said as we thundered off, 'I promised Ma we'd ring her when we arrive to tell her everything's okay.'

'Why shouldn't everything be – okay?' If Dan could say it so could I though we weren't supposed to, the way we weren't supposed to say 'thanks'.

'If Granny's really gaga she won't be able to look after you – feed you and stuff. You don't want to end up starving to death, do you?'

True I was always hungry at Granny's, but I couldn't imagine *starving*.

'If she can keep eight big lorry drivers alive just on potatoes she can keep us alive,' I said. 'If the worst comes to the worst we can run wild like deer, and eat berries and mushrooms – can't we, Hattie?'

15

'I suppose so. Anyway, Aunt Lynette'll be nearby.'

'Have you ever seen her make anything other than a gin and tonic?' said Dan.

'There's Mrs B to keep an eye on us,' I said.

'Didn't Ma tell you?' Dan said, lighting another Player's. 'Jesus.'

'No. What?'

'Er ... she's snuffed it. The old bugger of a winter again.'

I stared at a row of cottage chimneys. None of them had smoke coming out because it was a sunny day. Mrs B always had smoke coming out of her 'chimbley' because she said it gave the place a nice welcome, a fire did. I didn't cry the way you're meant to when you're told someone you love has died but I did have an aching feeling deep inside that summers at Granny's were never going to be the same again.

'How come you knew and we didn't, Dan?' I said crossly.

'I can't remember to tell you everything that goes on.'

'Just think,' said Hattie, 'we'll never again hear her say ...'

'... *I'll raise my hat*,' we said for that was Mrs B's very favourite expression, regardless of whether she was wearing one.

'Poor Jack,' I said. 'He must be lonely on his own.'

'And poor Granny,' said Hattie. 'I bet she misses him as much as Jack. Well, almost as much, anyway.'

'Actually,' said Dan, 'Granny's got someone to take her place.'

'No one could take Mrs B's place,' I muttered. 'Honestly. No one tells us anything.'

'A young girl by the name of Dawn Potts, apparently,' he said, driving unnecessarily fast round a z-bend.

When Mr Beaver first mentioned the name 'Aslan' in *The Lion, the Witch and the Wardrobe,* Peter had felt brave and adventurous, Susan had felt as if some delightful strain of music had just floated by, Lucy had got that feeling when you realise it's the beginning of summer, and Edmund had felt a sensation of mysterious horror. On hearing the name 'Dawn Potts', my feeling most closely resembled Edmund's, plus an urge to be car sick.

'Let's sing a song to cheer ourselves up,' I said. 'And please don't light another foul cigarette, Dan, I'm feeling as sick as a dog already.'

So Dan sang a stupid song about seven little girls sitting in the back seat a-kissing and a-hugging with Fred.

'What a vile song,' said Hattie.

'Yes and even if there was someone called Fred sitting in the back seat I wouldn't dream of kissing or hugging him, would you, Hattie?'

'Certainly not.'

'Oh, hoity-toity,' said Dan. 'All right, we'd better go for something tamer for the prim and proper members of the party.'

Eventually we agreed "Summer Holiday" by Cliff Richard would be appropriate. So we sang it at the tops of our voices, Dan doing descants, and oh, this was the life!

We were now in Norfolk and it was time to look out for the things we always looked out for at this stage of the journey.

The piebald horse wasn't in his normal place by the gate in the long thin meadow. Don't say the old bugger of a winter had got him, too. But there he was, under a chestnut tree, and he can't have been a he because he'd had a foal! It was black and white which meant its father must have been piebald, too. The foal looked round at us but the piebald horse didn't. She had seen enough cars in her time.

'Oh, isn't it sweet!' cried Hattie. 'We must remember to tell Granny.'

'Boy, that horse must be as old as I am,' said Dan. 'You'd have thought she'd be past it.'

'Past what?'

'Having a foal.'

'Eighteen isn't too old to have a foal, is it?' said Hattie.

'Horses are like dogs, aren't they?' I said. 'One of our years is worth four of theirs. That makes her ...'

'Seventy-two.'

'Blimey O'Reilly,' said Hattie. 'That would be like Granny having a baby.'

'Does it hurt more, having a foal when you're old?' I asked.

'Don't ask me,' said Dan. 'I'm not an old horse.'

'Well, does it hurt for a young one?'

'I'm not a young one either! Yeah, I expect so. A bit, anyway.'

'As much as having a filling at the dentist without an injection?'

'Or falling out of a tree and breaking your arm?' suggested Hattie.

'I'm only guessing, but it's probably the same as being tremendously constipated.'

So that was all right then. As long as the piebald horse hadn't suffered too much.

There was no washing on the line outside the little old woman's tumbledown cottage. 'Perhaps she's died,' I said. 'Or got a spindrier,' said Dan. 'Or changed her washing day to a Tuesday,' said Hattie. And as for whether or not the scarecrow was wearing his straw hat ... We rounded the bend, and *'Blimey O'Reilly,'* we yelled.

It felt the same as watching an interesting nature programme on the BBC and your older brother flipping to the commercial channel (without asking first), where American cops and robbers are being rude and shouting; for the field of golden wheat had turned into a forest of red monstrosities with car ports and no garden fences.

'Holy macaroon! How foul,' Hattie said.

'One less field to provide food,' said Dan.

'People have to have a roof over their heads,' I said.

'They also have to have food in their bellies,' said Dan and muttered something I didn't catch about birth control.

'I wonder what happened to the scarecrow,' said Hattie.

'Probably got flattened by a bulldozer.'

'*Dan!*'

'All right then, he's probably sitting with his feet up reading his horoscope in the *Daily Sketch*.'

'Don't be silly,' said Hattie. 'Scarecrows can't read.'

'You don't say!' said Dan.

We survived the z-bend that had on the left a brambly wood concealing a black bottomless pond in which a milkman had drowned on New Year's Eve in 1952, which always prompted Dan to mutter 'Milko! Milko!' in a ghostly voice. We soared over the hump-back bridge that took your breath away and passed Granny's gardener's cottage, hiding slyly behind hollyhocks and sunflowers, and the silvery, slippery snake in the grass of a river where you sometimes saw a one-legged heron. Then we were turning off at the long, low, winking Rat-catchers public house, past the tiny thatched church that had a corner of the graveyard reserved for Hillington bodies, past the Milly Molly Mandy house and a row of dark cottages with a fern in a brass bowl or a china carthorse in each downstairs window, past the fighting sisters' house and the Untidiest Farm in Norfolk.

And now at last we were in the heart of England's green and pleasant land – Granny's land, with not an eyesore in sight, just field upon field of glorious golden wheat and oats and barley, of dark green sugar beet and peas and potatoes, stretching on and on until they reached the sky.

'Blast it's bootiful to be home,' said Dan not looking where he was going and having to jam on his brakes to avoid crashing into Jack on his blue tractor.

'There's not room,' I said. 'You'll have to reverse.'

'Want a bet?' said Dan, driving up the bank so the old Morris was almost on its side. 'This is the summer for playing with fire, yeah?'

'For dicing with death, don't you mean,' I screamed. 'We'll tip over.'

'Want a bet?' said Dan, driving further up so Hattie was on top of me. 'How ya doing, Jack?' he said leaning unnecessarily far out of the window.

'Good to see you, Master Dan,' he roared over the tractor's chug-chug. His face looked leaner but that was hardly surprising; Mrs B had been a very good cook. 'And you two little uns,' and he bent down to look at us. 'Blast, you look as though you could do with some good old country air, an' there's no shortage of that round these parts, tha's for sure,' and he threw back his head and laughed, revealing teeth which were starting to go the same way as Elizabeth the First's.

'It's Dan's awful driving that's made us pale, actually, Jack,' I said but he didn't hear.

'You'll find a few changes up at the hall,' he said and winked at Dan. 'Cheerio for now then.'

'See ya, Jack,' said Dan and by a miracle we ended up back on the road in an upright position. 'I wish he wouldn't call me Master Dan. It makes me sound like something out of *The Archers* or Thomas Hardy.'

'And I wish you wouldn't say "ya" instead of "you",' said Hattie. 'It makes you sound like a Teddy Boy or something out of *The Rag Trade*.'

'Why did he wink?' I said. 'Is there something *naughty* going on? If there is I bet it's something to do with that Dawn Potts person. I know I'm going to hate her. I can feel it in my bones. As soon as you mentioned her name I felt sick, and if that isn't a bad omen I don't know what is.'

We turned left at the crossroads, past the row of flint and brick cottages including the one in which Mrs B had died, down the narrow, cow parsley lane, and in through the white gates past the birds'-messy sign that said Gressenham Hall and up the crunchy drive, past the shady rhododendrons that made ace hiding places, past the park and lawns on the right and the lilac tree, the chestnut tree and rose beds on the left.

'Nothing's changed so far,' said Hattie. 'Apart from the weeds in the drive.'

'We haven't seen the house yet,' I said. 'Five ...'

'Four,' we yelled. 'Three. Two. One. *Zero!*'

And there, basking in the sun and half-hidden by the copper beech, was Granny's house.

CHAPTER TWO

Miss Rose believed in magic and even at her age dressed a bit like a fairy in flowery dresses with white collars and stiff petticoats and red-button shoes. She often talked, in her little-girl voice, about goblins and witches and wizards.

'The wicked ice wizard is behind this fearful weather, girls,' she had said, standing at the ice-fern classroom window wringing her cherry-mittened hands. 'Why, this winter will go down in the history books as the cruellest ever.'

'Does that mean the wicked ice wizard will go down in the history books, too?' said Sheila Page. 'How strange, I always thought that the weather was caused by cloud formation.'

Miss Rose's cheeks matched her bobble hat. 'You're quite right. I . . .'

'So why did you tell us it was the wicked ice wizard?' persisted Sheila and crikey she was brave, she would grow up to be a riding instructress or a trade union leader or a prime minister, even.

After the class Sheila Page said The Thorn was a frustrated old spinster, a brainless crank trying to fill our heads with ruddy mumbo-jumbo. Why, she didn't have the intellectual capability to teach a kindergarten and she bet two quid she hadn't been to teacher's training college, let alone university. Valerie Lake said how could anyone take a woman with a northern accent and child's shoes seriously, and how typical of this day and age that the state schools should get the best teachers and the private ones the dross. She was going to complain about her, in the strongest possible terms, to her father who was on the board of governors.

During the Easter holidays I used my magic formula to stop Miss Rose getting the sack, not because I wanted her to be my teacher so much as because if she didn't have us she'd be stuck in her tiny, terraced, tomcat-smelling house with her mother who looked and sounded, according to Valerie Lake, like a cross between Ena Sharples and Minnie Caldwell in *Coronation Street*. And the spell obviously worked because there she was at the front of the class, blinking and beaming behind her pink swept-up spectacles on the first day of the summer term.

But I should have eased up on the magic, for two days before the end of term she said she was leaving, 'for a rest, my pets', and Valerie Lake muttered that we all knew the real reason.

There was much speculation about Miss Rose's replacement.

Valerie Lake said at least we couldn't have anyone worse than Miss Rose sat on a pin, Miss Rose, and Veronica, my best friend, tossed her yellow ponytail and said yes we could, we could easily get a smelly, deaf old crone like Miss Grimes, who stank of ciggies and thought the Beatles were insects, and Susan Fisher said given the choice, her ideal teacher would be young and kind and pretty and clever and laugh a lot and most of all be *with it*. Rosie Alston (who needed a brassiere at her age!) said wouldn't it be a hoot if we got a man, a young, shy man whom we could tease and we all groaned and told her she was boy-mad.

When the classroom door opened, we scraped back our chairs and slouched to attention. But instead of the waddling, spitting maths teacher, Miss Braithwaite, it was the marching, dry-mouthed headmistress, Miss Sargent. And marching in imitation and winking at Miriam Poole to show this wasn't the way he normally walked, was someone who would have made you gasp out loud if you had been on your own. He was the tallest, most handsome man I'd ever seen, handsomer than William Tell or Robin Hood or Adam Faith or Cliff Richard or President Kennedy or even Dan.

He had slicked-back hair as black and glossy as the healthiest raven's feathers in the world, with a ruffled bit at the front that was in danger of falling forward, lean cheeks and a lop-sided, smiling mouth. He pulled a face at the back of the Sargent Major's head then raised his finger to his lips but he needn't have done that; not one of us would have betrayed him, not even Rosie Alston.

He was wearing a tightish pair of black corduroy trousers (please not too tight to be a teacher) and no jacket, just a jumper that wasn't quite a Sloppy Joe but would have been if it had been a shade baggier, with the weeniest knot of a tie showing, like a shy, embarrassed animal peering over the top of a navy-blue hedge, and I racked my brains but I couldn't think of one man teacher I'd ever come across who didn't wear cavalry twill trousers and a tweed jacket with leather elbows. I didn't see his shoes till later (please let them be sensible brown lace-ups or even Hush Puppies) but they weren't shoes at all but funny boots with elastic sides. Chelsea boots, Dan said later, and the very latest thing; the Beatles wore them and he wouldn't say no to a pair.

'Sit down, girls,' said Miss Sargent and the scraping of sixteen

21

chairs hopefully muffled our hysterical whispers. We sat down and there wasn't one pair of fingers uncrossed apart from Anne Pond's, who took life very seriously because her parents were divorced.

'Come along, girls, settle down, settle down,' said Miss Sargent because Rosie Alston was having a coughing/giggling fit. 'Now I have great pleasure in introducing you ...' and you couldn't help noticing that her voice had turned softer, like tough career women's voices in films when the man they love appears at their side ' ... to Mr Richards', and she turned and grinned her false teeth at him.

He had been standing with his arms folded and one knee bent as casually as a pop singer on one of Dan's posters, but now he turned to Miss Sargent and gave a small smiling bow.

'Mr Richards, I expect you'll be delighted to hear, girls, is going to be your form and English, er, master next term. He is an ex-RAF fighter pilot, and I for one feel most privileged that he has agreed to join our humble establishment.'

She beamed at us, her bosoms heaving with pride under her peach twinset, and if we had bosoms they'd be heaving, too.

'Mr Richards kindly agreed to meet you today so that you can get to know each other before the term ends, and so that he can set you some homework to do over the summer holidays. Well, I'll leave you in Mr Richards's capable care,' and, flashing her teeth at him one last time, she strode off.

We were now alone with him. How *thrilling!* All eyes were on him as he sauntered to the front of the teacher's desk, perched on it and lifted his booted feet on to the edge of Mary Jones's desk (and I'd have given her five bob to swap places at that moment). He sat there with his legs apart, his forearms resting on his knees, his long, gentle artist's or musician's fingers relaxed and dangling. Then, half-smiling and one eyebrow raised quizzically, he looked at each of us in turn (look at me longer, I'm far more interesting than her – and her – and her).

His eyes were blue or maybe green; whichever, they were bright, sharp, penetrating eyes that had seen more, been around more as Dan would say, than anyone's you'd ever encountered before; they were the sort of eyes that understood exactly what it was you were thinking.

Still half-smiling, he said in a deep rich voice that sounded like Aslan's in fact, or James Stewart's without the American accent and with a delicious lilt to it, 'Do you know, I've never been in the same room with so many pretty girls before ... Ah, I tell a lie. There was a certain night in Bangkok, but that's another story.'

How flattering to be compared to girls living in an exotic place like Bangkok! And if Rosie Alston giggled because he'd said 'cock' I would personally snip off her ginger pigtails later. But she didn't.

'And now girls, I have a question for you – who can tell me how they know I'm not related to Cliff Richard?'

I shot up my hand like a rocket. I know, I know, ask me, Sir, please; God I'll never ask you for anything ever again if you make him pick me.

'Because your surname ends in "s" and his doesn't,' said Valerie Lake triumphantly and it wasn't fair because she hadn't put her hand up ... But wasn't there another reason? Didn't Dan say Cliff Richard's real name was something like Harry Worth or Cobweb or – what *was* it? – and he changed it because it wasn't glamorous enough? I hesitated. Say I was wrong, I'd be a laughing-stock. But say I was right ...! I half put my hand up but it was too late; Mr Richards had changed the subject.

'Now girls, as well as teaching you about grammar and syntax and précis, I plan to teach you about Life with a capital L. What do you say to that?'

What could we say but yes please and nod and smile, and Valerie Lake, in order as always to have the last word, said 'That would be very nice', and Mr Richards said 'Did I hear someone say the word *nice*? For future reference, there's no such word as "nice" in my book. Interesting, fascinating, delightful, agreeable, anything you like so long as it isn't "nice". All right? Now, I plan to broaden your horizons, teach you a bit about the outside world. Hands up those who've seen the outside world – travelled abroad, that is.'

About half the class put up their hands. Mine wasn't among them. Should I put it up anyway and risk him not asking me where I'd been? I'd been to Scotland and on a boat to a sort of island that was a bird sanctuary but I couldn't remember its name. And I was the only one in the class who had ridden on a combine harvester and in a helicopter. But none of them counted as abroad. Unless I pretended I thought he meant 'a Broad'; I'd been on the Norfolk Broads loads of times. But that was babyish. I stared at my inkwell. It would be the absolute limit to catch his eye without my hand up.

'Fair enough,' he said. 'And now let's go round the class and you can all tell me where you're going for your holiday this year. Tell me your names too. Starting with you at the back.'

At least I wasn't as badly off as Vera Patterson, who wasn't going anywhere, and at least he said, 'Never mind, that's fine,' to her. He just nodded when I said a farm in Norfolk. Three people got a 'very nice' because they were going to places like the south of France, and Susan Pritchard got a 'Lovely. Very nice indeed' because she was going to Boston to visit an aunt. Valerie Lake would have probably got a 'Lovely, very nice indeed' if she hadn't gone on and on about her father's yacht and Mr Richards, recognising her as the show-off that she was, simply gave her a nod.

'Anyone been to Yorkshire?' he asked and a few hands, including mine, shot up. He looked round and nodded. 'Good. I spent a holiday on the Yorkshire Moors when I was around your age, and it fuelled my imagination and left a lasting impression on me – I suppose none of you has tackled Emily Brontë's *Wuthering Heights* yet? It conjures up the atmosphere brilliantly, all that suppressed passion and vivid imagery ... Extraordinary family, the Brontës ... But this is my point: you are at an impressionable age and I want your holidays this year to make an *impression on you*. It doesn't matter if you are going to France, Spain, Scunthorpe or your back garden, just so long as something, somewhere, stimulates you, whets your appetite. Your homework for this summer is to keep a diary – not any old diary, mind: what I *don't* want is: "Got up, had bacon and eggs for breakfast, read my comic, kicked the dog." What I want is *colour*; incidents – and it doesn't matter how trivial they are – brought to life through smell and sound and feelings. I don't want to hear how large your father's yacht is or how much he paid for it, I want to be able to *smell* the tang of salt in the air, *picture* the porpoises dance through the waves.'

We thought about this and thick Miriam Poole said, 'Please, Sir, the trouble is I'm only going to a hotel in Bournemouth and nothing exciting ever happens there. It's full of old ladies and really boring.'

Mr Richards stood up and sauntered over to her. 'Your name?'

'Miriam Poole.'

'So, Miriam, you find old ladies boring, do you? What *does* interest you then?'

Miriam went beetroot. She was only interested in her pony Moonshine, but she wasn't going to tell Mr Richards that.

'Do you mean to tell me, Miriam, that not one of these old ladies has a *past*? That not one has anything to say about either of the World Wars they've lived through, the advent of the motor car, the General Strike?'

'Don't know, Sir.'

'Precisely. That's why I want you to keep a diary. Find out. Play detective. Open your eyes to what's going on around you. *Learn*. And I don't want to see the word "boring" appear once. Is that clear?

'I'm already looking forward to reading your accounts,' he said smiling lop-sidedly and rubbing his hands. 'I'll pick my favourite extracts to read out in class. Who knows? I might discover a Samuel – or should I say Samantha? – Pepys among you, or even a modern-day Emily Brontë,' and just at that moment he chose to look at me. Had he instinctively known that *I* would turn out to be the Emily Brontë of the class? As our eyes met, I felt an awakening of an instinct deep within myself, an emotion I had never experienced before.

'Right, any questions, anyone? Anything you like,' he said slapping his thighs.

No one dared ask whether or not he was married, so Rosie Alston asked him how tall he was and he said six foot four, and then someone asked if he could tell us what it was like to be a fighter pilot and he said he'd save that for next term, and then someone asked where he was going for his holiday and he said the Emerald Isle, and only Katherine Preston knew where that was because her mother was Irish.

'Please, Sir – are you Irish, actually? Originally, I mean,' she asked and Mr Richards said, 'To be sure, to be sure', and Katherine said, 'My mother's Irish', and he nodded and smiled but you could tell he just thought she was sucking up. Then, although the bell hadn't gone, he ambled to the back of the class as casually as a man leaving a public house after a drink with friends. At the door he turned and grinned at us all. 'Good luck with your diaries,' he said. 'And be good now, girls. Don't do anything I wouldn't,' and with a wink and a wave he was gone.

As soon as I got home I talked and talked about Mr Richards to anyone who cared to listen.

'Honestly,' I said at supper, 'it's like a miracle. Out of the thousands of dull, dud teachers there are, we've got a brilliant, interesting one.'

'Tall, dark and handsome, too, by the sound of things, eh? Eh?' said Dan infuriatingly, digging me in the ribs. 'If she's like this after one lesson think what she's going to be like after a whole day with the bloke.'

'Well, you'll never know, will you, Dan, because you'll be at Cambridge next term,' I snapped, my cheeks burning.

'I say,' said Dan, 'I do believe my sister's having her first crush.'

'Don't tease, Dan,' said Mummy frowning at him, and Daddy hid his laugh behind his table napkin and Hattie said, 'What's a crush?' and I shouted, 'I hate you, Dan. And you, Daddy, because it's not funny in the slightest', and stumped up to my bedroom, slammed the door, lay on my bed and thought and thought and thought about Mr Richards.

'Sarah is a spirited, sensitive girl . . . Sarah has a vivid imagination' Miss Rose wrote in my school report term after term; exactly the qualities Mr Richards was looking for! I might not be much good at spelling and maths and science, and I might not be the prettiest in the class, but one thing was sure, to be sure; I was going to be the best diary writer.

'Sarah Hillington – or should I say Samantha Pepys – or even Samantha Brontë – would you stand up, please?' Mr Richards would say, and he would look deep into the heart of my soul and we would exchange another of our private, knowing smiles . . .

Tomorrow I would buy a notebook with hard covers that would contain information for my and Mr Richards' eyes only. Meanwhile, I opened my Deadly Secret exercise book at the page headed *IF PEOPLE WERE HORSES*. So far I'd written:

HATTIE: pretty little black pedagree Fell pony; filly. Small boned, inclined to be delicate; broke leg hunting which at times makes her tempramental, as does her artistic nature. Overal sweet-natured, loyal, willing, and inteligent for her age.
ME: rich bay Exmoor; pedagree; outstanding strength and stamina; dependable, brave, VG nature, supurb allrounder, equally at home in showring or galoping over hill and dale on life or death mission. Would keep going until dropped. Sweet natured, spirited, obediant and cheerful at all times. In private calls herself Black Champion to spur her on, because even though a filly shows promise as future Black Beauty or Champion the Wonder Horse (NB this is my aim not always what I am!).
DAN: musculer, spirited, fearless, brave pedagree hunter. Outstanding strength and stamina. Perfect bone structure and fine, inteligent head. Could well develop into Champion the Wonder Horse but too early to say as still a colt. (Owner, beware: go steady on the oats with this one!!!)
MUMMY: Arab show horse. Well-mannered but slightly horghty; prefers the glamour of the show ring to the mud of the hunting field. Enjoys being groomed, having main platted. Very kind with ill foals.
DADDY: black stallion. Impecable pedagree. Broad and strong, equally at home in showground or hunting field. Some qualities similar to Black Beauty, though can be secretive, and a shade obstanate when gets bit between teeth. Sometimes queralous, usually cheerful and spirited. (NB Has sired some exallant foals!!!)
GRANNY: dainty, ladylike grey pedagree Dartmoor. Beautiful

manners, gentle yet spirited, now suitable only for light carriage work (eg taking her mistress to church); entirely to be trusted with foals.
AUNT LYNETTE: high-spirited nervy piebald racehorse; fiery temprament; has strong likes and dislikes. Resembles Ginger in 'Black Beauty' in character (although Aunt L wasn't ill-treated as foal). Mischevous and not to be trusted with foals.
GRANNY P: a plump roan mare. Inclined to bolt food; prone to colic. Inquisative nature and nips if startled, but basically good natured.
VERONICA: thin, nervy, prancy Palameno. Inclined to shy, wouldn't complete a cross-country course and fussy with her food. Handle with cortion at times, tosses head if driven hard. Loyal companion.
And now I proudly added another name to the list:
MR RICHARDS: every horse lover's dream come true – the heavenly, divine, perfect mixture of Black Beauty (gentle, sensative, hard-working, handsome) and Champion the Wonder Horse (fiery, brave high-spirited, handsome) plus a pinch of magical Aslan thrown in for good measure.

And in tiny writing underneath: *I have found my kindled spirit at last!*

27

CHAPTER THREE

Like Toad Hall, Gressenham Hall is a handsome, dignafied old house of mellowed red brick I would write in my diary because Mr Richards was sure to appreciate quotes from the classics. *It isn't vast like a stately home or Valerie Lake's mansion, but it's certainly bigger than average. It is either Queen Ann or Georgian, I'm not sure which, with a conservatry which opens onto the Tea Lawn. If houses were people it would be a friendly, rosy-cheeked gentleman farmer, who in his prime walked with a swing in his step and a sparkle in his eye. These days his step is creaky and his eye dull, and he allows birds to nest in his whiskers and beetles to dwell under his hat but I still love him dearly. He is my haven, and makes me feel the way Black Beauty felt on the last page of the book: 'My troubles are all over and I am at home'.*

'Gee whizz,' said Dan, as we shied and whinnied to a halt outside the front door. 'The old bugger of a winter hasn't half taken its toll.'

The paint on the front door was flaking and the house martins had made a dreadful mess under the eaves. There wasn't the usual vase of roses at the drawing-room window, and several curtains were drawn which made the house look half-blind, or like a hospital. The only sign of human life was a trug full of dead heads in the drive.

'Look at the state of some of that brickwork,' said Dan.

We looked, and listened. Apart from a distant bird orchestra, conducted by a cooing wood pigeon, no one was stirring, not even a mouse.

'You don't think Granny's ... you know, dead,' whispered Hattie.

'Come off it,' said Dan. 'Pa was only talking to her this morning.' But he didn't sound his normal devil-may-care self.

'We aren't getting much of a welcome, are we,' Hattie said in a small voice.

Normally when we arrived three things happened. First, Clifford, Granny's spaniel, bounded up, barking and wagging and licking and jumping, then running in small dizzy circles on the lawn to show how pleased he was to see us.

Second, Mrs Butterworth came waddling round the side of the conservatory, a very stout short person whose eyes went twinkle twinkle and who was like Mrs Tiggywinkle in every way apart from the lack of prickles, wiping her hands on her apron and saying, 'Coo, *Dan*, I'll raise my hat! You've gone and grown as big as an old ox! And how are my two little treasures? Coo, you've both gone and grown, too. I can't keep up with you, that I can't.'

Third, the front door opened and there would be Granny; slim and elegant and smiling, wearing a heathery tweed skirt and a blouse with a brooch and smart grey shoes and medium-high heels. She would have visited Eileen her hairdresser that morning, and she'd be wearing face powder and pale-raspberry-coloured lipstick that wouldn't suit everyone but really suited her.

'Darlings,' she'd say, her arms outstretched. 'Darlings, I can't *tell* you how lovely it is to see you,' and she'd give us each a violet-smelling kiss, standing on tiptoe to give Dan his and saying, 'Dan, you're getting far too tall for your shrinking old Granny' (which prompted Dan later to make a hysterical joke about shrinking violets). Then she'd turn to Mummy (Daddy always came a fortnight later) and say 'Hello, Evelyn dear. Not too much ghastly traffic, I trust?' Then she'd say to Hattie and me, 'Now, darlings, if you peer among the roses you might just find a little something.' And we'd pretend to hunt around, though we'd spotted the red tissue paper from the car, and it would always be a tube of Smarties each. Dan normally got a bar of chocolate – plain, and not hidden among the roses because he was older, but last year Granny gave him one of Grandpa's cigars she'd found at the back of the davenport. He puffed away politely but later told us it tasted like a rancid pre-World-War-One sock.

Today, though, it didn't look as if any of these things were going to happen.

'I'll do a recce,' said Dan, getting out of the car. He marched across the gravel, whistling *From Me to You* like a cheeky but nervous postman, put his head round the front door and shouted 'Anyone at ho-ome?'

He beckoned. Cautiously we followed. Would we find Granny lying on the flagstones, her hand two inches from the telephone which would have saved her life?

The hall was cool and dark and smelt, as it always did, of a rarely used though not unpleasant cupboard.

It looked much the same, too. The lorry drivers hadn't chopped up the umbrella stand for firewood, or the oak chest in which gloves and hats and scarves and road maps and prayer books lived, or the table upon which the telephone sat like a square, black, sleeping cat. Nor had they stolen the portrait of Grandpa's father, a stern frowner of a man with white Father Christmas sidewhiskers though no beard, who according to Dan had been quite a one with the ladies (and if I'd been a lady in those days he certainly wouldn't have been a 'one' with me; he reminded me far too much of Mr Grouser in the Toytown books).

'Is anybody there?' shouted Dan, but apart from the solemn tick-tock of the grandfather clock all was as quiet as a church. I took Hattie's hand and Dan casually folded his arms and shouted, 'Yoo-hoo, Granny. We've arrived!'

But answer came there none.

Then Hattie said, 'What was that?'

People often asked that question in Granny's house. But this wasn't the usual bird-rustling or floorboard-creaking or scurrying of little tiny feet sound.

'Blimey O'Reilly,' gasped Hattie, pointing at the drawing-room door. 'It's Clifford.'

He walked in slow motion towards us, as stiffly as if his legs were made of wood. His eyes were a strange blue colour; but the biggest shock of all was his face, which had turned as grey/white as snow.

'Boy, oh boy,' muttered Dan. 'Here, old chap, remember me? Uncle Dan?'

Clifford waddled stiffly up to him, whined in the back of his throat, held up his head to be stroked and thumped his tail feebly on the flagstones.

'Ugh. Why are his eyes blue?' said Hattie and Dan said it was because he was going blind, poor fellow, and bent down to stroke his face. Hattie said he might have some contagious disease and she didn't want *her* hair to turn white or her eyes blue, thank you very much, and I said your eyes are blue already and Hattie was just saying all right, clever dick, blind then, when ...

'Darlings,' said a dull, crackly witch's voice. We spun round and there, on the second to bottom wide wooden stair, stood Granny.

If Clifford had been a shock, the equivalent, say, of an electric fence to ward off sheep, the shock Granny caused was enough to kill five fully grown men.

Her arms were outstretched as usual but they weren't Granny's arms, they were a skeleton's with blue veins painted on, and what had happened to her blouse and skirt, her stockings and smart grey shoes? For she was wearing a pink nylon overall, the kind maids wear, and foul pink fluffy slippers and nothing on her legs which had painted veins on, too.

Her face was still Granny's face, just, but her eyes were dull and red-rimmed and had sort of sunk. They stared at you funnily like glass eyes, and you assumed they saw things in a different light to her proper ones.

But the biggest shock of all was her hair. Like Clifford's face, it had turned as white as snow; but worse, it was as straight as a ski slope and how, I'd like to know, would we be able to decorate it with wild flowers? They'd all come sliding straight out. And even worse than it being straight was its sparseness round the parting and her *head* was showing through, and it's a hard thing to admit, and you'd never tell your schoolfriends in a million years, that your beloved Granny is going *bald*.

She no longer looked special. My once beautiful, elegant, dignified grandmother, the only grown-up I knew who understood the things children understand, now looked just like any other old woman you saw staring vacantly through the window of a county-council-run nursing home.

She shuffled on to the last step, one foot then the other, and again on to the floor, and it was then you realised how small she was. Why, she was barely taller than I was!

Dan's voice sounded too cheerful by half when he said, 'Hello, Granny!'

'Darlings,' crackled Granny, shuffling – not as slowly and stiffly as Clifford; at least her knees could bend – towards us. 'I'm so sorry I wasn't about to greet you. I've taken to having an afternoon nap. Beg pardon indeed.'

At least she was still using her expressions. If you kept telling yourself *she* was the same, she just looked and sounded different, things would be all right.

You didn't really want to kiss her, the way Hattie didn't want to stroke Clifford, but it would have been rude not to. It wasn't a violet kiss by any stretch of the imagination, more a damp-pantry-smell one though quite *bearable*. When she kissed Dan, instead of standing on tiptoe she just tilted her cheek and waited for him to bend down.

Then she stared at us with her funny eyes and said 'Blond, brown and dark. What pretty colouring you all have', as if she'd never seen us before.

There followed an embarrassing silence, filled only by the grand-father clock and Clifford's tail. If only Clifford would speed up a fraction they would be in time.

31

'Er, Granny?' Hattie said cautiously. 'Clifford didn't seem very pleased to see us at first, but I think he is now.'

For a moment, Granny looked puzzled. Who was Clifford? her glass eyes seemed to be saying. Then she said, 'Oh, I'm sure he is, darling. He's just not used to visitors,' and she slowly bent down and patted his neck with stiff fingers. 'We're both a bit doddery at the moment, aren't we, old chap.'

'Yes, how *are* you, Granny?' asked Dan, as loud and boisterous as a large puppy, and for a dreadful moment I thought he was going to go on to say, 'You're looking well', and if he had I'd never believe anything he ever said again.

'I'm feeling rather woolly, darling, because I've just woken up. That wretched winter . . . None of us has been quite the same since.'

'Not even Aunt Lynette?' said Hattie.

'Not even Aunt Lynette,' she said, straightening her back. 'I'm afraid she's on the brink of . . .' and her voice trailed away and there was another tick-thump-tock-thump silence.

'Granny?' I said. 'You know the piebald horse. She's had a foal.'

What piebald horse? her funny eyes were saying.

'You know, the one we pass in the car. We worked it out. She must be seventy-two.'

'Well, she's eighteen really, like Dan,' said Hattie. 'But if you multiply a horse's age by four you get the human age. At least it's four for dogs, it might be less for horses. Do you know, Granny?'

'Er, I'm sorry, darling, I've lost the thread somewhat.'

'Well, if horses . . .'

'Look, why don't I unload the car,' interrupted Dan.

'What a good idea,' said Granny. 'And perhaps you two would be very kind and help me prepare tea.'

Tea? It was only five past two! We hadn't had lunch yet, and I was starving. And Granny wasn't exactly known for her hearty teas – a dry biscuit or two and, if you were very lucky, a piece of cake. I stared at the grandfather clock in the hope Granny would say, 'What are you looking at, darling? Oh, good gracious, it's not nearly teatime! Lunch, I think, would be more in order, don't you?' That's what would have happened with the *old* Granny. And anyway, children shouldn't have to be stuck in the kitchen on a sunny day. Where was that Dawn person?

We followed her like snails along the twisty passage. Although it wasn't a sandy passage – the walls were a pre-World-War clotted-cream colour – it still reminded you of Mrs Tittlemouse's home, and you half-expected to end up in a nut or a seed cellar amongst the roots of the hedge. When Grandpa was alive, Hattie and I once followed him down the passage and the likeness to Mr Jackson the toad's back view made us want to die laughing; although he didn't twiddle his thumbs or put his feet on the fender or say 'Tiddly widdly widdly, pouf, pouf, puff!' he did have a 'fat cough'. And Granny reminded us of Mrs Tittlemouse herself, a most terribly tidy, particular little mouse. Or that's who she used to remind us of. This year the house smelt suspiciously damp and musty, and there was a strange new sweet and sour hairdressery smell, too. Granny can't have had her annual spring clean, when Reggie's wife Betty and Mrs Finch, Ron Green and Elsie from the village came up for the day to take down the curtains, beat carpets, paint and polish. That meant there was bound to be a mouse's nest somewhere, and insects munching in droves, and maybe even at this moment a large rat was setting up home in an attic.

Granny's kitchen had been untouched by modern times. It didn't have an electric cooker or a washing machine or a spin-drier. She cooked on an Aga and used a washboard and a mangle. If it was raining the clothes were hung on a wooden airer that squeaked when you lowered it on its pulley. The fridge stood on legs and was big enough to house a small girl. It blocked out half the light from the window which overlooked the cobbled courtyard. In the middle of the kitchen was a large table scrubbed white. It didn't look as white as usual and sitting on it was a small, cheap, ill-at-ease wireless.

The scullery, like Mrs Tittlemouse's house, was prone to unwelcome visitors: creepy-crawly people in the plate rack, Babbitty Bumble bees and big fat spiders. The mouldy cheese in the mouse-trap on the stone floor looked suspiciously like last year's. If so, the lorry drivers can't have been that famished. In the corner the old copper stood below its damper that bit into the wall. There were two shallow sinks, so low even Hattie could reach without standing on tiptoe. Granny said this was because people were shorter when the house was built. It had two taps which didn't have 'H' and 'C' or red and blue dots because they were both 'C'. This meant that to wash up you had to boil water on the Aga. I hated washing up at Granny's, and now Mrs Butterworth wasn't ... Where *was* that Dawn person? And then I spotted something that looked as out of place hanging in Granny's scullery as, say, a kipper hanging in the National Portrait Gallery. It was an Elvis Presley calendar! He was playing a guitar and grinning lop-sidedly at a Hawaiian girl in a grass skirt. The colours were so lurid it looked as though he were wearing make-up which, come to think of it, made his cheeks the colour of a kipper!

33

Even so, my heart gave a sharp twitch. Kipper cheeks or no, he still bore a striking resemblance to Mr Richards!

'Granny, where did that foul calendar come from?' Hattie asked.

'Which ... Oh, that's Dawn's – Mrs Butterworth's replacement. She says looking at it helps her get through the washing up,' and Granny almost managed to laugh. 'It's her afternoon off in case you were wondering.'

She filled the kettle to the brim which meant it would take years to boil. 'I'll carry that,' I said. 'What's this er, Dawn person like?'

Granny said she was afraid she could only concentrate on one thing at a time these days and she'd tell us while we were having tea. 'Hattie dear, would you fetch the biscuits? They're in the George the Fifth tin on the second shelf.'

Biscuits? What about cake? A huge fruit one with sultanas and fat cherries that I could have three slices of when Granny wasn't looking.

'I'll help you look,' I said, because I wanted to investigate the food situation.

The pantry was large, about as big as our spare room, and cool, with a high-up window that had small mesh holes to let the air in and keep the flies out. The pre-World-War exhibits were still on the top shelf gathering dust: National Household Dried Machine-skimmed Milk in a red-striped tin with USA in blue written across it; Captain Kettle Grill Sauce in a bottle with a disgusting-looking cork; a huge Bisto tin; Pure Dried Whole Eggs in a gold tin with black stripes, again from the USA. We sometimes dared one another to look in one of them, but that was as far as it got; goodness knows what would be festering – squirming maggots, maybe, or pea-green mould or wriggling worms. It made a great insult, though: 'Oh, go and stick your head in Granny's Dried Eggs tin!' Next to them were forgotten china and glasses and silver wrapped in green felt.

The next shelf was full of home-made jam and marmalade with Granny's neat sloping writing on the labels, and bottles of plums, raspberries, blackcurrants and gooseberries. There was also a large brown earthenware pot filled with rancid old butter wrappers. On the shelf below were boring things like flour, tea, Bird's custard powder, Colman's mustard powder, sugar, porridge oats, tins of dog food and ... Daddy's Sauce, HP sauce and tomato ketchup! 'Look, more evidence of that Dawn person,' I whispered to Hattie, pointing. 'She's obviously got no *taste*', and we giggled.

I peered into the safe: a dry-as-a-bone leg of lamb stared out, the type that Clifford or a caveman might enjoy; a small piece of cheese that was about to go the same way as the mousetrap, and one portion of rock-hard rice pudding with a thick yellow skin in a Pyrex dish.

'Dan was right – it looks as though starving to death could be on the cards.' I whispered and even though it wasn't funny we giggled again.

'Let's hope all the decent food's in the fridge,' whispered Hattie.

'I think we'll have the rose-bud tea service as it's such a special occasion,' croaked Granny from the kitchen. 'And perhaps the silver teapot.'

'Never mind the teapot, what about the cake?' I whispered, and we giggled so much we had to pretend to cough.

'I trust you haven't brought colds with you,' said Granny and we said it was just a spot of dust and could we have tea in the garden, please, as it was such a lovely day, and Granny said she didn't see why not.

Despite the rose-bud tea service, Dan lived dangerously by carrying the silver tray shoulder-high on the palm of one hand as casually as an Italian waiter.

We sat round the garden table on chairs that made a curly pattern on the backs of your thighs if you were wearing shorts, looking out over the rhododendron bushes and cedar tree. I was about to say at least that Dawn person hadn't put a grinning gnome in the garden, when Granny appeared out of the conservatory wearing a straw hat covered in purple and yellow flowers made of *plastic*! If she *had* to wear a hat, what was wrong with her old black felt gardening one? That Dawn must be really cruel to make her wear such a monstrosity. Only one good thing could be said about it: hideous though it was at least it covered her straight hair and the bald bit.

I was just wondering whether to comment on it – you couldn't say you liked it, that would be a real whopper – when Dan cleverly said, 'I say, Granny, where did you get that hat!'

She didn't answer because she was concentrating on pouring the tea with a hand that shook like a blue-veined autumn leaf. I longed to say 'So *that's* where the scarecrow's hat got to,' and to give me an excuse to laugh I said, 'That reminds me of that joke. Mrs Brown said to Mrs Jones, "When I'm down in the dumps I buy a new hat." "Oh," said Mrs Jones. "So that's where you get them!"'

'Dawn bought it for me,' Granny said, crashing the teapot on to its silver stand with such a force it was a miracle its little legs didn't snap. 'It's not really *me*, is it, but she said I needed brightening up, and I dare say she's right. And now, darlings,' she said, not looking

35

us in the eye, 'we've got so much news to catch up on. Where shall we begin?'

We thought, and chewed on our biscuits in time to the coo of the wood pigeon. They were plain, home-made biscuits that went round and round in your mouth like cement in a mixer and barely made it to your throat.

After an age, Dan said in his trying-not-to-laugh voice, 'We were very sorry to hear about Mrs B.'

Granny said yes it was very sad but at least she died peacefully in her sleep.

'Will she go to heaven?' asked Hattie.

'You mean, is she there already?' I muttered. 'It wouldn't take five months to get there.'

'How do you know?' said Hattie. 'She was a very slow walker.'

'You don't walk to heaven. You fly.'

'I expect so, darling,' said Granny, taking a mouse-size sip of tea. 'She was a good Christian.'

'What did she die of exactly?'

Granny said it was called hypothermia, and quite common among old people. 'I suppose I should count my blessings,' she added.

'Rather!' said Dan too loudly, making Granny jump. 'And if the weather stays like this and you get some sun on the old bones you'll soon be as good as new.'

'I wouldn't quite say new, Dan,' said Granny and smiled for the first time.

'It's funny, isn't it,' I said. 'I loved Mrs B very much but I haven't felt like crying yet.'

'That's because of her age, darling. If someone young dies then it's a tragedy – a pitiful waste. But if you've had a good innings, like she had . . . I trust you won't cry when I die, for example.'

'Oh, Granny, you're never going to die,' said Hattie.

'No, none of us will – ever,' I said, just for something to say, and took a biscuit without asking.

There was another awkward pause.

'The barometer wavers between Fair and Change and the forecast says a storm's brewing,' said Granny, suddenly. 'No doubt harvest will be late as usual.'

'I hear you've found a replacement for Mrs B, then,' said Dan changing the subject. 'By the way, mind if I smoke?'

'Darling, how grown up. Your own cigarettes! Just so long as you don't stub them out on the lawn. What were you saying?'

'Mrs B's replacement.'

'Oh, yes,' said Granny. Every word she spoke seemed to require

36

enormous effort. I could hardly bear to look at her in case the hat made me either laugh or cry. 'Her name is Dawn Potts. Thoroughly modern is the way I think one would describe her. She spends all her money on clothes and fashion fabrics and cosmetics and gramophone records. I do so hope you'll like her. She's not to everyone's taste, but I personally find her cheerfulness and high spirits most refreshing.'

'Aren't *we* most refreshing, Granny?' I asked.

'Of course, darling, but you're not here all year. And I need someone to do my cleaning and make up the Aga and all the other tedious chores.'

'Is she from round these parts?' Hattie asked.

'No, she's a Londoner. Her family moved to Norfolk a year or so ago. She's got the most glorious cockney accent, something I haven't heard since the war.'

Hattie and I pulled a face at each other.

'I would very much like you to be specially kind to her, darlings. She comes from a most humble, underprivileged home – a family of eight, I believe. She hasn't had the advantages you've had. She's bright, but not what you'd call well-educated. Incidentally, she's engaged to Albert Thirtle, the butcher's son.'

'Oh, I *like* him,' I said meaning Why's someone as nice as him marrying someone who sounds so awful?

'So do I,' said Hattie. 'He tells hilarious jokes.'

'Granny, this, er – Dawn won't be in charge of us, will she?' I said. 'We won't have to do as she says, surely? You'll still be the one who looks after us, won't you?'

Her reply was drowned by the sound of a car hooting, and the scrunch of tyres on gravel. It was Aunt Lynette in her open-top shiny-red MGB. She was wearing a very white headscarf and very black pointed sun-glasses.

'Yoo-hoo, you lot!' she shouted, screeching to a halt which caused the canvases in the back seat to tip forward.

'She looks like Grace Kelly in what's-its-name,' remarked Dan.

Aunt Lynette leapt nimbly from the car like Jeremy Fisher, and strode over in black slacks, a white blouse not tucked in and white slip-on shoes with pointed toes. Hattie, Dan and I watched her. Clifford and Granny didn't. Like the piebald horse, they had seen it all before.

'Is it a private party or can anyone join in?' she said, her voice shrill like a bird's.

Aunt Lynette lived in the stables which had been converted into a studio and a flat. She was an artist; portraits, gardens and salivating pets were, she said, her bread-and-butter money. Her heart lay in bold abstracts, in pinks, purples and oranges, which I thought foul but Hattie said were good examples of Modern Art; several had been exhibited in London.

Daddy was quite proud of his arty sister, but Mummy thought her a Bad Influence. Although I admired Aunt Lynette, I felt rather dull beside her, like one of Granny's biscuits beside a Black Forest gâteau. Dan could always discuss banning bombs and Hattie wanted to be an artist too when she grew up. But I didn't really have much to say to her at all.

'Greetings, one and all,' she said, all black and white with red lips and nails, which reminded me of a joke I'd have to tell the others later: 'What's black and white and red all over?'

'A newspaper.'

'No – Aunt Lynette!'

'I've just spent the day painting Sir Edward's horrendous Pekingeses, and I don't know which was more trying: Sir Edward yapping about the Socialists' nuclear policy or the hirsute rodents piddling on the Wilton. Lummy, I need a drink. How are you, Ma? As well as can be expected, I suppose, beneath that shocker of a hat. My God, *Dan*! Is it really my schoolboy nephew I see before me? God, Ma, doesn't it make you feel ancient to have a *man* as a grandson? Look at those cheekbones! I've simply *got* to paint you, if it's the last thing I do.'

Dan turned red as a brick and studied the lit end of his cigarette.

'Let's see,' she said, plonking herself on a chair and sitting with her legs apart, so it was a good thing she was wearing trousers. 'How about if you were leaning against my car, looking towards the open road – i.e. your future, à la Jack Kerouac. It can be fearfully vulgar and symbolic. We can call it something crass like "In his Prime", or what was that Yeats poem? "Of boyhood changing into man: the unfinished man and his pain".'

'How do you mean, vulgar, Aunt Lynette?' asked Hattie.

Aunt Lynette laughed her cocktail-party laugh. 'I don't mean vulgar in the sense of undone flies or trousers round the ankles, if that was what you were thinking, Hattie darling. Vulgar in the clichèd, obvious sense. I mean if *you* were going to paint a man in his prime, wouldn't you have him standing by a sports car looking at the open road?'

'I suppose so,' said Hattie. 'Or I might have him holding up a cricket cup, or being presented with a prize on Speech Day.'

'But that would symbolise what he's already achieved, not what he's about to.'

'If you have him looking at the road, how do we know he's looking *forward*?' I said. 'How do we know he isn't looking back?'

'Shrewd thinking, Sarah, and this is where the skill of the artist comes in. It's that optimistic, expectant glint in his eye; the glint that says *anything can happen round any corner*.'

'Can I paint him, too?' asked Hattie.

'Course you can, darling. We can compare notes.'

'Anyone would think I'm a Pekingese,' said Dan, his face still red, and half laughed to show he was half joking.

'God, you don't mean you piddle on carpets, too!' screeched Aunt Lynette lighting a cigarette, and her laugh caused the wood pigeon to go quiet so he could listen in on the conversation.

What was Granny going to say Aunt Lynette was on the brink of? Going mad, perhaps? Whatever, she was definitely diary worthy.

'Would you care for some tea, Lynette?' said Granny quietly.

'No thanks, Ma. A large G and T would be more in order after a day spent with the hairy rodents. God knows what Sir Edward sees in them. I just hope they yap at his constituents and lose him thousands of votes at the next election.'

'He's an old friend of the family,' muttered Granny at the same time that Aunt Lynette said, 'I say, Sarah, haven't you got *huge*.'

'Granny was just telling us about this Dawn person,' I said.

'Oh, God, Dawn! Haven't you met her yet? Lummy, you've got a treat in store. The Busty Blonde Bombshell of Gressenham.' said Aunt Lynette taking off her sun-glasses. She looked rather disappointing without them, like the Lone Ranger would without his mask. 'She's a character and a half. Ma's very taken but ... Oh, I suppose I am too. Your mother wouldn't be, though. She'd yell blue murder if she knew someone like that was in charge of you two.'

'Lynette ...' began Granny.

'And you'd better watch out, Dan. She's got an eye for a pretty face.'

'I thought she was engaged to Albert Thirtle,' Dan said going red again and that was the thing about Aunt Lynette; she had that sort of effect on people.

'Of course she is,' said Granny. 'Really, Lynette, I ...'

'Ah, but I suspect she has her sights set on higher things, given half the chance,' said Aunt Lynette, winking at Dan before returning her sun-glasses to their proper place. 'She has elaborate ideas about opening boutiques and becoming a fashion model. I'm afraid I encourage her. Your grandmother doesn't approve, she thinks ...'

'I wish you wouldn't talk about me as though I wasn't here,

39

Lynette,' said Granny. 'I simply said she ought to count her blessings because nice young men like Albert don't grow on trees.'

'But, Ma, that's the beauty of being young these days. Why *should* she be content with marrying the rather worthy Albert and bearing countless red-haired children? Fine if that's what she *wants* but I'm not sure it is. Gone are the days when one had to be content with one's lot. The young – and I include the working-class young – have expectations. Who knows, Dawn could make a wild success of something. She's certainly got the spirit for it, and now's the ideal time. I mean, look at David Bailey, cockney as they come and our number-one trend-setting photographer. Look at all the hairdressers and fashion designers and pop stars and actors – Michael Caine, for one – springing up in polite circles everywhere. They're the new aristocracy. As soon as we get rid of this archaic government ... I tell you, working-class heroes are all the rage. I rather wish I was young and working-class, if the truth be known.'

'Lynette, I would rather you didn't fill the children's head with such rubbish,' said Granny. 'Really, it's most unsuitable.'

'A thousand pardons,' said Aunt Lynette. 'Just trying to bring a slightly more worldly element into the proceedings. Oh well, I'd better go and finish off the rodents. Let's hope I don't dip my brush in the gin and knock back the paint water, ha, ha! Cheerio, one and all,' and she jumped up, swivelled round on her heels, saluted and stode to her car in a puff of cigarette smoke.

'I find her rather wearing,' sighed Granny. 'Take no notice of her, darlings. She's going through a slightly peculiar phase.'

'Because of the old bug ... the winter, I expect,' I said. After all, if *heat* could make people go mad, why not *cold*?

'Where is – Dawn, by the way?' asked Dan, helping himself to the last biscuit which I had had my eye on.

'It's her half-day,' said Granny. 'I fancy she's gone to Shotestead to do some shopping, and then she'll meet her young man. They're looking for a bungalow to buy, I believe. She's so looking forward to meeting you all. I daresay she finds it a bit dull here with just me. She won't be back till after your bedtime, so you'll meet her at breakfast.'

At breakfast ... Did that mean ...? Hattie and I looked at each other.

'Surely she's not staying *here*?' I said.

'Of course, darling. This is her home. Her family live too far away for her to come every day. Besides, it's reassuring for me. If something were to go bump in the night ...'

'Which room is hers?' asked Hattie very quietly.

'The middle attic. She's made it look frightfully gay, with pictures of pop stars – do I mean pop stars, Dan? – on the walls.'

'That's . . . right above our room,' I said.

'I know, darling. I've told her she must keep the television's volume down.'

'She's got the *television* in her room?' squealed Hattie.

'Well, I never had it on, and I'm sure if there was something you fancied watching she wouldn't mind you going up there,' said Granny wearily, still not looking us in the eye when she spoke.

Hattie and I had been so looking forward to having Dan and Granny to ourselves all summer, and now this foul-sounding person would be here, interfering with family matters that were no concern of hers. I for one would be going nowhere near her smelly old maid's room with pop stars on the wall to watch television. There was nothing good on in summer and besides, I had better things to do with my time. And then I had an even worse thought. Would she be *sharing our bathroom*?

'I expect you two want to explore your old haunts,' said Granny as we cleared away, and asked if we'd mind giving Dan a hand with the washing up first. She was going to have another lie down; the excitement of seeing us had exhausted her.

'You are pleased to see us, though, aren't you, Granny,' said Hattie.

'Darling, of course I am,' she said, but her funny new eyes didn't look pleased at all.

CHAPTER FOUR

Dan washed, Hattie dried, and I put away.

'That's another bad omen, her not being here to do the washing up on our first day,' I said.

'The poor girl is allowed an afternoon off,' said Dan.

'Trust you to take her side,' I said. 'Just because she's a blonde bombshell. Dawn. What a foul name. I think we should call her Red Sky in the Morning.'

'I bet *she's* foul, too,' said Hattie. 'She must be to have bought Granny that straw hat. That was the last straw.'

'You mean the last straw hat!'

'Well, I think the last straw hat is her staying here, right over our bedroom. What's the betting she snores.'

'And do you realise she'll be using our bathroom? We might catch some foul disease.'

'Shut up, you snobs,' said Dan, pouring boiling water into the sink. 'She comes from an underprivileged home, remember. The least we can do is be nice to her.'

'As long as she doesn't stick her big nose into things that don't concern her,' I said. 'By the way, talking of underprivileged homes, I'm *starving*. We haven't had lunch yet.'

'I bet you're not as starving as I am,' said Hattie. 'You had an extra rasher of bacon at breakfast.'

'So? I'm bigger than you. Anyway, you've just had a huge glass of milk and I only had watery tea.'

'So? You hogged all the Murray Mints in the car.'

'I'm starving, I'm starving, I feel faint,' I said and fell dramatically to the hard stone floor.

Dan turned round, his hair damp from the steam. His face wasn't hot red or embarrassed red but angry red. 'Stop being so bloody infantile, Sarah. You miss one meal, one bloody meal in your whole life, and you behave as if the world's been blown up. Do you realise there are children in Glasgow who survive on one packet of Smith's potato crisps a day? That there are children in Africa who only have one meal a *week* ...'

'And then it's only rice,' said Hattie, and who's side was she on?

42

'What you've just had for tea would keep them going a whole *fortnight*. Anyway, it won't do you any harm . . . Oh, never mind.'

'It won't do me any harm to do what? To eat less because I'm fat? I hate you, Dan, and I wish you'd go and stick your head in the Dried Eggs tin,' and I stood up and thumped his corduroy bottom, tears scalding my cheeks.

'Sorry, Sausage, I didn't mean it,' he said, squeezing my shoulder with a hot, wet hand. 'Even so, we don't half have easy lives compared with most people. It won't hurt us to rough it a bit this summer.'

It's all right for you, I wanted to say, looking down at my Clark's sandals. You're a man who likes to roam around. We're still children and need a bit of looking after.

'Now the point is,' said Dan, turning to the sink and rattling the rose-bud china unnecessarily loud. 'What are we going to do? I've got mixed feelings about the place.'

'Why? Granny isn't gaga exactly, is she? She's just older and her hair's gone funny.'

'Her hat's gone funny, too,' said Hattie.

'Yeah, but can she cope with us without Mrs B? This Dawn sounds a bit of a rum'un. I mean, if Aunt L has her doubts . . .'

'But she's not going to look after us,' I said. 'Granny and you are.'

'Yeah, well,' said Dan, and I wished he wouldn't say 'yeah', it was so common.

'By the way what is it you're going to do this summer that will bring you fame and fortune? You promised you'd tell us when we arrived.'

'Did I?' said Dan, crash-bang-walloping in the sink. 'All right, then. I, sisters dear, am planning to form a pop group.'

I stared at the mousetrap cheese. My brother in a pop group! What about the harvest and the cricket match – and us? And to be in a pop group didn't you have to be poor and come from a northern slum, not be an ex-public schoolboy about to go to Cambridge next term to read law?

'Are you, er, the right type?' I asked.

'If you mean, have I got a fringe and a Liverpudlian accent, the answer's no. But nor has Little Richard or Howlin' Wolf or Muddy Waters.'

'Who on earth are they?'

'Black American rock 'n' roll singers.'

American *negros?* Rocking roll? Had Dan gone round the bend?

'You're not going to sing like *them,* are you?'

43

'Only wish I could,' said Dan, piling plates unnecessarily high on the draining board. 'Or that guy,' and he jerked a soapy thumb at the leering Elvis Presley.

'Can Hattie and me be in your pop group?' I said. 'I could play the recorder and Hattie could pay the triangle.'

'Sorry, girls, electric guitars only.'

'Or I could play the drums,' I said. 'Or I know – we could wear sparkly dresses and sing the chorus. Cliff Richard has girls singing the chorus sometimes, doesn't he.'

'Sorry. Wrong image.'

'We could stand right at the back of the stage so the audience wouldn't really see us. We are in the school choir, in case you'd forgotten.'

'To be honest, the sort of songs we plan to sing wouldn't suit girls' voices.'

'You're not going to sing soppy songs about love with an American accent, are you?' said Hattie.

'We might,' said Dan. 'If the mood takes us.' And he started singing in a silly quivering deep voice about a heartbreak hotel.

'Well, who's going to be in it then?' I said, but Dan said the final line-up had yet to be decided.

'What are you going to call the group?' said Hattie. 'How about Dan Hillington and the . . .'

'Pop groups are named after insects these days, like the Beatles,' I said.

'All right then, how about the Spiders?'

'Or the Bluebottles?'

'Or the Rattlesnakes?'

'Or the Warthogs?'

'That's a foul name for a pop group,' said Hattie.

'Actually, I think it's quite good,' said Dan.

'*Good?*' screeched Hattie. 'Warthogs are stupid and ugly.'

'So's our music.'

'I think you've gone off your rocker,' I said.

'Actually,' said Dan, 'I was hoping for some moral support from my siblings.'

'We *will* give you moral support,' I said doubtfully. 'Er – you're not going to grow your hair like the Beatles, are you?'

'Ner, I was planning on something a little longer, actually.'

'Dan!' gasped Hattie. 'You'll look like a *girl*. What will Granny say?'

'She'll probably say "It's a phase Dan's going through",' I said. 'Or "In my young day boys of his age went on hiking holidays to let off steam." Or, most likely, "Why isn't Dan doing the harvest?" '

'Anyway, the point is,' said Dan, 'I won't be around for a lot of the time. I'm hopihg we'll get our act together in time to play at the Shotestead Show dance, which means a whole lotta practising going on. And I'm not sure I like the thought of you two here on your own.'

'We won't be on our own,' I said. 'Anyway, we can entertain ourselves, can't we, Hattie.'

'For example, the beds aren't even made up,' said Dan.

'We can make up our own beds,' I said, though I saw what he meant.

'Plan A is we stay here and make the best of a bad job,' said Dan. 'Plan B is I stay here because I can look after myself and you two go and stay with Aunt Daphne.'

'Oh, no, not Aunt Daphne,' I said. 'It's our last summer with you, Dan. Next year you'll probably go grape picking in France with your student friends. We can't be split up like children taken into care by the county council.'

'They've got ponies,' said Dan. 'You could ride in the Shotestead Show if you wanted.'

Yes, but in return for the ponies, there were our snobby cousins to contend with, and being on your best behaviour at all times and having to have a rest after lunch even if you weren't the least bit tired, and only being allowed to watch *Blue Peter* and nature programmes on television, and having to put up with Aunt Daphne herself, who was as strict as the Red Queen and sometimes smacked you even though she wasn't your father. But worst of all, I'd have nothing interesting to say in my diary. It would end up just us uninspired as everyone else's: *Got up. Groomed Tinkerbell. Went for a ride across the heath. Tinkerbell shyed at a pheasant. Had lunch. Had a rest* ... For whatever Mr Richards said about being able to make anything interesting, there were a few things – and Aunt Daphne's was a good example – that were just dull through and through.

'Oh, please can we stay here,' I said. 'You said we should live dangerously this summer, Dan, that it was good for the blood pressure. It would be an adventure. We can look after ourselves. We could even sleep in the black summerhouse and wash in the river and live on berries and catch rabbits if we *had* to, couldn't we Hattie.'

'I suppose so,' she said. 'I don't think I could kill a rabbit, though.'

'But do you want to stay?'

45

'I suppose so,' she said uncertainly. 'Aunt Lynette has arranged some painting expeditions.'

For a moment I wavered. Did that mean I'd be stuck on my own with that Dawn person? And I'd just spotted on the window-sill the most disgusting piece of evidence of her yet: a willow-pattern saucer full of tipped cigarette ends smothered in vile pink lipstick.

'Look, before we take a vote, are you quite sure?' said Dan. 'I can't help feeling . . . Do you promise to look after Hattie when I'm not around, Sarah?'

I nodded and Hattie said, 'I don't need looking after, if you must know.'

'Right. All those in favour of staying at Granny's say Aye.'

'Aye,' we said and I put my hand up, too.

'Okay, vote carried,' Dan said, drying his hands on a Union Jack tea cloth. 'Let's go and ring the parents and stop them fretting.'

Mummy answered and Dan told her that yeah, everything was fine, and yeah we had had lunch and winked at us, and how could he lie like that without even going red?

I pictured her sitting on the high stool in the gleaming, black and white linoed kitchen in our house in Hertfordshire, the fridge defrosting, a casserole using up the leftovers in the oven, Daddy hovering nearby half-listening and half-wondering whether to pack his golf-clubs. She'd be wearing her green and white checked apron and her polka-dot scarf tied behind her head rather than under her chin like Aunt Lynette. Mummy was very pretty, with gold hair and grey eyes; Daddy was very handsome, with black hair and blue eyes; Dan took after Mummy and Hattie took after Daddy; I was somewhere in between. 'Sarah's going to be the plain one, poor soul', I once overheard Aunt Lynette say to Granny, and I ran like a hare into the wood, picked a Destroying Angel toadstool and was about to take a large bite when through my tears I caught a glimpse of myself on television on the back of Black Champion winning the Horse of the Year Show. I wrapped the Destroying Angel in dock leaves and hid it in the roots of a beech tree. I wondered if it was still there.

'Right, over and out,' said Dan. 'I'll pass you over to your eldest daughter.'

'Bags tell her about the piebald horse,' Hattie whispered.

Mummy asked me twice if everything was all right, *really* all right, and how Granny was, and I told her apart from her funny hair she was fine. She said she and Daddy were missing me already. 'Look after Hattie, darling. Remember, she's only little' were her last words.

I handed the phone to Hattie, and she was just saying yes, everything's fine, when there was a creak on the polished stair.

Dan and I looked round. It was Granny.

The afternoon sun streaming through the window behind her formed a halo round her straight white hair. It made her look like ... a *witch*.

Hattie hadn't seen her. 'And Mummy, you know the piebald horse ...'

'Dan,' crackled Granny in her duchess voice, 'in future, kindly ask before you use my phone. It's a trunk call, I presume, and not yet the cheap rate.'

This time Dan did turn red, and I did, too.

'Sorry, Granny, we were just ...'

'I know perfectly well what you were doing,' said Granny, advancing straight-backed down the stairs, and surely a witch wouldn't wear a pink overall and fluffy slippers – would she?

'... and he worked out her age was seventy-two – that's four times Dan's age, so ...'

I nudged Hattie. 'Belt up,' I hissed.

'When your sister has finished her involved conversation, I would like a word with my son.'

I'd only seen Granny angry four times. Once when Hattie coloured in Piglet and Eeyore in *The House at Pooh Corner*; once when she caught Dan at the drinks cupboard; once when I pretended to be dead after falling out of a tree; and once when we locked Cousin Susan in the downstairs lavatory.

'Granny wants to speak to Daddy now,' said Hattie. 'Goodbye, Mummy, have a lovely Second Honeymoon.'

Granny snatched the receiver from Hattie. Her hand shook not with old age but rage. 'Gerald? Oh, Evelyn, I'd like a word with my son. Gerald? Your wretched children are telephoning at peak time long-distance without my permission. Even if you have failed to teach them about the value of money, at least you could have taught them about manners.' There was a pause while Daddy said something, then she said, 'Whether they promised or not is beside the point; it is my telephone, and I will not be taken advantage of.'

Dan nodded at the front door. We ran out into the bright, warm, welcoming big outdoors, Dan swung Hattie on to his shoulders and we tore round the side of the house, across the courtyard, along the wall of the kitchen garden and flopped, panting, on the grass under the walnut tree.

'Phew,' said Dan lying on his back, crossing his feet and putting

47

his hands behind his head as if he were tucked up in bed or on a lilo floating out to sea. Hattie and I did the same. Then he said 'Jeepers creepers.' Then none of us said anything while our heart beats died down.

'Dan,' I said softly because I didn't want to disturb the peace. 'Was that a sign of Granny being gaga?'

'Yeah, probably,' he said and sighed. 'Does anyone get the feeling we've made the wrong decision?'

Hattie and I said no, we didn't think so, but in small reedy voices, and I said, 'We'll just have to watch our Ps and Qs like hawks, NB, Dan Hillington.'

'Didn't she look frightening, like a witch,' Hattie said. 'Mind you, if that was her being gaga, perhaps when we go back she'll have forgotten it happened.'

'Perhaps it *didn't* happen,' I said. 'Perhaps it was all a figment of our imaginations. That can happen to people as close as us.'

'Dan, you didn't half tell a whopper,' said Hattie. 'You know, about lunch.'

'Sometimes people don't want to hear the truth,' he said. 'It was only a *white* lie.'

'You'll always tell *us* the truth though, won't you,' I said.

'Sure.'

'Do you swear?'

'Sure. Bloody, blimey, hell, bleeding . . .'

'And do you swear that all the time you aren't rehearsing with your pop group you'll be with us?'

'Sure. Bloody, ruddy, bleeding . . .'

'You're the last straw – hat, isn't he, Sarah,' said Hattie.

We lay in our little row and Dan held our hands and we swore we'd have no secrets from each other and Dan said gruffly, 'Bugger the rest of 'em. As long as we three stick by each other, we'll be all right, Jack.' And gradually gaga grannies were pushed to the back of my mind and a warm safe aching feeling glowed through me; never mind the future or the past; it was now, this precise moment that mattered, this perfect precise moment lying beside Dan on the grass in Norfolk, England, Europe, World, looking up through the green-plum walnuts to the sky. I wanted to tell him I loved him more than anyone else on earth but I didn't because he would have gone red and Hattie would have said, 'Do you love him more than me?' So instead I snuggled up to him, and Hattie snuggled up on the other side, and he put his arms round us and we lay there breathing in his shirt which smelt of Tide and warm sweat and cigarettes, and I wouldn't have said no to life staying like this for ever and ever.

And then Dan ruined the magical moment for ever by saying 'That pigeon's got an ace sense of rhythm. Hey, *you*. Wanna join a pop group?'

CHAPTER FIVE

It wasn't the birds that woke us the next morning, or Clifford growling at Mr Ridley the postman on his bicycle whistling 'Que Sera Sera', but a loud crash from above followed by a roly, poly, roly noise and the words *'Oh, gawd!'*

When we had gingerly returned to the house the day before, Granny was in the kitchen in a pinny and, a miracle ... we could smell cooking! And, even more of a miracle ... she was smiling, and maybe the telephone incident *had* just been a figment!

'Darlings – I was about to call you. There's a shepherd's pie in the oven and I thought perhaps a little ice cream to follow. Would that suit?'

We said it would suit us very nicely (as long as it wasn't *too* little, I thought) and Granny suggested we unpack and change into our dressing gowns and perhaps Dan could fill hot water bottles because the beds weren't aired and goodness, she hoped Dawn had remembered to make them up and we didn't let on that she hadn't.

Our room, which once upon a time had been Aunt Lynette's, still had the same orange and lemon chrysanthemum curtains at the windows, Grandpa in water colours on the wall along with the abstract of a purple eye on yellow stripes and the small framed photograph of Frank Sinatra in a white suit. The beds were high like hospital beds and had iron bedsteads and thick knobbly mattresses covered in ticking and bumpy buttons – the buttons didn't stop us sleeping, though, so we can't have been princesses in disguise.

The window looked out over the copper beech, the sycamore tree, the 120-year-old sweet chestnut, rose beds, a sweeping sloping lawn and, beyond, the park with its four healthy-headed oak trees and two stag-headed ones under which shorn sheep and a hairy pony grazed. The pony was called Snap Dragon and stood at the far end in the dappled evening light swishing his tail at a strutting hen pheasant. There was no sign of Smiler, the retired Suffolk Punch who in his prime had pulled a dead elm out of the ground which had roots a yard long, and who never turned a hair when all three of us rode on his back and pretended he was Champion.

We stuffed shorts and T-shirts and trousers into nut-brown mothball-smelling drawers and hung frocks and skirts in the large, sly wardrobe, checking in passing (and knowing full well only wardrobes in books ever lead to magical lands) that it had a back to it, and I hung a vest over the purple eye because it did stare so. We threw sheets and blankets over the beds, put in the hot water bottles and tucked up Teddy and One-Eyed Lamb, changed into our pyjamas and went into Dan's room.

It was Daddy's old room. You knew straight away it was a man's room; it was all brown and plain and sombre and somehow smelt of man. If furniture could talk it would have a deep, gruff voice. There were sports cups on a shelf, and a long yellowing school photograph in a brown frame.

'Third from the left, second row from the back,' said Dan, squashing his freshly ironed cricket flannels into a drawer. 'Good-looking devil, wasn't he. Like father, like son,' and he stuck his tongue under his bottom lip, rolled his eyes and grinned.

'He's nothing like you,' said Hattie. 'For a start his hair's dark.'

'And short,' I said.

'He looks a bit like a young Gregory Peck,' said Hattie.

'And think of him now,' said Dan. 'That's what getting married and having children does to a man.'

'What?' I said.

'Makes you old before your time.'

'I don't think he looks old before his time in the slightest.'

'Nor do I,' said Hattie.

I looked at Daddy, a cheeky, grinning, baggy-shorted schoolboy. How strange to think that when the photograph was taken he had no idea that one day he'd meet Mummy and have three children called Dan, Sarah and Harriet, or live in a Tudor house in Herts, or become a lawyer to give him a second string in case the farm packed up, or fight in the Second World War, or even know there was going to be a Second World War. Right then, at the time the picture was taken, all he knew about was telling jokes and collecting stamps and having conker fights and failing Latin tests and playing cricket and spending school holidays here at Gressenham Hall.

'I wonder if he'd started shaving when the photograph was taken,' I said.

'Expect so. I started at twelve, and these things run in families. Early developers, us Hillingtons.'

'I'm glad girls don't have to shave.'

'I'm glad boys don't have to wear bras.'

'Dan!'

51

Anyway girls *do* have to shave. Under there.' And he tickled my armpits until I begged for mercy.

On the way down I whispered, 'What's the betting that gnarled old caveman's leg has gone into the shepherd's pie', and Hattie giggled hysterically and said if anyone mentioned the word 'cave' at supper she would die laughing, honestly.

'How lovely to hear laughter in the house,' said Granny as we sat round the dining-room table. She was wearing a grey cardigan over the overall, and proper shoes.

'Doesn't, er, Dawn laugh?' I said.

'Oh, continuously, but there's nothing like an innocent child's laughter. Dawn's is rather coarse, if you know what I mean.'

'Of *course*,' I said and we laughed and even Granny joined in.

I took a mouthful of shepherd's pie and chewed and chewed but I just couldn't swallow it. When Granny wasn't looking I put the piece of lamb between by teeth and grinned at Hattie. For a moment she managed to contain herself and then whoosh! Peas, potato, meat exploded like a firework all over the clean white table-cloth. Neither of us could stop and Dan turned red and forced his mouth not to curl at the edges because now he was a man he could only laugh at grown-up things.

'What is it?' cried Granny. 'Is it something I've said?'

'Sorry, Granny,' I said, parking the bit of gristle on the side of my plate. 'It was, er, a funny joke Dan said in the car', and the look on Dan's face, a who? me? look, made me laugh all over again.

'Oh, do tell,' said Granny, so I said, 'Er, why is a ...' But I couldn't think of one joke, let alone one that warranted showering a clean table-cloth with one's supper. Then Dan said, 'Honestly, Granny, it's one of those silly schoolboy jokes that doesn't bear repeating – though I will if you insist' (and how *brave* of him).

After supper we went to the glory hole under the stairs to choose a game. It smelt even fustier and dustier and mustier than last year, the games seemed even more old-fashioned and pre-World War: jigsaw puzzles of Pip, Squeak and Wilfred at the seaside and George VI and Queen Elizabeth with the two little princesses wearing puffed sleeves; Housey Housey with Air Raid Wardens playing the game on the lid; Lexicon in an old red box with gold letters, the Bruin Boys' Jolly Ring Game. We chose Jaques' Original Happy Families, even though when I was younger the cruel red Victorian faces gave me nightmares.

It stood out a mile that Granny was collecting the Sweep and Brewer families and, with much giggling behind fanned-out cards, we let her win.

She read us a story in bed. Hattie chose *The Tale of Samuel Whiskers* because Mummy didn't allow it at bedtime in case it made us dream. (I, of course, was far too old for Beatrix Potter; nevertheless it would have been rude not to listen.) Granny's voice, as she read it, was almost like the old Granny's.

'Everything's more or less back to normal, isn't it,' I whispered in the dark when she had gone. Through the wall you could hear Dan's guitar playing softly, and Granny had kissed us both goodnight.

'Sort of,' said Hattie. 'Except the bathroom. Did you see all that foul stuff everywhere? The talcum powder and flowery plastic bath hat and hair stuff and foul pink sponge and cheap as chips soap?'

'I know. There's no room for *our* things. In fact I can sense her presence all over the house, like a ghost.'

'I bet she's foul,' said Hattie. 'Vile, in fact. We'll just have to *rise above her*. Goodnight, Sis.'

In my sleep I heard the rats' rolling pin going roly poly roly, and then Anna Maria say *'Oh, gawd!'* But . . . Beatrix Potter would never have written *that!*

It had woken Hattie, too. We said in unison 'Oh, gawd' and I whispered, 'What's worse than being woken by the dawn chorus? Being woken by Dawn!'

We got up so as to get to the bathroom before her, and decided to go exploring – in order to get out of helping with the breakfast. 'Assuming there'll *be* breakfast,' said Hattie.

We put on shorts and T-shirts and sandals and slipped out through the dark, quiet, early-morning-smelling house.

The enormous sky was a hazy lazy blue covered in cigarette-smoke wisps of cloud. The sun, glowing pinkly behind Lion's Mouth Wood, was not yet hot or high enough to dry out the dew which cloaked the dark-green, silent lawn on which a blackbird dared to tread with legs as thin as binder twine.

We crossed the cobbled courtyard past Aunt Lynette's sleeping window and under the archway through which coachmen once skilfully guided their horses and through which Aunt Lynette once unskilfully guided her old green Austin Healey. We walked down the red brick road whose potholes were filled in with crushed bricks, over the gate and into Long Meadow where we sang 'Oh, What a Beautiful Morning' at the tops of our voices. *'I've got a beautiful feeling,'* we bellowed, causing the bullocks to jerk their necks up and stop in mid-munch. *'Everything's going my way.'* We disturbed a hare, too, nibbling at his breakfast, and he bounded into the wood leaving a faint footsteps trail that a hound would have no trouble following.

Beyond the meadow's hedge, corn stretched in every direction. *'The corn is as high as an elephant's eye, and it looks like it's reaching right up to the sky . . .'*

'Good morning, Mr Bullocks,' I shouted and the bravest walked cautiously towards us and the others followed in a long line like a black and white army, huffing and puffing like the wolf in *Three Little Pigs*.

'Let's be generals,' I said. 'Men. Stand to attention,' and they halted hooshing and snooshing in front of us, their warm breath clouding up the morning air (perhaps in my diary I could describe their breath as 'swirling mists'). Then the ringleader stretched out his neck and touched my hand with his pink and black-spotted nose. Its texture reminded you of hard cod's roe.

'Sergeant Major,' I said sternly. 'That's no way to treat a general. Kindly show some respect', and I waved my arm and the sergeant major backed away, crashing into the soldiers behind.

'Right, men. Here comes the enemy. Prepare to do battle . . . Let battle commence', and we ran among them making loud machine-gun noises in a very ungeneral-like way and they snorted and puffed and bucked and jerked and galumphed away, their tails streaming behind them.

Hattie said later that just when I said 'enemy' she saw the dark shape of a man looming out of the corner of her eye.

'What the hell do you kids think you're a-playing at?'

We looked round. So did the steaming bullocks. It was a bulky parcel of a man wrapped in a Norfolk jacket, tweed plus-fours, thick speckled socks and stout leather shoes. On his head perched a deerstalker. If his intention was to blend into the background, he failed dismally on such a brilliant green and blue bright day, and wouldn't fool the most short-sighted rabbit. He had a beard the colour of curly crows' feathers and in the crook of his arm nestled a long gun. Beside him trotted a large yellow dog.

I wanted to shout 'And what the hell do you think *you're* a-playing at?' but instead I said, 'We're Mrs Hillington's grand-children, actually.'

'I don't give a bugger if you're the Queen of England's grand-children,' said the man still walking towards us, his legs slightly apart like a cowboy's or, as Hattie said later, a man who's wet his pants. 'You're trespassing.' And if the Yellow Dog hadn't been so well trained he would have chased us off, you could tell by the wistful look in his eyes and the way he licked his chops in anticipation.

54

'No, we're not,' I said, a trickle of sweat collecting in the small of my back. 'It's our grandmother's farm and even though our grandfather's died it's still *hers*.'

'Well, I don't know nothing about that. All I know is Mr English pays me good money to make sure strangers don't go messing around with things that don't concern them.' He rested his gun on his hip and delved in his pocket for tobacco and cigarette papers. The Yellow Dog sat down and stared at us. 'And what do you have to say to *that*?' he seemed to be saying with polar-bear-bright eyes. The bullocks snooshed round, keeping a firm eye on the dog.

To look at the man you'd expect his voice to be rough and gruff and loud, but in fact it was soft and quick, like the pitter-patter of rain on the window or a race commentator with the sound turned down.

'Anyway, we weren't doing any harm,' said Hattie.

'Like hell you weren't,' he said and his button-black eyes flicked from one to the other of us like a greedy pirate's. 'Do you know what them cattle is here for? To get nice and fat so that when they goes off to market they'll fetch a good price. And if the likes of you worry 'em and make 'em dance and prance around, do you know what happens to all that nice fat on them bones of theirs?'

'It wobbles around,' said Hattie bravely but we could afford to be a bit rude because of who we were. But just say we hadn't been ...

'That it don't,' said the man in his light, sing-along voice, and if Hattie had said 'Spotted dick and custard' he'd have still said 'That it don't'. 'It turns to muscle, and do you know what muscle means to you and me? Yep, gristle. And do you like eating gristle? Nope, neither do I. So you two run along now and leave them bullocks be. You're worse than terriers, you are.'

So off we went towards the gate at the top of the field, not exactly hurrying in order to show we weren't going to be bossed around by the likes of him.

'I was tempted to say we couldn't run because of a) your leg and b) we didn't want to turn into gristle,' I said.

'He'd make a good murderer in a film,' said Hattie.

'Or a pirate,' I said. 'Cut-throat Jake in *Captain Pugwash*.'

'Or Bluto in *Popeye*.'

When we got to the gate I glanced back. He was standing in the same spot, his gun resting on his hip, cigarette smoke drifting upwards and disappearing before it had time to turn into a cloud. The Yellow Dog sat as still as a china ornament, watching our every move. So did the man. To my surprise he was grinning in a most sinister fashion, and it was then I knew who he reminded me of exactly and the question was, had Mr Richards read Beatrix Potter's books in his youth? If he had I was laughing.

'*I* know who he is,' I said. 'Tommy Brock. A short, bristly, fat, waddling person with a grin.'

'Who's not nice in his habits,' said Hattie. 'And eats wasp nests and frogs and worms and waddles about by moonlight, digging things up.'

'And goes to bed in his boots and grins when he snores, one eye not perfectly shut,' I said.

We climbed the gate and walked down a short, wooded avenue and I sang, to the tune of 'On the First Day of Christmas', *'One gaga Granny, one loopy aunty, one common-as-muck maid, one brother who-fancies-himself-as-a-pop-singer and a man-with-a-gun who looks like Tommy Brock.'*

We walked between thick, silent hedges down Holly Tree Loke. A cock pheasant, cocky because he'd survived a shooting season, minced across our path in brightly coloured woman's clothing. We passed the rat- and mouse-inhabited brick and flint barn and the clucking, brooding black henhouse and the mud-up-to-your-waist pond in the meadow dotted with fat-uddered cows and goose-stepping ducks and feathery plus-foured bantams whose roost was ruled by a red-headed, chestnut-coloured cock.

Once upon a time the stables housed ten carthorses; you would walk in and be confronted by a row of large bottoms and tails in assorted colours. It was like a cool, quiet church which smelt of horse and hay and leather, with only the sound of munching and the occasional clomp of hoof on brick floor. Now it smelt of diesel and creosote and rats, and housed oily sacks and oil drums and bags of fertiliser and tins of poison and signs that said FOOT & MOUTH DISEASE and bits and pieces of rusting farm machinery. The stableyard where the horses were once hitched to ploughs and threshing machines and carts had been concreted over, and from every crack grew a stout weed. It wasn't only the horses you missed, but also the sound of cheerful men's voices. The crumbling red-brick farmyard had turned into a bit of a mausoleum.

We passed muddy tractors and a muddier plough, a baler, a sugar-beet harvester and a seed drill in the sagging, open-sided cart shed held up by tree trunks.

We walked into the cowshed and up the narrow passage that ran between the calves' feeding troughs. There was the same munching sound as there used to be in the stable but it wasn't as peaceful. The calves moved around more than the horses and the mealy,

56

sweet-milk smell was mixed with old damp straw and Scrubb's Ammonia.

'Look, isn't he sweet,' said Hattie stroking the curly bit on a calf's forehead. 'He's sucking my fingers. It feels all tickly.'

We stroked each calf in turn, and then wandered into Jack's shed beside the milking parlour where the calf food was mixed. Jack was sitting in his corner on a pile of empty sacks below a fly-blown 1957 calendar of a cow and calf and the words 'Allen & Brown – first for cattle feed', eating a hearty corned-beef sandwich and drinking cold tea from a glass jar.

'Blast, look who it isn't! You've caught me having a spot of nineses. Or should I say ...' and he screwed up his eyes to look at his watch '... quarter-past-eightses. It's hearing them calves go munch, munch, makes me a bit peckish, too. Now, come and sit you down and tell your old Jack what you've been a doing of.'

His dungarees smelt of meal, and there was meal in the cracks of his red rough hands and in his hobnail boots. Sitting on the sacks beside Jack gave you the same feeling as, say, sitting in an armchair by a blazing fire in winter, eating hot buttered toast and watching a good cartoon on television. Even though he was a grown-up you never felt shy with him, not in a million years.

'Now, can I interest either of you in what you could call a rough and ready sandwich?' he said, opening his greaseproof paper parcel. We thanked him politely but said we didn't want to spoil our breakfast.

'Er – we were very, very sorry to hear about Mrs Butterworth,' I said.

'Yes, very sorry indeed,' said Hattie, her voice quivering the way it always did before she laughed and I glared fiercely at her round the edge of Jack's large stomach.

'Yep, well, we all have to go sooner or later,' said Jack, returning his half-eaten sandwich to its greaseproof wrapper. 'Fact of life, dying is, and that's a fact. It was that there bugger of a winter ... Coo, lor, worse than 1947, that was. That took some getting over, I can tell you.'

It wasn't clear whether he meant his wife dying or the bugger of a winter took some getting over; we stayed silent for as long as we could and then I said, 'Er, Jack, did the old bugger of a winter kill off Smiler, too?'

'That it did,' said Jack, sighing. 'He was on his last legs, anyway, that poor old hoss. And then there were none.'

'And then there was *one*,' said Hattie.

'I don't reckon you can count that old Snap Dragon. That little

57

old devil's never done a day's work in his life. No, it's them tractors now. Tractors, tractors, tractors, machines, machines, machines. I reckon if the guv'nor had his way he'd get rid of old fogies like me and Reggie and get in more machines. I don't reckon they're much of an improvement meself. Break down soon as look at them and always needing spare parts. No, it's no companion a tractor in't, not like a good old hoss who listens to your troubles. Still, we mustn't get stuck in our ways now, must we,' he said, slapping his navy thighs. 'The guv'nor, he's what's called a progressive farmer, I believe. There's talk about going all arable, and growing foreign rubbish like them courgette whatsits and oilseeed rape. And then there's the old pheasant shooting. He's got a fancy new gamekeeper installed up at Woodman's Cottage. The guv'nor's planning to turn it into big business, inviting city gents up for a day's shoot and charging them a small fortune. And foreigners, too, so I've heard tell. Dutchmen and Belgiums and the like. I told him, 'as long as he don't have no Germans . . .'

'Why, Jack?' said Hattie, though she already knew.

'Every man in this village went to fight in that Great War, I said to him, and do you know how many of 'em came back? One. Yours truly. And then I go and lose both me sons in the Second . . . Still, let's not depress ourselves by talking about war. I'll tell you this much for nothing, though; things han't been the same round here since your grandad's day. It's all business and profit and milking the ground for all it's worth and no respect for the natural balance of things. Take sparrowhawks, for example. You used to see quite a few round these parts but not no more. Practically extinct they are thanks to some new old pesticide they've been using as a seed dressing.'

We nodded wisely, and Jack said, 'How's your grandma, by the way? The winter took the wind out of her sails fair and square.'

We said she was on the mend now, and Jack said she's as strong as an ox, that one, she'd got years to go yetawhile.

'Jack,' I said. 'We've just been shouted at by the new gamekeeper.'

'Have you indeed? You don't want to go taking no notice of old Brian Pike.'

'Is it true, Jack, that bullocks' fat turns to gristle when they run?'

Jack's tummy chuckled. 'Is that what he told you? I reckons they'd have to run all the way to Norwich and back and then do fifty press-ups for that to happen. He's a rum'un, that one. Likes to throw his weight around. Rum breed, gamekeepers. "Ogres of the wood" they used to be known as.'

'You liked Arthur,' I said.

'Ah, but he mucked in with other jobs, too. He weren't no professional who went to some fancy college. Arthur was one of the lads, unlike this one. He thinks he's above the likes of us farm labourers. They're in between two stools, I reckon. Lonely sort of life it must be. And an unpleasant sort of job. Tampers with nature.'

My ears pricked up. Mr Richards was bound to be interested in the tampering of nature. 'Why, what does he do exactly?' I asked.

Jack hesitated. 'Oh, this and that. You'll find out, soon enough. Puts his old pheasants before anything, he do. And what for? So they can be shot, not by country gents who know the law of the land but city slickers who if they've got a few whiskies inside them look cock-eyed down the barrel and maim the poor old buggers rather than kill 'em.'

'Pheasants don't blend in very well with the countryside, do they,' I said.

'That they don't. Them old cocks are far too gawdy and foreign-looking to my mind. Still, like I say, we must move with the times – that's something you young-uns don't have to worry about.'

'I don't like the new ways much, either,' I said and told him about the red monstrosities. 'By the way have you met Granny's new helper? Dawn's her name.'

Jack slapped his mealy hands on his thighs again. 'You haven't seen her yet? Blast you've a rum old treat in store. Talk about new ways – she's ahead of her time, I reckon. Cor dear me, she's a character and a half and then some. She blends into the landscape round here the way . . . a cock pheasant do! She keeps your grandma on her toes, I shouldn't wonder.'

We talked more about the old ways and the new ways, and about the Shotestead Show and Jack said if one of his cows didn't win this year he'd eat his hat, and I said don't you mean cap and he laughed and said 'That an' all.'

'Well, I can't spend all day mardling, much as I'd like to,' he said, standing up. 'Come and see me whenever you fancy. I've got me darts team at the Plough and me whist drives and me roses, but it gets a bit lonely at times, I don't mind admitting.'

We walked back by road to avoid the gamekeeper.

'Jack wasn't as jolly as usual, was he,' Hattie said.

'Well, would you be if your wife and your favourite horse had died and the Germans had killed all your best friends and your sons – and you had modern ways to contend with? I was just thinking. Wouldn't it be funny if Jack and Granny got married.'

'Don't be silly,' Hattie said. 'Granny's upper class and Jack's lower class. I bet he belches after meals and walks on carpets in his muddy hobnail boots.'

'Yes, but it doesn't matter so much about marrying someone of the same class when you're old, does it. It's not as if you'd have children and argue about their education. And I bet Jack would make a far better companion than that Dawn person.'

If Granny died before Jack he'd inherit the farm,' said Hattie.

We met Dan on the corner of the drive. He was wearing shorts. His legs were big hairy man's ones.

'Blimey O'Reilly, look at our legs compared with yours,' I shouted. 'Ours look like deserts and yours look like forests!'

Hattie laughed. 'And blimey O'Reilly, is this really our brother we see before us? I haven't seen him this early in the morning for years. Do you think the blonde bombshell could have anything to do with it, Sarah?'

'Come on, my little chickadees, we were about to send out a search party,' said Dan lifting us both up and swinging us round.

'What's she like?'

'Who?'

'*You* know.'

'Haven't a clue. I haven't seen her yet. Just heard her – and smelt her.'

'Oh, no. Not BO as well.'

'No, some pukey scent. She's made the place smell like a tart's boudoir.'

'Our grandmother's maid's got no nose,' I said.

'How does she smell?'

'*Awful!*' we all shouted at the tops of our voices.

CHAPTER SIX

Rabbits could not bear him; they could smell him a mile off, wrote Beatrix Potter about Mr Tod. Exactly the same could be written about us and that Dawn person. For as soon as we opened the front door her scent crashed into our nostrils like a Force 10 gale.

Holding our breath, we ventured into the dining room. Granny sat at the head of the table, pouring tea from a teapot covered in a maroon and blue striped knitted thing like a football supporter's scarf. Granny herself wore a smart navy blue blouse with a cameo brooch and, apart from her hair and eyes, looked fairly normal and not cross that we were late. She didn't ask us if we'd washed our hands and we'd been touching bullocks and calves and goodness knows what; could humans catch foot and mouth disease?

'Sorry we're late, Granny. We were talking to Jack and got carried away.'

'Ah, Jack. How is the dear old soul?'

I studied her funny eyes for any lovey-dovey signs.

'Very well,' I said, and added craftily, 'He's handsomer than I remember.'

'*Jack? Handsome?* What a weird taste in men you have, sister dear,' said Dan.

'I think he gets a bit lonely, though, Granny – in the evenings.' Later I would tell her what he said about the new ways, and the Germans, and his nineses really being quarter-past-eightses because seeing the calves munch made him peckish, too. Right then I wanted to concentrate on meeting *her*. You could hear her way off in the kitchen singing about walking like an angel in a flat, coarse, common voice. I pulled a face at the others. How *dare* she make such a din. Not only had she taken over the air we breathed smell-wise, but sound-wise, too.

'*You're the devil in disguise.*' Speak for yourself, I thought and just at that moment I saw, at *my* place, something more repulsive than the plastic dog's mess Dan had put on my plate on April Fools' Day. It was a table napkin in a cheap yellow plastic ring and, even worse, a copy of the *Daily Mirror*. As far as I was aware, up till now the only newspaper ever to have graced the breakfast table at Gressenhan Hall was *The Times*.

'I say, Granny, who's sitting in *my* place?' I said, forcing my voice to sound cheerful.

'Oh sorry, darling, I should have warned you. Dawn and I decided it was daft me sitting alone in here and her sitting alone in the kitchen, so she eats with me. We keep each other company. I've put you this side next to Hattie.'

'But *we're* here, Granny. We're your company now.'

'Yes, of course you are, darling, but I can hardly banish Dawn to the kitchen just because you've arrived, can I?'

Of course you can, I thought. You're her employer, you can make her eat in the henhouse if you want. Eat meals with a *servant* ... I'd never heard anything like it. Mummy would have fifty fits. And worst of all she'd be sitting in *my* place.

'I don't want to sit next to Hattie,' I said. 'She sticks her elbows out. I want to have a side of the table to myself.'

'Come on, Sausage, sit down, please,' said Dan, giving me one of his looks.

So I thumped into my new seat and sulked, something I hadn't done since I was at least nine.

We could hear a loud click click click on the passage floor and a wobbling egg-cup sound and a jingle-jangle noise like the White Witch's sleigh bells in *The Lion, the Witch and the Wardrobe,* and we held our breaths and stared at the door, and in walked Dawn Potts.

If Granny had been enough of an electric shock to kill five fully grown men, she was enough to kill five fully grown men *wearing rubber boots*.

Normally when you met a new person they reminded you of a character in a children's book or a Walt Disney film, or of an animal or a bird or *something* you'd come across before. Dawn reminded me of nothing on earth. Her hair, the colour of straw with mouldy black bits at the roots, was piled all higgledy-piggledy on top of her head as high as an elephant's eye. She wore a tight pink man-made lacy jumper that you could see her brassiere through as clear as day, a very, very pointed one that made her bosoms look like the wrong ends of ice-cream cones, or perhaps that was the shape they actually were. She wore rings on all her fingers and scuffed white stilettos on her toes and a black skirt that ended *above her knees*. From her ears hung tinkly gold ear-rings like the cheapest sort of Christmas-tree decorations you see in Woolies, and her wrists were smothered in jangly bracelets that had hanging off them little gold dogs and other things too vile to look at that probably came out of crackers. And blimey O'Reilly, her *eyes*! They had black all round them, like our neighbour at home's dog or an ancient warrior, and eyelashes as long and black as sweep's brushes, and thin black arched eyebrows like Cruella de Vil's. Her mouth was sugary almond pink like a plastic doll's, and the pong of her scent was so overwhelming you didn't want to breathe in too deeply in case it took over your lungs and cast a spell on you and the wind changed and you ended up *looking* like her.

'Hi, you lot,' she said in a loud foghorn voice, her silly mouth smiling but her black-as-soot eyes remaining as hard as nails, crashing the plate of eggs on the table, causing Mother Goose – *my* egg cup – to wobble over. 'Oh gawd, why am I so frigging clumsy? Come here, missus,' she said stretching over to put it upright and if Dan had wanted he could have seen up her skirt to her ... But he didn't. He was far too much of a gentleman.

'Dawn, dear, may I introduce you to my grandchildren,' said Granny, trying to bring some dignity into the proceedings.

'Don't bother, I'll guess, Mrs Aitch.' (Mrs *Aitch!* What a disgusting cheek!)

'Now, you,' she said staring at me and narrowing her eyes so they looked like two lumps of coal, '... must be Sarah.' I nodded and managed a flicker of a smile just to be polite. 'Blimey, you're bigger than I imagined. And you're Hattie – cor, are them waves natural? Lucky sod. And you – must be Dan', and she put her hands on her hips which made the ice-cream cones stick out even more, and if she'd been standing a shade closer she could have poked out one of his eyes. 'Cor, you're right, Mrs Aitch. He *is* a looker, ain't he.'

I watched Dan's reddening face closely for signs that he thought she was a 'looker', too (though if he did he'd want his head examining). But he wasn't even looking at her but at his cornflakes bowl while jiggling his leg.

'Shy, is he?' she said, looking at me.

'Er, yes. We all are really, with people we don't know,' I said. *And don't like* I tried to convey by my expression, though of course she was far too thick-skinned – and thick – to notice.

'Well, I expect it won't take you very long to get to know Dawn,' said Granny quietly, smiling faintly at us.

'Oh, no time at all. I'm an open book, ain't I, Mrs Aitch? Oooh, that reminds me. Can I have a butcher's at your leg, Hat? Mind if I call you Hat? Hattie reminds me of Hattie Jacques and makes you think of a round cuddly person which you certainly ain't. Don't worry, I'll look under the table so you won't have to stick it up in the air or nothing', and she dived under the table-cloth.

We sat open-mouthed. No one ever mentioned Hattie's leg. She had caught polio just before the vaccinations came in; the doctors said she had a fifty-fifty chance of making a complete recovery and we all prayed like mad; but she was in the wrong fifty. It was the first time I'd seen Mummy cry. Too many muscles had been damaged, the doctor said, and though the leg would be under-developed and she'd always walk with a slight limp she'd be able to lead a perfectly normal life. Apart from running races, said Hattie without a wobble in her voice though she sobbed her heart out in the car going home; and dancing and climbing trees and riding bicycles and playing rounders and hop-scotch, but the doctor just smiled and said there's more to life than those things; why, she could be in a wheelchair for the rest of her life and she wouldn't like that very much, would she? I told Hattie later that in a way it was fairer that she had got polio rather than me as she was good at painting and I wasn't specially good at anything, and also she was bound to be prettier than me when she grew up, and Hattie said she supposed so, though it would have been fairer if neither of us had caught it and anyway, she already had her glasses to contend with. A withered leg was one thing, but a withered leg *and* a squint was the last straw. Sometimes, and I'd never tell Hattie this in a million years, I wished I was the one with polio and glasses and long dark wavy hair and could paint, because then I'd get all the attention and sympathy and be people's favourite.

'Oh, *blimey*,' squealed Dawn from under the table. 'It's nothing like as bad as I thought it would be.' She bobbed up, a piece of hair hanging down her cheek like yellow wool. 'All you've got to do is wear slacks and no one will know the difference.'

'Yes, they will,' Hattie said. 'I limp.'

'Yeah, well,' said Dawn, 'when you're older and go on dates, just make sure you're the first to arrive at the pub and just stay put all evening. Oh, except you wouldn't be able to go to the toilet. Oh, well, at least you don't have to wear one of those thingamy-jigs – you know, caterpillars or whatever they're called – like what me cousin has to wear.'

Toilet? Pub? Date? Who did she think we were? As common as muck like she was? Was she aware my sister would never go to the *toilet* in her life? And talking about it at meal times ... Why didn't Granny say something?

'We'd better get cracking on the eggs,' said Granny.

I opened my mouth to comment on Granny's joke, when Dawn crashed in with 'Funny joke, that, Mrs Aitch. Cracking – eggs.'

'Oh. Oh, I see,' said Granny, a whisper of a smile crossing her lips. 'Would you be kind enough to pass me one, dear?'

'One egg coming up, Mrs Aitch. They might be a touch on the hard side, I lost all track of time. They say hard-boiled eggs are binding but I can't say as I've noticed.'

Her voice would have been loud with cotton wool in your ears, and as for the accent – it was worse than Miriam Karlin's in *The Rag Trade* or a fishwife's. And what, come to think of it, was a fishwife – not a woman married to a fish, surely? This made me think of a Dawn joke which would end up, with many others, in a special section in the diary: *What did the fishwife say to Dawn? You talk a load of CODSwallop!!!*

'What does binding mean?' asked Hattie.

'You're pulling my chain!' shrieked Dawn. 'You *must* know. Or don't you toffs ever ...'

'Not at table, please, dear,' said Granny.

'Sorry, Mrs Aitch. I must remember me Ps and Qs now I'm in polite company, mustn't I,' and I knew she would; I just knew it. Instead of passing us our eggs first and taking the one left as a proper servant should, she just helped herself first, and, even worse, to *my* Mother Goose.

Hattie, Dan and I looked at each other. Although I couldn't bear the thought of her hands on it – they were bound to be smothered in germs, and who knew what horrors lurked under those long pink painted nails – I didn't want to embarrass her. It was Dan who came to the rescue. 'Er – I think you've got Sarah's egg cup there.'

'Oh, sorry. I didn't realise ...' She looked quite crestfallen and for a second I felt almost sorry for her.

'And mine's Sooty on Television,' said Hattie.

'And I suppose yours is the pink elephant, eh, Dan?' said Dawn in the kind of voice Sheila Page used when asking Miss Rose about wizards.

'It really doesn't matter.'

'Yes it does. He's just too polite to say,' said Hattie.

'Oh, all right, I'll have the flowery one. Makes no difference to me. The eggs will all taste as flipping rotten.'

'Yes, they are a trifle hard,' said Granny, digging away as if her spoon were a trowel and the egg frozen earth. 'Do use the timer next time, dear. I've shown you how it works.'

Yes, do, I thought, because now we can't have soldiers, the whole point of a boiled egg. Like the biscuits and the shepherd's pie before it, my egg didn't want to be swallowed. (*It is the summer when food clings to the sides of the mouth like clay, when cheep scents poison one's breathing aparatas ...,* I would write.) I was tempted to help it on its way with a mouthful of tea but that was common, the sort of thing Dawn would do and one really ought to be setting a good example; standards round here were low enough already.

'*Dig* these eggs!' I said for Dan and Hattie's ears only, but of course Dawn had to go and say 'Yer what?' so I said 'It's a family joke, actually.'

Dawn opened the *Daily Mirror* and everyone got on with eating their breakfast except Granny, who sat with her hands folded and a faraway look in her eyes. Maybe she was thinking back to when Grandpa was alive and the Hillington family was in its prime, when the boiled eggs, served in silver cups, were always cooked to perfection, and when servants would no more eat meals with the family than take a bath with them.

I looked across at Dawn; her table napkin (or as she would call it, serviette) was still in its plastic ring and she was piling butter on her toast as if there was no tomorrow. I could feel another joke coming on: *Why is Dawn like her butter? They are both disgustingly thick!*

' 'Ere, what's your star sign then, Dan?' she said with her mouth full.

'Er – Sagittarius.'

'Oh yeah? Half man, half beast, eh? I'm a fire sign, too. Aries.'

'I'm a fire sign, too,' I said. 'Leo.'

'Yeah? Anyway, Dan, according to Leon Petralengo changes are in the wind. You'll be branching out into something new.'

The fact that she could read came as something of a surprise, though of course she could have been making it up.

'I don't believe in astrology,' said Dan. 'It's a form of brainwashing.'

'No, it ain't,' said Dawn. 'It's a science.'

'We met that new gamekeeper this morning, Granny,' I said to change the subject. The less Dawn and Dan had so say to each other the better.

'Oh, did you, darling?' said Granny. 'His name's Mr Pike.'

'Yes, and I bet it's no coincidence that he's named after Britain's fiercest freshwater fish,' I said.

'He reminded us of Tommy Brock,' said Hattie.

'Who's he when he's at home?' said Dawn.

'A badger,' I said, and added gleefully, 'but he's never at home. He's always in other people's!'

Hattie and I roared with laughter, and Granny and Dan smiled

66

and Dawn said 'What are you on about? I don't get it', which was exactly the intention.

'He told us off for playing with the bullocks,' said Hattie, 'so Sarah told him we were your grandchildren and he was a bit nicer after that, though not very nice.'

'You were playing with the *what*?' screeched Dawn, her black, delinquent seagull's eyes round with wonder. 'Oh, bullocks. Blimey, I thought you said something rude there for a moment.' (*Dawn is the Enid Blyton of literature, the Carry On films of the cinema*, I would write.)

'Is Mr English going in for pheasants in a big way then?' asked Dan ignoring Dawn and quite right too.

'Yes, indeed,' said Granny and sighed. 'But not like in your grandfather's day when just a few were reared each year with broody hens. Mr English, I gather, is doing it as a profit-making venture and chicks are reared by the hundred in incubators. Continental businessmen will pay large sums of money for the privilege of a day's shooting on the Gressenham Estate.'

'I think it's cruel, if you ask me' (but we weren't, so just shut up), said Dawn. 'Poor little things.'

'They're not very little,' said Hattie.

'Oh, I thought they were,' said Dawn. 'Maybe I've only seen teenage ones.'

Dan smirked and it made me feel even more bad-tempered, him finding something *she* said funny, especially as it wasn't.

'What do gamekeepers do, exactly, Granny?' I said. 'Apart from feeding the pheasants and looking out for poachers. Jack says they tamper with nature.'

'They see to it that no harm comes to the pheasants. So any animal that is their enemy he, er, disposes.'

'What sort of animals are the pheasant's enemy?'

'Oh, weasels, rats, birds with hooked beaks, foxes, stoats, squirrels.'

'Not sweet little squirrels!' said Dawn.

'Grey ones, not red ones,' I said crossly. 'Grey ones are just rats with bushy tails, and you wouldn't feel sorry for rats, would you.'

'Yeah, I would as it happens. I feel sorry for all living creatures who're mucked around with by humans,' and what a typical stupid Townie attitude. 'How does this geezer dispose of them then, Mrs Aitch – just out of interest?'

Granny said by various methods – traps, snares, poison, the gun. 'I so worry that Clifford might get caught in a trap,' she added.

'Would he die?' asked Hattie.

67

'Mr Pike is supposed to inspect the traps at regular intervals, but if he forgot one day, and we didn't hear his barks ...'

'He might starve to death,' I said.

'Yes, but what would the trap actually do to him?' said Hattie.

'It would catch his leg so he couldn't get away,' said Dan and muttered something about nature being red in tooth and claw.

'I heard about this dog, right?' said Dawn, getting excited. 'A collie, I think it was, yeah? who got his leg caught in a gin trap so he chewed his ...'

'That'll do, Dawn dear,' Granny said quietly.

'He chewed his what?' Hattie said.

'I said that'll do.'

'Clifford isn't the pheasants' enemy, is he?' asked Hattie.

'All dogs love chasing pheasants,' said Granny. 'So yes, in theory, Clifford is on Mr Pike's "wanted" list, too.'

'He's a bit past it if you ask me,' said Dawn. 'Clifford, I mean, not the Pike bloke', and she let out a great cackle of laughter that was so loud Granny flinched her shoulders, and what on earth was funny about that? 'That geezer gives me the creeps,' she said and *who cared?* 'Well, it stands to reason that you can't trust a man who carries a gun. And those black piercing eyes that stare at you as if they can see what you look like without clothes on.'

It wouldn't be difficult, I thought, with that see-through jumper.

Granny laughed politely. 'My dear, I don't think ...'

'I reckon he's got gyppo blood in him.'

'Oh, I don't *think* so, dear,' said Granny, and I wanted to ask what gyppo blood was but as I wasn't going to show any interest in anything Dawn said I didn't.

'Well, I certainly wouldn't fancy meeting him down a dark alley, ta very much,' she said. Then she did something that really made my hackles rise. For without a by your leave, her seagull-jawed jingly-jangly hand swooped across and snatched the last piece of toast.

CHAPTER SEVEN

'I refuse to have a meal with that rough, rude *apparition* ever again, and that's final,' said Hattie.

'Hear, hear,' I said, but only out of loyalty to Hattie. For I had decided to make the best of a bad job by persuading myself that the rougher and ruder Dawn was the better my diary would be.

We were waiting for Granny in Austin of England, her small grey round car, in the gloom of the coach house. Thanks to Dawn saying, 'What are we going to feed this little lot on then, Mrs Aitch? The cupboard's more or less bleeding bare,' Granny had suggested we go shopping. Dan sat in the front with his guitar. Afterwards he was going to meet his 'pop-group blokes'.

'You'll go hungry, then,' said Dan. 'You heard what Granny said. Can't you just ignore her?'

'*Ignore* her? It would be like ignoring chronic toothache, or a tiger in your bedroom. It's all right for you, she doesn't sit right opposite you. Even when I'm looking at Granny I can see her foul black eyes and yellow hair out of the corner of my eye.'

'So can I,' said Hattie. 'And her table manners are appalling.'

'She treats the place as if it's hers. And she's only a servant.'

'If you two had your way we'd still be living in the Dark Ages,' said Dan.

'No, we wouldn't, we'd be living in the *civilised* ages, when people are polite and know their place.'

'Yeah, but life's not like that any more. The class system's on the way out, or haven't you heard.'

'I'm not talking about class, I'm talking about manners. I mean, if I went to *her* house I wouldn't throw my weight around.'

'But this *is* her house,' said Dan. 'And the sooner we realise that the better.'

'If she calls me Hat again I'm going to call her Brassiere,' said Hattie. 'I mean you wouldn't want to be called Scarf or Pullover, would you? And her brassiere was peculiar. It made her bosoms look like spears.'

'Perhaps it's because her bosoms *are* like spears.'

'Yes, perhaps all common girls have pointy bosoms.'

69

'Mrs B didn't. They were round and squidgy like beach balls.'

'Yes, but she wasn't a girl.'

'All right then. Vera Finch in the baker's.'

'Girls, girls,' said Dan.

'And I thought it was really off, her crawling under the table to look – have a butcher's, rather – at Hattie's leg, as if it was something at a fun fair.'

'Yes, like a bearded lady,' said Hattie.

'Oh, I don't know,' said Dan. 'It's preferable to what other people do – pretend nothing's wrong and then take sly sideways glances when they think no one's looking. That's what's known as hypocrisy.'

'What's that?'

'I've just told you. Or it's when people in high places tut-tut about someone misbehaving when on the quiet they're doing exactly the same.'

'Is it like if you were to say "Fancy Dawn reading the foul old common *Daily Mirror*" and when no one was looking have a sneaky read of it?'

'Exactly,' said Dan. 'Hey, that's not a bad idea.'

'I can't believe that's her real accent,' I said. 'She sounds like an actress playing the part of a cockney.'

'Yes, you keep expecting her to start talking normally,' said Hattie.

'Boy, you two are so unworldly,' said Dan. 'Thousands – millions – of people speak like that in London. Anyway, we're stuck with her so we might as well try to get on with her. You never know, she might turn out to be a bit of a laugh.'

'A bit of a *cry,* don't you mean,' I said. 'You must admit though, Dan, she is pretty frightful. You don't, er, like her, do you?'

'I wouldn't say *like,* exactly. But she makes a refreshing change from most of the boring, stuffy old squares we usually meet up here. And at least she's not a hypocrite.'

'You don't think she's . . .' and I took a deep breath, 'pretty, do you?'

Dan threw back his head and laughed. It sounded a bit on the hollow side to me, but maybe the acoustics in the coach house were to blame. 'That's like me asking you if you think Mr Ball's handsome.'

'No it's not. Ball's old and a man and she's young and a girl.'

'Who wears tons of make-up. Bucketfuls, in fact,' said Hattie.

'That's precisely why I don't find her pretty,' said Dan. 'It looks as though she put it on with a trowel.'

'Like the butter on her toast,' I said.

'She's not my type at all,' said Dan. 'Far too pushy and obvious. I go more for the *au naturel* type.'

'I don't know what type she is. I've never met anyone like her in my life,' said Hattie. 'It would be impossible to play that game – you know, if this person were an animal, what sort would they be.'

'Not without insulting the animal,' I said. 'I know, if she were a fun-fair attraction, which one would she be?'

'The Big Wheel,' said Dan, 'because she's a *dizzy* blonde. Or a hoopla stall with that chest.'

'The dodgems,' said Hattie, 'because you'd be trying to dodge her the whole time.'

'No. The Tip the Lady out of Bed stand. Do you remember that one we saw with that foul blonde woman with pouting lips and men were aiming balls at the thing which tipped up the bed so she'd fall out and they would see her in her baby-doll pyjamas? That's who she reminds me of.'

'Yes a Tip the Lady out of Bed woman,' said Hattie. 'Though you could hardly call her a *lady*. More a peasant or a serf.'

'That's just given me a great idea for a song,' Dan said. 'Thanks, Sarah. Here comes Granny. Let's hope the old bugger of a winter hasn't impaired her already dubious driving skills,' and he got out to open the door for her.

'Sorry to have kept you waiting, darlings,' she said, climbing stiffly into her seat. 'I was sorting out Dawn and lunch.'

She was wearing a tweed jacket over her blouse, sensible lace-up shoes and *that dreadful straw hat*. She would be seen in it in *public*.

As if she could read my mind she looked round and said, 'The hat doesn't look too frightful, does it? You would always tell me, darlings . . . When you get to my age you can go so wrong.'

Wat it because I was a hypocrite that I didn't say anything? Hattie obviously wasn't one though. 'If you don't mind me saying, Granny, I'm not sure about the plastic flowers.'

'Oh, aren't you, darling? I thought they were rather jolly. It would look so – bald without them.' (And you would look so bald without the hat, I thought; on balance, it was the lesser of two evils.)

'Are you sure you wouldn't like me to drive?' asked Dan.

Granny said she was perfectly capable, thank you, then proceeded to kangaroo forward and jerk on the brakes to avoid crashing into the stirrup pump and the brick wall, causing us to cry with silent laughter. Then with a roar she reversed out without looking behind her or in the mirror. There was a shriek. 'Good gracious, have I killed someone?' she cried.

It was Aunt Lynette. Her toe nails were painted the same red as her finger nails but not the same red as her dressing gown. She wore a thick white hairband which looked like a bandage, and no lipstick. 'In the nick of time!' she shouted. 'You couldn't be loves and get me a couple of pairs of nylons from Bryants? Do you mind, Sarah, darling? Size nine and any shade so long as they're vaguely flesh coloured. Avoid the Old Dragon like the plague.'

'All right,' I said, pleased she'd chosen me for such a grown-up assignment, the way I was pleased the foul Dawn – and the others didn't know about this – had chosen me to give her fiancé a message.

We careered off, leaving Aunt Lynette standing in a cloud of exhaust, and got as far as Cow Parsley Lane without once changing gear.

'Er – Granny? Is the choke still out?'

'Oh, thank you, Dan. One gets so forgetful.'

Then Dan said wasn't it round about time to be thinking about changing gear, and Granny said one should always be in a low – or did she mean high? – gear going up a hill, otherwise one was in danger of losing too much power and going backwards which would never do.

Dan looked round at us with an 'I see no hill' expression and Hattie and I quietly roared while Austin of England noisily roared down the middle of the main road at two miles an hour like the Queen, and a man hoeing onions looked round expecting a large farm machine and seemed surprised to see a little grey mouse of a car. 'The mouse that roared,' I said quietly.

'Mummy says, you can never trust country roads,' Hattie said.

'As long as people know you're there,' said Granny, gaily pressing the horn. It sounded like the tiny squeak of a very shy girl mouse and Jack and Reggie on their tractors would never have heard it in a million years, and Hattie and I rolled around on the back seat weak with silent laughter. (There was no fear Granny would see us in the mirror because she hadn't looked in it once so far.)

It was only two and a half miles to Shoteshead but it seemed like twenty-two and a half. We went so slowly you could see whether or not cattle had rings in their ears, whether scarecrows were wearing ties, what every cottage had growing in its garden and hanging on its washing line and the black middle bits in the poppies that bobbed in the cornfields.

'I bet there are tons of harvest mice living in there,' said Hattie. 'Someone should warn them their homes are going to be mown down soon.'

'They don't die,' I said reassuringly. 'They hear the combine coming and leap out in front of it.'

'Yes, but I bet they'd prefer more warning. Then they'd have time to pack.'

'Don't be daft. Harvest mice don't have suitcases,' I said, though I knew what she meant.

The journey was taking so long it gave me time to think about how I would describe Norfolk to Mr Richards.

I'm sure you would love Norfolk as much if not more than the Yorkshire Moors, Mr Richards, I would write. *Although it is an odd, lonely sort of a place, it is not as bleak and hostile as the Moors, but nor is it pretty-pretty, with green hills and cream-tea villages, like, say Deven or Sussex. And dispite what George V said (or was it Noel Coward?) Norfolk is not as flat as you think. If I had to chose between spending the rest of my life watching television or a Norfolk sky, I would chose the latter. And the light is always changing ... Aunt Lynette says speaking with her artist's hat on the Norfolk light is the reason she could never live anywhere else.*

The scenery is as varied as its inhabitants (rum'uns, good'uns, bad'uns but almost all nice'uns). It is a county of wheat and water and water meadows and willows ('willas', as local people say) and wildlife and wild fowl and wild woods and wild winds. Agriculture is its main industry, plus there are the Broads, of course, and 600 medievil churches all in all, and the sand and pebbled bird-haunted coastline, and muddy isolated villages and spick-and-span matey market towns and Norwich itself, a fine city which brisels with history. It is very hard for me to convay Norfolk's beauty to you in a couple of sentences. I think that the only way you could really appreshiate it basking in its full glory, Mr Richards, is to see it for yourself. Perhaps, if you don't think it is too forward of me to ask, you would like to come and stay at Granny's next year? She would make you feel terrably welcome, and so would I.

But ... what was I thinking about! That was the sort of thing Rosie Alston rather than a prospective Samantha Pepys would write. I'd be asking him to marry me next! If I wanted my diary to be the best in the class I would have to keep to the straight and narrow.

'What's ticking over in your brain, Sarah?' said Hattie, narrowing her eyes at me behind her pink spectacles. 'You look all sort of misty the way you do when you watch *Champion.*'

'She's probably thinking about her Mr Richards,' said Dan, and I clouted his shoulder so fast and furiously we didn't hear a squeak out of him for at least five minutes.

CHAPTER EIGHT

'You'll notice a few changes in Shoteshead. Look, darlings,' said Granny, making me long to sing, *'Keep your snoopy ey-es on the road ahead',* and she pointed to a row of new orange houses up a tarmac-ed road that last year was a bumpy track with a sign saying 'Unsuitable for Motors'. 'I believe that's the sort of thing Dawn and Albert have their eye on.'

'Ugh. How foul,' I said without thinking.

'They should be encouraged,' said Granny. 'Shoteshead needs all the young people it can get. The young are moving away and the old are moving in,' and her shoulders sighed.

'Why's that, do you think?' said Dan.

'There are no jobs, and there's nothing much for them to do. Apart from the youth club and the picture house ... The council wanted to build a bowling alley – do I mean bowling alley, Dan? – on the cattle-market site, but there was so much opposition from residents that a ghastly red self-service place – do I mean self-service or should it be *supermarket?* – appeared instead.'

'*Why* didn't the residents want a bowling alley?' I asked.

'I suppose they thought it would attract the rougher element who would rev up their motor cycles late at night.'

'And drop litter everywhere,' said Hattie.

'If they're not careful the town will die,' said Granny.

'Why will it die?' Hattie said.

'Because old people can't have babies,' I hissed.

'Just wait. When my pop group gets going the young'll come flocking back in droves,' said Dan cockily.'Hey, watch that goose, Granny.'

We roared in slow motion past the gates of the huge haunted workhouse that was now a hospital; poor people who remembered it as a workhouse refused to go there, even when they were very ill, in case they never came out again. We went over the blind bridge that straddled the weeping willow river, and past the musty-fusty mill with its cobwebs at the windows and rats at the sacks, and grand, red-brick houses and not-so-grand, red-brick cottages, the coal merchant's, the blacksmith's, The Maltings, the stonemason's yard, the Stonemason's Arms, the barn with the sign saying 'Price's: Best Antiques, Best Prices', the white doctor's surgery with its stone lion head on the porch and the grey Baptist church with its tiled tiger pit in the floor where people (naked, fully clothed or in a bathing costume I'd like to know) were baptised.

And then we were in White Lion Street, which had secret yards and dark alleys leading off it and whose pavements were too narrow for a pram or a person with a wide shopping basket or a dog on a lead.

'Just look what's replaced Fisher's, where we bought our cotton and buttons', said Granny. We looked and saw a shop called Knick-Knacks, its window full of glass and china ornaments and cheap plastic things, the sort of place where someone like Dawn would have a field day. 'And even more tragic,' said Granny with a sniff, 'is Ponds which has become, of all things, a *launderette* – do I mean launderette, Dan? Poor, dear Mr Pond. Your grandfather always bought his suits and trousers there. But after the War people started buying clothes off the peg and the business went downhill. The final straw came when his son decided to join the Merchant Navy and see the world.'

'Can't say I blame him,' said Dan. 'If I had the choice between running an old-fashioned men's outfitters and seeing the world, I know which I'd choose. Er, Granny, watch that dog.'

Granny swerved unnecessarily wide and narrowly missed a truck coming the other way.

We turned into the market-place, whose church spire towered above the steep sloping roofs of what were once wool and cloth merchants' houses but were now shops, and the old pink pub where Horatio Nelson once had a drink. We shuddered to a halt outside the Town Hall, in exactly the spot where the Number 10 bus always stopped while the driver dashed to the gents. (Dan once pointed this out to Granny and she said she wasn't going to change the habit of a lifetime just for the bus driver's convenience and Dan said, 'At the bus driver's *public* convenience, don't you mean, Granny!')

I carried the hen basket and skipped in front, Hattie held Granny's hand and Dan strolled a good distance behind, whistling casually.

We saw along Hart Street, past the post office and the baby Woolworths, the self-service monstrosity that had signs in the window saying TOP CAT 9d to 6½d; ICOL 2/6 to 1/3, WINDOWLENE 1/9 to 1/3. Wall's Pork Luncheon Meat, Heinz Salad Cream and Carnation Salmon could also be had for a bargain price.

75

'Why don't we go in there, Granny?' I shouted. 'We'd save tons of money.'

Granny said Dawn had dragged her in once because they were giving away stamps of some sort – Green Shield, did she mean? – and she couldn't find a thing she wanted and there was no one to ask, of course. 'I'm the wrong generation for such a place,' she said, pausing to catch her breath. 'Give me the Higgens way of doing things any day. So much more *civilised.*'

'I'm just going to pop into Pilgrim's,' shouted Dan. 'I'll meet you later in Higgens's, okay?'

'Dan just made a joke,' I said. 'He said he was going to *pop* into Pilgrim's, and they sell pop records.'

'No, they don't, darling. They sell electrical appliances.'

'Upstairs they do,' I said. 'Dan says it's Shoteshead's in-place.'

'Well, fancy that,' said Granny.

'It would have been an even funnier joke if one of us had been Daddy,' said Hattie. 'Then he could have said, "I'm just going to pop into Pilgrim's to look at pop records, Pop."'

'It would have been even funnier if he'd been thirsty, too. Then he could have said, "When I've finished this bottle of pop I'll just pop into ..."'

'I do wish Dan wouldn't say okay,' interrupted Granny. 'It's so frightfully ... *American.*'

We walked past the chemist and the florist and the saddler and the pet shop and the tobacconist where men could also have their hair cut. Higgens's smelt of coffee and cheese and sage-and-onion stuffing and black pepper and smoked bacon. The little white dog was still begging on the counter: if you put a penny on its tray it bent over and the penny fell into the kennel money box in aid of suffering animals.

Mr Higgens wore a white coat. If he hadn't been standing behind his counter, you would have mistaken him for a cowman.

'Good *morning,* Madam,' he beamed, and Granny said, 'Good morning, Mr Higgens. I've brought my granddaughters with me today. Their parents are on a motoring holiday in France.'

Mr Higgens remarked on how we'd both grown (as if we were runner beans, Hattie said later), and you couldn't quite see his eyes because the light was winking in his pebble glasses. He gave us each a lollipop, Hattie a red and me a yellow.

'Thank you very much, Mr Higgens,' we chorused and Granny handed him the shopping list and said we'd be back in half an hour if that suited.

'That'll suit me very nicely, Madam,' said Mr Higgens, giving a small bow. 'It'll be ready for collection in the customary brown box.'

'Darlings,' said Granny when we were outside. 'I really don't think penny lollipops warrant a "very much". "Thank you" would have been quite sufficient.'

'Would, say, sixpenny bars of chocolate?' said Hattie, but Granny pretended she hadn't heard.

'Swapsie?' I said to Hattie, offering her my lollipop. 'You're too young to wear lipstick.'

'No, I'm not,' said Hattie. 'Anyway, what's wrong with yellow lipstick? You might start a new fashion.'

We went into Bryants and, while Granny looked at tea cloths in the summer sale, Hattie and I strode purposefully upstairs to the hosiery department, which was next to the *underwear* department!

'Oh, good, we can have a good old look,' I said because when we were with Mummy or Granny it was rude to stare.

Stretched across plastic women's bottoms and torsos was a wicked white forest of roll-ons and girdles and corsets and corslets 'for those who need extra figure control'. Some had little legs, some did up at the front with laces, or at the side with zips or hooks, 'to help you adjust your figure to fashion'.

'Why don't they just say, "For those who are fat"?' Hattie said.

'Because they'd never sell any,' I said. 'No one likes to admit they're fat.'

'I'm never going to wear one of these contraptions when I grow up,' she said lifting a girdle out of a tray marked 'All 10/6'. 'Feel. It's got *bones* in it. Ugh. It would be like wearing a skelington. I bet Aunt Lynette doesn't wear one.'

'She must wear something to keep her nylons up,' I said. 'Bet she wears one of these.' And I held up a sort of belt with suspenders jangling from it like silver catkins. 'I dread to think what the foul Dawn wears.'

'Probably nothing, not even knickers,' said Hattie. 'Or if she does I bet they're black so they don't show the dirt.'

Plastic bosoms were covered in brassieres in all shapes and sizes, some pointed like Dawn's, others round and motherly, some with narrow daring straps, others with wide fuddy-duddy ones.

'What I'm going to do is what Chinese women used to do with their feet: wrap my chest tightly in bandages the whole time apart from when I have a bath,' said Hattie. 'Then I won't grow bosoms and won't have to wear a silly brassiere.'

'That would be tampering with nature,' I said. 'I think it would be nice to wear a bra. Look, does this suit me?' And I held one up

77

to my chest that was large enough to house a rabbit family and a large owl, and Hattie laughed so much she had to bend over, and suddenly a voice behind said, 'Can I help you young ladies?'

We looked round, scarlet-faced. The shop assistant didn't look like an Old Dragon; more like a plump pig in spectacles and a ginger wig and with plump pink legs ending in trotters crammed into too-tight shoes, and bosoms like a bolster. Perhaps her bosoms were the reason she worked in the underwear department; to make the larger customers feel at home.

'Er ...' I gave Hattie my lollipop to hold while I slithered the brassiere back in its box. 'I'm sorry, we were just trying to imagine what it would be like to wear a – brassiere.'

The Ginger Pig smiled and then laughed, a strange wobbly hiccup of a laugh. 'I'm only laughing because it's funny to hear young 'uns call them brassieres. Everyone calls them bras these days. I'll tell you something. By the time you two are ready to wear them, they'll be light as feathers. The manufacturers have at last cottoned on to the fact that girls don't want to be all trussed up like chickens. And them new stretch fabrics ... Why, you won't even know you're wearing one.'

'But if you don't know you're wearing one, wouldn't that mean it wasn't doing its job properly?' said Hattie.

The assistant hiccuped again, and her bolster shook like a jelly. 'Ah, it's all been scientifically worked out,' she said and sighed. 'I envy you two, I don't mind admitting. You should have seen the horrors me mum used to put me into. Everything is so much *freer* these days, and I don't just mean underwear, I mean life generally. You only have to look at America, and what happens there happens here, sooner or later.'

'May I ask you something too, please,' I said, because friendly grown-ups like her didn't grow on trees. 'Why does underwear have to be white?'

'Ah. It doesn't,' she said. 'But only white is considered *respectable*. You can get other colours elsewhere – that shop Joleen's in Norwich, for a kick-off. But not here at Bryants. There'd be an uproar among our older regular customers. I suppose we'll change with the times eventually. Who knows, in ten years the Queen will be wearing a green bra and red petti ...' and she hiccuped '... but at present, it's white, white or white. Though I'll let you into a little secret. For my last birthday, to cheer meself up I bought meself,' and she lowered her voice, 'a *black bra!* I haven't got a husband or anyone to see it, but *I* can see it, and it makes me feel ever so wicked.'

Out of the corner of my eye I could see the Old Dragon staring disapprovingly at our sticky lollipops.

'I would like to purchase two pairs of nylons for our aunt,' I said loudly to the assistant. 'She wants flesh-coloured ones, size nine.'

'Certainly, Madam, step this way,' she said. 'Now I wonder if your aunt cares for seams.'

'I don't think so,' I said. 'You might know her – she's Lynette Hillington.' And the assistant said oh, yes, she's a regular customer and ever such good fun, and come to think of it she could see a slight family resemblance. 'These Pretty Polly's are ever so nice. Runproof, and only six and eleven.'

We explained we had ten shillings for two pairs and eventually settled on some micro-mesh ones. 'She'll get three bob change she wasn't expecting,' said the girl chattily, ringing up three and six twice on the till.

The Old Dragon, who had been breathing hotly down the assistant's neck, now said, 'Hilda, when you've quite finished wasting time with these two, there are other customers waiting to be served. And may I assume you still haven't found time to sort out the new Playtexes?'

It would have been easy to have said to Hattie afterwards, 'I wish I'd said ...' But there was going to be no taking the easy way out for me this summer. For my diary's sake I had to say something. *I felt the Old Dragon needed taking down a peg or two,* I would write.

'Excuse me,' I said in a voice that wasn't my own but a Girl Guide leader's, 'I would just like to say how charming and, er, helpful, your assistant has been. Even if you think we've been wasting her time today, I can assure you that when the time comes and we have the need of your, er, undergarments, Hilda – may I call you Hilda? – has convinced us Bryants is the place to come. We shall be regular and valued customers like our aunt and grandmother. Well, goodbye for now, Hilda, and thank you for all your advice,' and picking up the candy-striped paper bag off we stalked, leaving Hilda with a pink round face and the Old Dragon with a white pinched one.

'You were *brilliant*,' said Hattie as we went down the polished wood stairs. 'Blimey, I've never heard you like that before.'

We found Granny wandering in a daze among the table-cloths, and what a mercy the Old Dragon hadn't seen her in that hat! Hattie began to tell her what had happened but she interrupted to say, 'I've bought Dawn some dress overalls. Reduced to twenty-one and six. Man-made fabric, of course, and in rather lurid colours, but I don't think she would mind that, do you?'

'Will they cover her knees, Granny?' I asked but she can't have been listening.

We went into Edith Church's for an extra cottage loaf, and Pratt's (which we called Spratt's) for bloaters, herrings and haddock. We were served by Melanie Pratt who was, according to Dan, the most beautiful girl in Shotestead. I studied her carefully. She had silky brown long hair, hazel-nut eyes and a pretty, gentle mouth. She looked as much like Dawn as, say, a sea trout did an ugly red lobster. Good. If Dan found Melanie beautiful, he couldn't *possibly* find Dawn even remotely so. Not only was Melanie beautiful, she was nice, too, and never minded filleting your fish for you. Nice *and* beautiful. That must be the best combination in the world for a girl. Apart from working in a fishmonger's I wouldn't say no to being just like Melanie Pratt when I grew up.

If there was an Untidiest Shop in the World award, T. Bone & Son ironmongers would win hands down. Higgledy-piggledy nails and knives and screws and Brillo pads and batteries and light bulbs and paint brushes and mousetraps tumbled from cobwebby shelves and dusty cardboard boxes and paper bags and woodwormy drawers, binder twine and paint pots and lavatory brushes and feather dusters and tins of glue and Hoover bags and everything including a kitchen sink lay in wait for unwary blind people on the splinter-riddled floorboards. 'You want it, m'dear, we've got it,' Mr Bone would boast, waddling off down narrow passages and emerging several minutes later holding up a rare nut or screw that hadn't been manufactured since the war and he would only charge a penny if that for it. A sign on the counter said 'YOU DONT HAVE TO BE MAD TO WORK HERE BUT IT HELPS'.

Mr Bone was a stout, sandy man who always wore a knitted old waistcoat that stretched round his plump tummy like a tight hot-water-bottle cover. His wife on the other hand was sharp and pointed like her spectacles. Their son Ronnie was half-way between the two and quite handsome in a pale, rough, untidy sort of way. He was wearing the tightest pair of jeans I'd ever seen which made you want to be rude and stare. Ronnie wasn't such a dedicated ironmonger as his father and one got the impression that he, like Mr Pond's son, would rather be seeing the world than cloistered in a dead-end shop.

With Mr Bone, you didn't feel embarrassed about plastic flowers on hats the way you did with other shopkeepers; he was the type who even if you wore a watering can on your head wouldn't turn a hair. He didn't bow and scrape like the others and was sometimes quite rude; that was the way he was, and you either liked it or you lumped it.

'You two keeping an eye on your old gran this summer, are you, then?' he said. 'Get us some flypapers and a kettle de-furrer for the lady, will you, Ronnie.'

Ronnie slouched off, his jeans making him stiff-legged like Clifford, down a passage and Mr Bone talked to Granny about the Shotestead Show.

'Should be a good 'un this year. Record cattle entries – and sheep so I've heard,' he said, scratching his armpit.

Grandpa had organised the first show in 1949 and it was still going strong, in fact for many it had become the major social if not agricultural event of the year. It was certainly ours. Granny was Hon. President and Mr Bone was on the committee and ran the hoopla stall.

'I reckon people'll come flocking this year. They like a good old show,' said Mr Bone as Ronnie reappeared with the required items which were placed in a used brown paper bag by his father.

Ronnie put his thumbs into the belt loops, looked at me and said, 'What's that old brother of yours a-doing of, then?'

'He's in Pilgrim's,' I said. 'Upstairs', and Ronnie nodded and wiped his nose with the back of his hand and said 'I want a word with him. By the way, how's that blonde bombshell of yours? Keeping well, is she?'

Of *ours?* She certainly wasn't mine. I just smiled and nodded.

What did he want to speak to Dan about? I had no idea they knew each other on a personal level. Perhaps it was something to do with the pop group.

R. Thirtle and Son had sawdust on the floor and plastic cress round the meat display. On the wall behind the counter a life-size plastic bullock's head stared morosely down at the customers. In the corner was a giant-sized fridge. Once Mr Thirtle had let us look inside. Red and white half-cattle and half-pigs hung upside down. The pigs still had their eyes on, and there was blood on the floor. 'You wouldn't want to spend the night in there, I'll be bound,' he said, and as luck would have it that was exactly where I did spend the night in my dream.

The Thirtles were always raising money for this, that and the other; 'Pillars of the Community' they were known as and how sad, I thought, that they of all people were about to be lumbered with the Foul Dawn as a daughter-in-law.

Mr Thirtle was a lean wire-terrier of a man. Mrs Thirtle was a fat, smiling bulldog who sat at the hatch with her biro poised waiting to make up the bills. They were Jack Sprat and his wife to a T.

But it was Albert I was interested in.

ALBERT THIRTLE: Suffolk Punch. The strongest horse of them all. Gentle, sweet-natured and kind. Fine chestnut coat. Hard worker. Has one unfortunate tendency: an unusual taste in mares. Could this be his downfall?

He had thick strong arms that last year had won him the title The Strongest Man in Shotestead for hitting something with a hammer and making a bell ring. They were covered in golden hairs and freckles. The hairs on his head were more the colour of the peel in Chivers Old English Marmalade; Aunt Lynette called it burnished auburn, a colour she didn't find terribly becoming on a man but would have chosen it for herself if one had a say in such matters. His sideboards were lighter, more the colour of the peel in Granny's marmalade.

I screwed up my eyes and stared at his face. He certainly wasn't as handsome as Dan or Mr Richards or Cliff Richard, but he wasn't *ugly*. His cheeks were reddish, the colour of pork fillet, and clashed slightly with his hair and his sideboards. His nose was long and slightly crooked and his eyes, a pond-life green colour, were very, very slightly crossed. His mouth was ordinary, though, in fact very nice, and his teeth were all right, too, not too yellow and there weren't any missing. But the best thing about him was that *he* was nice, he was always having private little jokes in an almost cheeky but not quite sort of way. Like he'd say 'Only the best for her Highness' and winking when Granny wasn't looking, or 'How's that Stirling Moss aunt of yours – driven through any red lights lately?'

I searched for traces of lipstick on his collar or a hint of a black eye, even, but he didn't look any different or worse for wear now he was engaged to Dawn. Had he started to say 'Oh gawd'? Did he approve of her knees showing? If his lips kissed her foul pink ones did they get covered in her lipstick? Had his huge red hands which at this moment were slicing lamb's liver ever touched Dawn's ... *bra*? I watched him pick up the liver as gently as if it were a new-born kitten. Had he even touched Dawn's *bosoms* in that way? What did they do during their evenings together? Go to the pictures or a public house or the Rec or walk by the river, watching the sun go down holding hands and saying 'I love you' to one another? Would they get married in a church? *What would their children look like?*

As if he could sense I was staring, Albert looked up and gave me a quick, secret wink, and I blushed furiously because it was the sort of wink that said 'I know what you're thinking.'

Mr Thirtle was cleverly combining chatting to Granny and getting her order ready. 'And how are your two charming grand-daughters? – pass over that there best end of neck, Albert – Coo, dear, they're growing up fast – not that one, Albert, I said *best* – you'll be here for the Show, will you? – bone and roll that top rib, will you, son? Nicely now – I bet you look forward to staying with your granny, don't you? – And we'll slip in the usual for Clifford, shall we, Madam? On the house, ha, ha, ha!'

'That would be most kind, Mr Thirtle.'

'The usual for Clifford. No charge, Ma,' shouted Mr Thirtle and Mrs Thirtle shouted, 'Okey-dokey.'

Granny began to discuss the Show's flower tent with Mrs Thirtle and Mr Thirtle weighed sausages for the next customer and Hattie had turned to talk to a large brown dog. It was now or never.

'Albert,' I hissed. He leant over the wooden, bloodstained counter, the bib of his white apron dipping into the meat. 'Dawn says hello and could you pick her up at eight o'clock tonight.'

Albert did the thumbs-up sign and gave me another wink.

'She sends her love, too,' I lied but I wanted Albert to be pleased. As Granny had said, nice men like Albert don't grow on trees, especially where someone as ugly as Dawn was concerned.

Albert's cheeks went one shade darker, a fillet steak colour, and he smiled and winked again and said softly 'Ta', and then 'Send her mine, will you.'

Even though the hen basket was weighed down by meat I still skipped down the street. It gave one such a light, happy feeling to make someone's day.

Dan was discussing cricket with Mr Higgens and fidgeting his foot. He carried the box of groceries on his head like an African woman, and Granny told him not to be irresponsible, there were lots of glass things, but Dan said not to worry, it'd be okay.

Austin of England looked small and old-fashioned and out-of-place all on his own in the middle of the market-place. We filled him up with the shopping and Granny, saying she had to return a library book, gave Dan a pound note to buy ice creams. On our way to Finch's I told him Ronnie Bone was looking for him and he said yeah, he'd seen him, they were going to have a lunchtime drink at the Wheatsheaf. (My brother in the *Wheatsheaf*? Where there were fights and the landlord kept a Dobermann Pinscher to be on the safe side?)

83

'I've been plagued by the flipping cricket match wherever I go,' said Dan.

'There is going to be one, isn't there,' I said. 'You did promise Daddy.' And Dan muttered something that included an extremely rude word.

Dan bought cigarettes, too and Mr Finch, a large-beaked man, said, 'Them things aren't going to make a Donald Bradman out of you, Mr Hillington! I reckon you Gressenham lot stand a fair old chance this year. It's still on, I take it?' and Dan muttered maybe, maybe not, he'd have to see.

Mr Glister, the elderly, red-faced, stout, slow, kind policeman strolled in and asked for a quarter of aniseed balls. He carried his helmet by its strap, perhaps so it could act as a shopping basket for the aniseed balls. As we went out, Hattie pointed at his back view. We rushed into the gateway of the churchyard where we collapsed in hysterics, even Dan joining in. For sticking out of his back pocket and rucking up his jacket was a blue budgerigar ladder!

'Can you imagine if he had to arrest someone, putting his hand in his pocket for his handcuffs and pulling out *that!*'

'*I think that sort of thing's what nice* about this country. You'd never see it in America.'

Granny was still in the library, so we strolled along the churchyard's narrow path licking our ice creams, just for luck touching the iron cage built round a grave to ward off body snatchers, and Dan nodded at the huge grey church, whose spire you could see fifteen miles away on a clear day, and said talk about a white elephant and I said don't you mean grey elephant, and Dan said it's amazing these places kept going, he bet it was never even half full. Hattie told him he shouldn't talk about it as if it were a fish and chip shop and Dan said there wasn't much difference really and I said, 'What, you mean you go to church to worship *Cod* instead of God?' which Hattie and I thought terribly funny.

We passed, all hunched up on a bench amongst the gravestones, a rough-looking group of boys smoking cigarettes and drinking Abbot Ale. They wore wintery black leather jackets and their hair glistened like oil slicks. From a transistor radio blasted forth a song about blue suede shoes which they sang along to, clicking their fingers and stamping their black-pointed, silver-buckled feet.

'How *could* they have it on so loud right by a church,' I said.

'Yes, people come here for peace and quiet and to visit their dead relatives, not to be disturbed by a foul din.'

'Where else can they go, poor old sods?' said Dan. 'They're not even allowed a bowling alley.'

I pointed out there were hundreds of miles of countryside all round and Dan said 'Yeah, ninety-five per cent of it privately owned.'

'Are they Teddy Boys?' Hattie asked and Dan said 'Maybe.'

'I still don't think it should be so loud,' said Hattie. 'It's selfish.'

'Yes, it's disturbing the peace.'

'You know what you two are,' said Dan. He hadn't touched his ice cream and I was half-way through mine. 'You're a couple of Miss Prims. In fact that's what I'm going to call you from now on. Or, even better, Prissy Sissies.'

'That's *horrible,* Dan. We aren't prissy or prim.'

'Oh, no?' he said. 'I think you are, and I bet you'll end up as po-faced shopkeepers or bossy hospital matrons. Spinsters, too, because no man would want to put up with your prissiness.'

'And you'll be a bachelor because no woman would want to put up with your rudeness and scruffiness,' I said.

'Do anything you wanna do, but honey lay off-a my blue suede shoes and don't ya, step on my blue suede shoes ...' reverberated round the gravestones and woke up the dead.

'Why should anyone want to sing about blue swede shoes?' said Hattie.

'Suede shoes, you chump,' said Dan. 'Why shouldn't they?'

'Does it mean you could chop off his feet so long as you don't step on his blue suede shoes?' I said.

'Or spill a bottle of ink over them as long as you don't *step* on them?'

'Don't take everything so literally,' said Dan. 'It's the general feel of the thing that counts. The mood. The rawness. The anger. The beat. That's the beauty of Elvis. And it's a good tune. A bloody great tune.'

'But bloody daft words,' I said. There. I'd used a swear word in a churchyard. There was no crack of thunder overhead, no one appeared to be rising up out of their grave. 'Do you promise you'll never sing anything silly like that in your pop group?'

'Maybe, maybe not,' said Dan and then he did a disgraceful thing. A Coca-Cola can lay in his path. Did he pick it up and put it in the nearest litter bin? Not on your life. He kicked it, as hard as he could, at a gravestone.

If Beatrice Clover, loving wife and mother who passed peacefully away in 1903, could see how the modern world behaved she'd be turning in her grave as fast as a chicken on a high-speed spit.

CHAPTER NINE

Beyond the kitchen garden, in a cool, quiet clearing surrounded by brambly undergrowth and a tangly wood, where the only passers-by were squirrels, pheasants and the occasional mind-its-own-business train, stood the black summerhouse. Its blackness was due to being painted with pitch to weatherproof it. It had a bristly roof in which a robin had built a nest, a door, two windows and a veranda with high crisscrossed log sides. Lion's Mouth Wood, thick and dense on the other side of the railway track, blocked out its sun, making it seem more like a winterhouse.

The black summerhouse used to be beside the old tennis court (which was now lawn and flower beds), and housed deckchairs and croquet mallets. Two summers ago, soon after Grandpa had died, Granny said the summerhouse had outlived it usefulness. She found its blackness sombre and out of keeping with its surroundings, and it always seemed to be in her line of vision like a big black cloud. 'Its purpose was for people to sit in and watch the tennis, but as no one's played since the war ... It would keep us going in firewood all winter.'

Hattie and I begged her to keep it, saying it was ideal to play in when it was raining. Eventually she reluctantly agreed, as long as it was moved out of her sight. 'It brings back so many memories, you see.'

'Nice memories or nasty ones?' I asked.

'Oh, nice, mostly,' she said. 'Your grandfather ... proposed to me. Rather an odd place, I know, for a proposal, but it was pouring with rain.'

We imagined the rain beating like birds' wings on the thatch while Grandpa got down on one knee and asked Granny if she'd be his wife.

'And what's a nasty one?' asked Hattie.

'Oh, nothing in particular, but I've always found it rather – spooky I think's the modern word, but that's probably me being fanciful in my old age.'

Dan and Daddy and Jack and Mr Ball borrowed a tractor and trailer and chains, and with much sweating and swearing and groaning and jokes and bottles of brown ale to 'sustain them', the summerhouse was uprooted like a large, square, black vegetable and replanted in our chosen spot.

To remove any 'spookiness', Hattie and I pinned a picture of Pat Smythe on a horse on the wall, and one of the Royal Family with Princess Anne in a pink dress, and a Dogs of the World poster. We acquired some old curtains and bits of furniture and Hattie painted a fireplace on the wall, above which Mr Ball nailed a piece of wood to serve as a mantelpiece. She added painted flames, which looked more like red bendy snakes, and when we'd moved in a few toys, we had our own secret home.

Except ... there was *something* about the place. We rarely went there, even when it was raining, and Granny said she trusted we were playing in it after all the palaver of moving it. It was then we formed the Flaming Snakes Secret Society, and began to use it the way one could a church, kneeling in front of the fireplace, staring at the flames of snakes and concentrating on anything good you wanted to happen.

'This is daft,' Hattie said one day. 'Kneeling in front of silly red paint.'

I told her she was worse than Alice accusing the courtroom of being nothing but a pack of cards, and she had ruined any magic spell there might have been.

One day I was in the library van when quite by chance my eye alighted on a book of witchcraft. I flicked through it, cramming my head with as many facts as I could while Mummy discussed Patricia Highsmith's latest novel with the librarian.

'A witchcraft ritual may be devised to suit any need, whether for healing a person, lifting some distress, alleviating a broken romance. There is a saying from the Ancient Wisdom: "When the pupil is ready the teacher appears..."'

I must have been ready, for he appeared on a holiday in Scotland. We were in a stately home looking at silver stags and tartan rugs and Victorian paintings, and I was getting a bit bored when I spotted *him*. He was called a Snuff Mull, and it said on a gold inscription it had been won by Lady Someone-or-other at the Aberdeen Show in 1889 for the best two-year-old fat ox.

It was a ram's head.

He had cold, haughty, pale-green eyes and long curly horns with silver- and blue-jewelled tips. The head, which was on small wheels, was covered in white wool like wizard's hair. On the crown of his head was a small lid which you would have opened to get out the snuff with a long-handled spoon.

'What does Mull mean?' I asked, and Daddy said it was Scottish for headland, as in Mull of Kintyre, and also, as in this case, snuff box.

The Snuff Mull stared through your eyes and into your very soul. You could feel his power radiating out through the glass case and sucking you into his spell. I couldn't stop looking at him.

'Did you see the Snuff Mull?' I asked Mummy in the car and she said she wished she hadn't, beastly thing, it was most macabre and would probably give us all nightmares.

'Certainly had you spellbound, didn't it, Sausage?'

Daddy had used the word spellbound! So he had sensed his power, too.

'What an extraordinary lot those Victorians must have been,' said Mummy. 'Imagine having that *apparition* wheeled under your nose at the dinner table! Enough to give anyone indigestion. Now let's forget the monstrosity and concentrate on finding a suitable picnic place.'

But I thought about him – a lot more. From then on, whenever I wanted something to happen. I closed my eyes and concentrated all my thoughts on him. But clearly just thinking about him wasn't enough. I needed him to *be* there, in front of me, in *person*.

So that morning, after we'd helped Granny put the shopping away, I persuaded Hattie to accompany me to the black summerhouse so I could tell her my plan.

STRICKTLY PRIVAT. ALL INTROODERS WILL BE SEVERLY PUNISHED was still pinned to the door though fading fast and splattered in birds' messes. Cautiously I opened the door. The pigeon feather we'd left just inside was in place, so there hadn't been any 'introoders'. It smelt musty and stuffy but that was all; there were no rotting animal smells or signs that the old bugger of a winter had wormed its way in. The patchwork quilt hadn't been ravaged by more moths and there was no evidence of mice or rats.

'It's funny to think we're the very first people to come in here for a whole year,' said Hattie. 'Just think, the air we're breathing in is the air we breathed out a year ago.'

She sat on the camp bed and I sat on the rocking chair, and I told her about the Snuff Mull, and her eyes behind her spectacles turned as round as when she listened to *Billy Goat Gruff*.

'Won't it make God cross?' she whispered.

'He will be God, sort of. I mean, if we could see God we wouldn't have to do this. Snuff Mull will just act as a sort of middleman between us and God.'

'Don't you mean middle*ram*,' said Hattie. 'Anyway, why does it have to be a ram? Why can't it be something nice like a cat or a rabbit or a Dalmatian? Goats and sheep belong to the same family, and goats are the devil, aren't they. Therefore we would be nearly devil worshippers, wouldn't we.'

I explained that goats and sheep were as similar as, say, lions and tigers, and, besides, we had to have something we were a bit ... *in awe of*, otherwise we wouldn't respect him.

Hattie said wouldn't we be dabbling in evil? and I said magic can be good or evil, and ours was only going to be good. We'd be like sort of doctors, making things better when they go wrong. Witch doctors, in fact.

'I don't want to be a witch,' said Hattie. And just at that moment a train thundered past, causing the summerhouse to shake and rattle, and because you couldn't actually see the train, with its passengers reading papers or drinking coffee from Thermos flasks, it made you think of rampaging wildebeests coming to get you, and Hattie began to cry.

'I hate this place and *please* don't make me be an ugly old witch.'

I put my arm round her and explained witches are only old and ugly in fairy stories, in real life they are often very beautiful. 'Come to think of it I don't fancy being a witch much, either. I suppose we needn't be anyone really. All we have to do is use our powers when things need changing.'

'I don't see what's wrong with things as they are,' Hattie said. 'Apart from the Foul Dawn and there's nothing we can do about her.'

'Everything's all right – at the moment,' I said. 'But we should be prepared. Please help, Hattie.'

'Oh, all right. But if someone breaks their neck or falls into a bottomless pit we'll know who to blame.'

I took out of my carrier bag a roll of lavatory paper and a bottle of water and two bowls. We had just put the paper in to soak when an unpleasant thought struck me: if Dawn was Aries, that meant she was a ram.

Suddenly there was an almighty shout that would have made you jump clean out of your skin if you were a snake: 'Lunchtime, kids. Come out, wherever you are!'

'I'll distract her,' I said and sped off like a hare.

Round the edge of the kitchen garden wall I met her head on. We both screamed.

'Gordon Bennet, you scared the living daylights out of me. Where were you?'

'Oh, nowhere in particular,' I said. In the bright light of day her face looked even more grotesque. Talk about not wanting to meet the gamekeeper down a dark alley; I'd rather meet him than her any day! 'By the way, do you mind not calling us kids? We're humans, not baby goats', and Hattie, puffing up behind, said 'That's just what I was thinking.'

'Oh, lardy-da,' said Dawn cheerfully, digging me in the ribs which was one thing I couldn't stand. 'Everyone says kids these days.'

'*We* don't.'

'Suit yourselves. It's cauliflower cheese for lunch, by the way. It's the first time I've made it so it might be a bit dodgy.'

We walked behind her to avoid her nauseating scent and digging elbow. You could see through her skirt right to the tops of her white spindly legs. Her bottom wiggled like mad.

What's round and wobbly and sometimes wiggles? A pig's bottom. What's round and wobbly and always wiggles? Dawn's bottom!!!

'Did you like the overall Granny bought you?' I said, though what I meant was *Why aren't you wearing it?*

'Yeah,' she said, 'A bit sweaty in this weather, though. Specially when you're slaving over a hot stove. Christ, I hate cooking.'

'You're going to have to do a fair amount when you're married to Albert.' I said.

'Don't remind me,' said Dawn.

We walked across the lawn and her heels sunk into the grass like golf tees.

'You're making holes in the lawn,' said Hattie.

'Helps the worms breathe, according to your gran,' said Dawn. 'Anyway, it's doing far more harm to my shoes than it is to the lawn. Look at the poor old sods.'

'Don't you mean poor old *soles*?' I said. Dawn looked as blank as a sheep for a moment then, winding herself up, roared her clockwork laughter.

'You are a card!' she said.

'Do you mean a birthday card or a Christmas card?' said Hattie, and I muttered, 'Knowing her, one of those vulgar seaside post-cards.'

That was another thing she reminded you of; that busty blonde woman saying something rude to a small, red-faced, sweaty man on those postcards you weren't allowed to look at because they weren't suitable.

Why is there no getting away from Dawn at the seaside? Because

Dodgy wasn't the word for the cauliflower cheese. The sauce was as runny and lumpy as unstirred packet soup with hardly any cheese in, and the cauliflower stalks were as tough as telegraph posts.

'How much milk did you say you put in the sauce, dear?' said Granny. At least she wasn't calling her darling – not yet, anyway.

'Er – three-quarters of a pint, Mrs Aitch – roughly, that is. It could have been a fraction more.'

'It's essential with sauces to be very accurate with one's measurements,' said Granny. 'I did tell you to use the measuring jug. And the cauliflower is a trifle underdone.'

'Yeah. Sorry, Mrs Aitch. Talking of trifle, that's what we're having for afters. My speciality, that. It should be an improvement on this load of codswallop.'

She'd said codswallop! It fitted in with my fishwife joke perfectly!

The trifle was just what you'd expect from Dawn. Unlike Mummy's pale pretty trifles, with apricot jam and pears and peaches and roasted almonds on top. Dawn's was as gaudy as the Elvis Presley calendar or the plastic flowers on Granny's hat, with its lime-green jelly, dazzling bought strawberry jam, tinned fruit salad, custard as yellow as her hair, all smothered in poisonous-looking sweets.

'It's very colourful, dear,' said Granny.

It was far too sweet, of course, and even though *she* had made it I still found myself saying that it tasted nice.

'Oh, ta,' said Dawn, looking pleased.

'Well, I think there's a *trifle* too much sherry in it,' said Hattie. 'I hate sherry.'

'She'll get to like it when she's older, eh, Sarah?' she said and winked at me like a boy, and I felt myself go red. Fancy her thinking I was old enough to like sherry! 'It's a shame your brother ain't here to sample my first – and probably last – culinary success. Anyone know what he's up to, by the way?'

It's none of your business, you nosy parker.

'I believe he's seeing some people about joining a pop group, dear – do I mean pop group, darling?' she said to me and I knew that sooner or later she'd get her darlings and dears mixed up; it was just a matter of time.

Dawn's black eyes widened. 'Blimey. That's really something! I can just see him on a stage. He's got the right face – and physique – to be a pop singer.'

'Surely it's his voice that counts,' I said gruffly.

'Not so much these days,' said Dawn. 'You have to have a bit of animal magnetism, too, and I reckon he's got that all right.' (How dare she liken my brother to an animal. Talk about pot calling the kettle black.) 'What sort of music is he into, anyway – pop? R and B? Rock 'n' roll or what?'

'How can you get *into* music?' said Hattie. 'It's not a box or a house', and Granny said 'What on earth is rock and roll?' and I thought to myself, Please don't let her know anything about music or it'll give her and Dan something to talk about.

'Rock*ing* roll I think it is, Granny,' I said.

'No, it ain't, it's rock '*n*' roll,' said Dawn, and how did she know? I bet her spelling was far worse than mine. 'It's music that's, well, untamed. Kind of wild, like an animal that's just been let out of its cage. Though I suppose some of it's like an animal still in its cage. That's the sad stuff. Blues, that's called. It's what American niggers sing when they're feeling pissed off.'

'Dear, I don't think we like the word "nigger" in this house,' Granny said. '"Negro" or "coloured gentleman" I think would be more appropriate.'

'Sorry, Mrs Aitch. Seeing as how that MP Gerald Nabarro said it on *Any Questions* on the radio it would be all right for me to. He said "big buck nigger", to be precise. Did you hear it? Anyway, rock 'n' roll is kind of exciting and fast and loud and ... *raw* ...'

'Like the cauliflower,' said Hattie, which I thought very funny. (*Why is rocking roll like the vegetables Dawn cooks ...?*)

'Or do you mean *roar*, as in lions and tigers being let out of their cages?' I said.

'You two!' said Dawn. 'Look, the best way to describe it is that you *have* to get up and dance. Rock 'n' roll has that sort of power over you.'

'Bet it wouldn't have over me,' I said.

'Bet it would,' said Dawn. 'When you're a bit older, anyway.'

'Bet it wouldn't make *me* get up and dance,' said Hattie. 'Bet you a pound.'

'Bet it would.'

'Bet it wouldn't because I can't dance with my leg. See, I won.'

'Oh, well,' said Dawn, not showing a flicker of embarrassment. 'That's different. Your *heart* would still want to.'

'Rocking roll songs have such stupid words,' I said.

'I trust this ... pop singing's not going to interfere with the harvest,' Granny said.

'Hey, that's a point,' said Dawn. 'Ain't he a bit top-drawer to sing in a pop group?'

'If you mean has he got a fringe or a Liverpudlian accent the answer's no. But nor has Howlin' Wolf or Muddy Waters,' I said and to my delight her blank face turned blanker and I knew she was working up to asking who they were when they were at home. 'Anyway, he's only doing it to let off steam between school and university. It's not *serious*.'

'It's all beyond me,' Granny said. 'In my day, young men went on a hiking holiday in the Pennines or Switzerland with a couple of chums to let off steam.'

'Perhaps Dan has run out of steam,' Hattie said quietly. 'Perhaps he's gone electric.'

'And about to go off the rails,' I muttered.

'Things are different now, Mrs Aitch,' said Dawn. 'Young blokes these days want to express themselves, show their feelings, their anger.'

'I haven't the remotest idea what they've got to be angry about,' said Granny, and sniffed. 'It's not as if they have to go and fight in muddy, rat-infested trenches or live in damp, dark houses or survive on bread and dripping or die through lack of medical attention. Thanks to the Welfare State they live in bright, light, airy homes with every modern convenience. You never see children without shoes, or with rickets, or in rags like you used to. I think Mr Macmillan was perfectly correct when he said "You've never had it so good".'

'I do, too,' I said.

'So do I,' said Hattie.

'And what on earth Dan of all people has to be angry about I can't imagine. He's had the most privileged of upbringings.'

'Yeah, but the thing is, Mrs Aitch...'

'Now I think we've talked quite long enough about ... pop music,' said Granny. 'Would anyone care for a spot more of Dawn's delicious trifle?'

I was itching to get on with the creation of Snuff Mull after lunch, but Granny asked us to help Dawn with the washing up. (*What's the difference between Dawn doing the washing up and us doing it*, I wanted to ask Granny. *Dawn gets paid for it*.)

She was a terrible washer-upper, not bothering to heat the water properly so the glasses were all smeary, pausing to puff on a cigarette every few seconds, crashing things about in the sink so loudly you were reminded of Baba Yaga, the bony-legged, the witch – *tongs and pokers tumbling down the chimney are nothing to the noise she made as she gnashed her iron teeth* ... nor did she get things clean,

93

and twice I had to return the cauliflower cheese Pyrex because it had bits on it.

'But they're stuck on,' she whined, and Hattie said in that case she should use the Goldilocks.

'A bloke I knew once called me Goldilocks,' she said. 'Bit of an insult when you think about it, being called the same thing as something you wash flaming dishes with.'

'Why would they be flaming dishes if you were washing up,' said Hattie. 'Surely the water would have put the flames out.'

'Ha, bleeding ha,' said Dawn. 'Honestly, I can never tell whether you kids are taking the piss.'

I decided not to bother to tell her about 'kids' again; it would only go in one ear and out the other; anyway, 'children' wasn't much better coming from her; why, in lots of ways she was no more than a child herself.

'You shouldn't swear in front of us,' I said. 'It's a bad influence.'

'I wasn't, was I?' said Dawn.

'"Bleeding" and "p-i-s-s" are swear words.'

'Suppose they are. Blimey, you see. I don't realise when I'm doing it. It's all part and parcel of the language to me.'

'Blimey's one, too,' said Hattie. 'Every time you're saying it you're asking God to blind you.'

'Blimey, so there's no hope for me then, is there,' she said.

'No,' we said.

And then she said, 'Okay, so what are we going to do this afternoon?'

We? I knew what Hattie and I were doing ...

'We've got something important to do. Hattie and me, that is.'

'Oh, yeah?' she said looking round. 'Is it private, or can I join in?'

'Er, sorry, Dawn, but it is a bit private.'

'Yeah? Well, the thing is, every afternoon between lunch and tea while your gran has a rest I'm meant to be looking after you two.'

Granny *must* be gaga. Dawn couldn't take care of a *tea cloth*.

'Mrs Thingamy-jig always took you for a walk, didn't she?'

'Not often,' I said. 'Mummy usually did.'

'Yeah, but *Mummy* ain't here,' said Dawn. 'Why can't you do this important thing you've got to do and I'll sit nearby and keep an eye on you?'

Hattie and I looked at each other. It was out of the question. She would ruin the magic and anyway, we didn't need an eye kept on us, thank you very much, especially not one of her black ones.

'I suppose we could go to the millpool for a swim,' I said, then added to put her off, 'It's very weedy and there are fish in it.' But she said she was game. 'As long as it's eighty degrees, chlorinated and with changing rooms,' she said. 'Don't worry, only kidding.'

'We can do *it* after tea,' I said quietly to Hattie.

'Blimey, that sounds rude,' said Dawn.

Her calling *me* rude! That was the biggest laugh of all.

CHAPTER TEN

What's ten times worse than going for a country walk with one of Cinderella's loud, ignorant ugly sisters? Going for a country walk with Dawn!!!

At last she was ready and off we set, me and Hattie in sensible T-shirts, shorts and sandals with rolled-up towels and bathing costumes under our arms, Dawn cheap-hairdresser-strinking, bracelet-clanking, high-heeled-shoe-and-tight-skirt-dinking, Teddy-Boy-leather-jacket-creaking, white-vanity-case-swinging. At least startling black sun-glasses concealed her startling black eyes. I just hoped that if we met someone we knew she'd keep them on.

'We're only going for a walk,' I said. 'Not ... (and I wanted to say along the streets of Soho, but I didn't quite dare; I'd say it in my diary, though; Mr Richards was bound to be broad-minded) ... a garden party.'

'Be prepared, that's me,' she said. 'You never know who you're going to meet. We might bump into some tall dark hunky farmer. Blimey, only kidding,' she said when she saw our faces. 'You two don't half take life seriously.'

'How are you going to tramp through soggy fields in those shoes?' I said.

'They're all I've got apart from a black pair, and they're even higher.'

'I suppose we'll have to go by boring old road then,' I said.

Because of her ridiculous attire she walked at the speed of an elderly crippled person. What was the point of clothes if you couldn't move in them? Say she was chased by a bull? The Black Champion in me longed to gallop ahead, but it wouldn't have been fair on Hattie. I held myself back on a very tight rein and said, '"Will you walk a little faster?" said a whiting to a snail. "There's a porpoise close behind me and he's treading on my tail."'

Dawn's sun-glasses looked at me askance. 'Are you a nutcase, or what?'

'Actually, it's a famous poem read by the Mock Turtle – or was it the Gryphon?' said Hattie, and the sun-glasses looked even more askance. 'Isn't Clifford coming?'

96

Dawn said he was having a kip with his mistress. ''Ere, talking of mistresses, have you been following the Profumo scandal? You know, with Christine Keeler and Mandy Rice-Davies. It makes every such juicy reading.'

'Never heard of it,' I said.

'You're kidding! Blimey, where have you been? The papers are full of it.'

Not *The Times* and the *Telegraph*, the papers we get, I bet. I decided to show as much interest in this Profumo Affair as a dog's mess that you almost step in and then never think about again for the rest of your life.

The sky had clouded over and the afternoon was turning humid and heavy.

'We've had the best of the day,' I said, wishing it would rain, *pour*, turning Dawn's hair into yellow rats' tails, making her black eye-stuff trickle like black ink down her cheeks, and just when she was looking her worst we'd meet Dan, who'd suggest we go home and play racing demon while Dawn got tea.

'Sugar in the morning, sugar in the evening, sugar at suppertime,' sang Dawn, disturbing two sparrows in the hedge and, way ahead, a cock pheasant who whirred into the air like a helicopter. *'Be my little sugar . . .'*

'That's a pheasant,' I said.

'Oh yeah. Big bugger, innit,' she said. 'That's right, mate, get the hell out of here before those flaming toffs with guns get you.'

Her voice, as loud as the loudest street trader, echoed round the fields and woods and disturbed all and sundry the way the boys in the churchyard had.

'Shhh,' said Hattie. 'Brian Pike might hear you.'

'Don't give a toss if he does,' said Dawn. 'It's a free country, innit?'

'But it's best to keep quiet sometimes. You wouldn't say to a vicar "I hate Jesus", would you.'

'Yes, there's a time and a place for everything,' I said.

'Bet that's the sort of thing your mum would say,' said Dawn and I said how do you know, you've never met her and she said she could tell, that was all and to keep my hair on, and I said my hair's firmly on, thank you, but is yours? Then Hattie and I sang 'Green Grow the Rushes-O' because Dawn wouldn't know it.

'That's a bloody weird song you kids are singing,' said Dawn. 'Blimey, and you complain about rock 'n' roll words. First mock turtles and snails and that and now lily-white boys dressed all in green-o. It all sounds a bit kinky if you ask me.'

'It's an old traditional English song if you must know,' I said. 'Anyway. I didn't know kids could sing, did you, Hattie?'

'You'll have to move with the times, you know,' said Dawn. 'Everyone calls children kids.'

'Mummy says it's American and vulgar.'

'There you are, you see. Your mum again.'

I have never actually hated, really hated, someone until today. I would write. Except say Mr Richards was a Christian – a Catholic, even, if he was Irish. He wouldn't approve of hate. I would just have to imply it through jokes.

Why's Dawn like a football? Because you're always itching to kick her!!!

What's the rarest sound in the world? Dawn saying please and thank you!!!

Why's Dawn like footwear? Because she's as rough as old boots!!!

How can you find Dawn in a strawstack? Follow your nose!!!

How can you tell Granny's gargar? Well would you *employ someone like Dawn?!?*

We crossed the main road and veered left down the Green Lanes past the Gooseberry Man's house whose black-faced alsatian barked through the bars of the gate.

'Give me the creeps, alsatians,' Dawn said. 'When we lived in the Gate – Notting Hill Gate to you – the rent collectors had them. If you couldn't cough up they'd have your leg off soon as look at it. Look at its fangs. Like bleeding needles.'

'They don't look as though they're bleeding to me,' said Hattie. 'That red thing's his tongue.'

Dawn laughed and said, 'All right, if you're in a joky mood, how about this? It's the only clean one I know. Why did the chicken cross the football pitch?'

'Because the referee said "Foul",' I said in a heard-it-a-hundred-times voice.

'What a *foul* joke,' said Hattie.

'Yes, it was nothing to *crow* about,' I said.

'Well, at least I didn't *cock* it up,' said Dawn. 'You two don't half give me the bird.'

'*Egg*sactly what I was thinking about you,' I said, and I couldn't contain myself any longer. I just had to gallop along the springy green turf, as any spirited horse would have done. I picked up Hattie and off we galloped, Dawn chasing us bumperty clack like Baba Yaga, shouting, ''Ere, wait for me.'

We hid in the gateway of a wheatfield to bo out at her, but needless to say she didn't pretend to jump like other grown-ups would have done. She just said 'Knew you were there', kicked off her shoes and flopped into the hedge.

'Blimey, I've had me exercise for the day,' she panted. 'How far's this whirlpool place? I'm bleeding knackered.'

'Only twenty miles,' said Hattie.

'Ha, bleeding ha. Whoops. I've got a bit of grass or something up me drawers,' and just at that very moment Major Smedley, his wife and their Jack Russell strode round the bend in the lane.

Unless they were as deaf as posts which I knew they weren't they must have heard. Partly because we didn't want to be seen with Dawn, and partly because Major Smedley always asked us what our favourite subject at school was, Hattie and I dived back into the gateway and behind the hedge, praying thay hadn't spotted us.

'Afternoon,' boomed the Major, and I could see round the edge of a piece of cow parsley he was raising his deerstalker.

'Er – afternoon,' said Dawn, and please don't let her have her hand down her knickers. 'Sorry, you caught me, er . . .'

'Storm brewing, I reckon,' said the Major, and Mrs Smedley shouted 'Come on, Jack, here, boy, here, boy. Naughty boy!'

'Blimey, you two,' said Dawn when they were out of earshot. 'Ta for landing me in it.'

'Why, what could we have done?'

'Talked to them or something. You speak their language, don't you. Fancy him raising his hat. I suppose he does it automatically to any female he meets, regardless of whether she's got a hand down her drawers or not.'

'I think that's what's called hypocrisy,' I said.

'What, a toff raising his hat to someone as common as muck?' said Dawn.

I suddenly felt hot. 'Well, maybe it's not . . .'

'I think it's hypocrisy of you two to disown me just because I get a bit of grass down me drawers. Don't tell me you've never had grass down your drawers.'

'Even if we had we wouldn't shout it out for the whole world to hear.'

'What whole world?' Dawn said. 'How was I to know Colonel Flaming Blimp and his missus were round the corner. As far as I was concerned, it was just you, me and that field of corn.'

'Ahh,' I said, 'but even the corn has ears.'

We all laughed, and Dawn said, 'I knew I was going to enjoy having you lot around.'

Townies would have turned their noses up at the millpond but I loved it wild and unkept and as nature had intended. The only sound was the rushing roar up the shady bridge end where we weren't allowed in case we got sucked under by the foaming white witch's cauldron. Fringed by lush reedy grasses and red campion, the millpond's far side was thick with pale sludgy-green-leaved trees among which we sometimes saw a kingfisher. Water boatmen rowed across the still surface, above which a dragonfly hovered and a cloud of midges danced. Plant life was allowed to flourish where it pleased.

It was like having our own private, secluded pool, with an old cart shed acting as our changing room. The weeds, I supposed, put people off. They sat in slimy clumps on the surface, like the sleeping backs of large, pale-green animals, and you could see them below the surface, too, green tangled rushes bending with the current.

'Blimey, is this it?' said Dawn, ruining the tranquillity, the magic of the place in one blow. 'What sort of fish did you say was in it?'

'Big fat carp,' I said.

'And long mean pike,' said Hattie.

'As long as their Christian name ain't Brian!' she roared.

I explained, as Dan had explained to me, that fish kept well away from swimmers, though you might come across a perch caught momentarily in an eddy.

'Eddy?' said Dawn. 'I can't see Eddie Cochran. You know, *"Three Steps to Heaven"* and all that.'

'Honestly,' I said to Hattie as we changed behind the old red cart while Dawn tested the temperature. 'It's like talking to someone from another planet.'

'Maybe she *is* from another planet,' said Hattie. 'Maybe God has picked us to teach her how to behave like normal people.'

'Personally, I have better things to do with my time,' I said and Hattie said she had, too.

'Jesus Christ, it's bleeding brass monkeys,' shouted Dawn, disturbing every bird and animal's afternoon snooze for miles and I said, 'See what I mean? It's another language.'

'You won't get me in there for all the tea in China,' she said as we came out in our bathing costumes. 'And it looks none too clean to me, neither. Look at all that green slimy stuff and them creepy-crawlies everywhere. You might catch cholera or typhoid or something. I wouldn't be surprised if we saw a bleeding dead sheep floating past.'

'If it was dead it wouldn't be bleeding, would it,' I said.

'Cor, these flaming midges,' said Dawn. 'I'm going to be eaten alive.'

'They only eat dirty people,' said Hattie bravely.

'I'll light a fag, that'll put them off,' said Dawn, not embarrassed at all. 'Don't go too deep. I don't fancy diving in to rescue you with all them weeds.'

'Well, I think it's very *weedy* of you not to swim,' I said and she said quietly to me, 'I can't. I've just remembered. I've got the curse,' and she kicked off her shoes, hitched up her skirt, sat on the vanity case and unfurled her *Daily Mirror*.

The weeds tickled your legs and the cold made you breathe in sharply, deliciously, cooling your body in a trice; but my mind wasn't on swimming but on whether dead sheep bleed and whether at that precise moment Dawn was bleeding.

Mummy had explained it was wrong to call it the curse because it was nature's way of telling you you had become a woman. It seemed too much of a coincidence that Dawn should chose to call it that. I looked at her pretending to read the paper, but who knew what was going on behind those black sun-glasses – it wasn't as if it was even sunny. Perhaps, at this very moment, she was putting a curse on us.

'Don't go out of your depth will you,' I said to Hattie. 'I'm going to ask Dawn something.'

'Shall if I want to,' Hattie said. 'Stop being a bossy-boots.'

I waded through the water, the weeds grabbing at my legs like gentle green ribbons, sat on my towel and fiddled with a piece of watercress.

'You didn't last long,' said Dawn, not looking up from her paper. 'Blimey. I feel sorry for this Stephen Ward geezer. Now, that's hypocrisy for you, if ever I saw it. Just because he's got an eye for a pretty face. That's been his only crime, you know, and they're doing him for living off immoral earnings.'

Got an eye for a pretty face. That again.

'Why's it hypocrisy?' Now Hattie was out of earshot, for my diary's sake I could take more interest in things Dawn said.

'Because they're all bleeding at it. The gentry, aristos, judges, politicians, the whole bang shoot. And yet he's going to have to swing for it. He's the scapegoat.'

'What's a scapegoat?'

'Someone who takes all the stick. The toffs have to look as though they disapprove, even though they're all up to it themselves.'

'Up to what, exactly?'

'You know, slap and tickle with good-time girls.'

'A friend of mine at school's mother is a witch,' I said staring hard at her like a policeman. What a shame her sun-glasses were

101

so black; according to Miss Rose, the eyes were the window of your soul. 'She had the power to put curses on people. She goes to a coven once a week.'

'What – to see the Beatles? No, I shouldn't joke. All that stuff gives me the creeps. I read about it in News of the Screws once. I reckon it's just an excuse for everyone to run around in the nude and have orgies.'

'Have you ever been to one?'

'What? An orgy?'

'No, a witches' coven.'

She paused, a very significant pause, I thought, and then she said, 'Give over. What do you think I am – some sort of pervert?' And then she went back to talking about this Profumo thing, on and on, about Russian spies and aristocrats and osteopaths.

'Do you believe in witchcraft, though?' I asked when I could get a word in edgeways, and she said, 'Blimey, you're obsessed. Dunno. Never really thought about it. Yeah, I suppose there are some people who have powers', and just as she said 'powers', two things happened: I saw a flash of kingfisher blue amongst the pale-green trees and Hattie, swimming dangerously near the foaming witch's cauldron, disappeared under the surface.

'*Take care of Hattie, darling, she's only little*' were Mummy's last words.

'*Hattie!*' With the strength of Black Champion himself, I crash-splash-thrashed through the watery weeds like a thing possessed, while Dawn stood up and frowned and shouted and pretended to look worried.

'*Hattie!*'

And then she bobbed up gasping and grinning, a green weed pigtail hanging cock-eyed from her hat.

'Fooled, you, fooled you!' she said. 'Coo, you should see your faces!'

'*So remember when you tell those little white lies that the night ... has a thousand eyes,*' sang Dawn, frightening the fish for miles both upstream and down (and me, too, if the truth be known; night-time was harrowing enough, thank you very much, without the thought of a thousand eyes on you).

We were walking back along the road that followed the river. If we'd been with Mummy or Mrs B we'd have stopped to play Poohsticks on the little white bridge near where Dan and Rupert went fishing, but because we were with Dawn we didn't.

'Major Smedley was right. There is a storm brewing,' said Hattie. 'Look, the cows are lying down.'

Due to Dawn's shoes though mainly, I suspected, due to her being a Townie and scared to be in the same field as cows, we skirted the meadows and, back on Granny's land, walked up a cart track along the edge of the dense, dark wood that was being throttled by ivy and bindweed and nettles and brambles and tangles. It gave you a suffocating feeling just looking at it.

Something rustled in the undergrowth and Dawn jumped.

'What the bleeding hell was that?'

'Only a pheasant, I expect,' I said.

'How do you know it wasn't a dirty great rat?' said Dawn.

'I thought you liked rats,' said Hattie.

'Jesus, the country gives me the creeps.'

So why don't you go back to filthy old London where you belong?

'Give me good old tarmac and shops and streets any day. At least there aren't creepy-crawlies lurking round every corner.'

'Yes, but there are rats. In London you're never fifteen yards – or is it feet? – from a rat.'

'Yeah but at least you can't see the buggers,' and then she stopped dead. 'Jesus bleeding Christ. Talk about Death Row,' and she pointed to the barbed-wire fence that bordered the wood.

At first glance it looked like a washing line full of animal skins. Except that no animal would hang its skin out to dry in such a dark, dank place. And anyway, it wasn't just their skins. It was whole, dead animals with little pink paws and dull eyes. There were two stoats, two moles, three grey squirrels, a jay, a crow, three magpies, a rat, two weasels and a barn owl. So this was what Jack meant by 'tampering with nature'.

If we'd been with any other grown-up they would have moved us on sharpish like policemen. Dawn let us look and look and look, and say it gave Hattie nightmares for the rest of her life?

Time stood still like a photograph as we absorbed every gorey detail, I would write. *The stoats' front paws in a begging position, the squirrels' white tummies, the blue wing of the jay, the rings on the rat's tail and his drooping whiskers ... It was very quiet and very still and very close. No birds sang, and there wasn't a breath of wind – or a breath of life. Here we were in the heart of England's green and plasant land staring death and decay slap in the face. If Beatrix Potter had been there she would have fainted clean away.*

Two young partridges bustled importantly by, like young men in tweed suits at a point-to-point hurrying to put a bet on the next race. 'I'm all right, Jack,' they seemed to say, not giving a dam about their fellow animals who had been sacrafised for them.

Due to the brewing storm, tea was in the dining room.

The plate of biscuits floated sadly in the middle of the table-cloth like a small, lonely boat on a large white lake.

'Honest, Mrs Aitch, it was the most disgusting thing I've ever seen,' Dawn said, slurping her tea like a central-heating repair man. 'Them hanging there all forlorn, their little faces begging for mercy. It made me want to throw up, honest it did. That Brain Pike geezer should be hung, drawn and quartered.'

Granny seemed to have shrunk since lunch. If she carried on at this rate, in a week's time you wouldn't be able to see her and when she talked it would be like the knitted tea cosy talking.

Why wasn't she annoyed with Dawn for letting us see the dead animals? For talking about "throwing up" at a meal time? Why didn't she say, 'Darlings, I'm so sorry, you've seen something unpleasant that Dawn should never have allowed you to see. Pretend it was something in a dream, and after tea we'll have a nice game of beggar my neighbour and forget all about it.'

But instead she said, 'Darlings, I'm afraid the world isn't all sweetness and light; man gets up to all sorts of unpleasant things that you're going to find out about sooner or later.'

'Doesn't woman too?' Hattie said.

'Yeah, but men are worse,' said Dawn. 'Look at prisons. Stuffed full of men.'

'But not all men are wicked are they, Granny?'

'Good heavens, no,' said Granny. 'You just get a bad apple cropping up sometimes.'

'Brian Pike must be a really bad, rotten apple. Rotten to the core and full of maggots,' I said.

'He's simply doing his job, darling,' said Granny. 'I agree it's a most disagreeable one, but then so many are.'

'He's a downright bloody sadist, if you ask me,' said Dawn. 'It's your land, Mrs Aitch. Why don't you tell him to leave off?'

'Part of Mr Pike's job is to keep down the vermin,' said Granny wearily. 'Your grandfather always said what notoriously stupid birds pheasants were. They'd lay their eggs just where a fox could get them.'

'But he hasn't killed any foxes,' I said.

'That's because he's scared of them,' said Dawn. 'He only kills tiny, helpless animals.'

'I think you'll find he does kill foxes, but buries them discreetly so as not to upset the hunting fraternity,' said Granny.

104

'So why can't he discreetly bury all the animals he kills?' I said. I didn't want to look as though I was on Dawn's side, but on the other hand . . . 'Instead of hanging them up like that and upsetting everyone who sees them?'

'Yes, because it makes sort of fools out of the animals, doesn't it.' Hattie said. 'When I die I would hate to have my body hung up on a fence for the world and his wife to see.'

'Perhaps they're there to act as a warning to other animals,' said Granny.

'If you ask me, it's Pike's way of showing his guv'nor he hasn't been sitting on his backside all day,' said Dawn, taking the second to last biscuit. 'I think it's flaming diabolical.'

'*You* don't agree with it, do you, Granny?'

But she – or rather the tea cosy – just went on about the barn owl. 'There are so few around, and from what I can gather they eat mice and rats, not pheasants' eggs.' she said sadly.

After the death row incident, Snuff Mull's presence was required all the more urgently. While Hattie squeezed out the soggy pieces of paper and mixed in the glue with a lolly stick, I blew up a large blue balloon, tied it with a piece of string and attached it to the back of the rocking chair. Then we carefully smothered the papier mâché over the balloon with our fingers, leaving a small gap at the top.

'It looks more like a round snowman's head,' said Hattie. 'Rams have long faces.' So I let out some of the air. We left him – or rather it, because he wasn't a proper Snuff Mull yet – dangling and just made it indoors before raindrops the size of half-crowns started falling.

We sat on wicker chairs in the conservatory and watched the sky turn as black as the end of the world or the middle of the night, the raindrops become stair rods which thundered off the roof like runaway trains clacking through a glass station. There was lightning, too, great white stabs of hope in the blackness, and thunder that made your ear-drums wince.

'I bet if we'd finished Snuff Mull this wouldn't have happened.'

'It's a bad omen for the summer generally isn't it,' Hattie said. 'I hope Dan's all right.'

I opened my diary and Hattie opened her sketchbook and, ignoring the ranting and raging going on outside, we worked in silence.

I told Mr Richards everything that had happened so far that I thought would be of interest. I finished by saying: *Outside, it is neither fit for man nor beast: the storm rages, flattening the crops and drowning the wildlife. All around is death and distruction. The force of evil, not content with the wicked winter, is at work again. Only one thing can stop it.*

We sat down to tinned ravioli and stringy boiled celery without Dan.

'You don't think he's been struck by lightning, do you?' said Dawn. Trust her to say what we were all thinking, and I flashed my eyes angrily at her through the gloom. The smell of hair spray fought the smell of scent like two rival skunks.

She had changed into a foul pink knitted dress that made her bosoms and bottom look huge, like Diana Dors. She'd changed because she was going out with Albert. Being a butcher he must like a nice piece of rump, I thought, then smiled because I'd just thought of a funny joke.

'Butcher, butcher, I'd like a nice piece of rump steak.'

'Certainly, Madam. Bend over, Dawn!!!'

''Ere, what you smiling about Sarah?' she asked. 'Not about your brother being struck by lightning, surely?'

'Don't be stupid,' I snapped. One wasn't even allowed to have a private joke with oneself without her sticking her nose in.

'Let's hope he's not sheltering under a tree,' said Dawn. 'That's the worst thing you can do,' and just as she said that lightning lit up the whole room and turned her into a black-eyed ghoul in a Hammer horror film.

There followed the loudest thunderclap yet which prompted Dawn to say, 'Hello. Someone's dropped their false teeth. Jesus, it scares the living daylights out of me.'

'It doesn't Sarah and me,' said Hattie. 'Does it you, Granny?'

'I can't say I care for it much,' said Granny. 'And the crops will be ruined, not to mention my roses.'

'The gods must be really pissed off with us,' Dawn said.

Speak for yourself, I thought, and don't ruddy well swear at table.

'Why's it *fork* lightning, by the way?' said Hattie. 'Why not knife or spoon?'

'Because it looks like a fork, I suppose,' I said. 'And why does a storm *brew*? It's not a pot of tea.'

'And why are you caught in the *teeth* of a storm?'

'Never mind storms, my teeth are caught in this celery,' I said, and Hattie roared with laughter.

'Blimey, look who it ain't,' said Dawn. 'Talk about a drowned rat.'

Dan was strolling through the teeth of the storm whistling *Singin' in the Rain* as casually as if he were walking along the seafront in the sun. His shirt sleeves were rolled up and the two top buttons were undone. He peered through the rain-spattered window and grinned his escaped-convict grin, waterfalls trickling down his cheeks, his hair plastered to his head like a swimming hat.

'Blimey, he'll catch his death,' said Dawn and for a second I thought of Snuff Mull; but all I could see was a blue balloon covered in sticky lavatory paper.

'We're going to knock spots off the Beatles,' said Dan and Hattie said didn't he mean ladybirds, beetles didn't have spots.

We were sitting in the conservatory in our dressing gowns and slippers drinking cocoa. Granny was in the sitting room listening to a Mozart concert on the wireless, Clifford was cowering under a bed and Dawn was peering into the dark and stormy night for the headlights of Albert's green Triumph Herald. You could see quite a long way up her skirt because she was bending over slightly, but thankfully Dan wasn't looking.

Dan told us how they had had a jam session in someone's dad's garage, and had hit it off musically straight away.

'Strawberry or plum jam?' asked Hattie and Dan actually laughed. He seemed a different person since he'd got back, and it wasn't just because now his hair had dried it looked funny. His eyes twinkle-twinkled like little stars and he had forgotten about being a rude and angry young man.

I asked him if Rupert, Dan's best friend, was in the group and Dan said, 'Give over. Rupert's about as musical as a fillet of cod.'

'Who is in it, then?'

'We haven't decided on the final line-up. Ronnie Bone's going to be on drums. He's bloody ace. The chances are Rick Benton – the bloke who overtook us in the red car – will be on bass guitar, Greg Hannant on lead guitar and Yours Truly on rhythm guitar, harmonica and vocals.'

'I thought there was more to that Ronnie Bone geezer than met the eye,' said Dawn not looking round, her bottom swaying like a pink balloon in a breeze. 'What sort of stuff did you play, anyway?'

'Oh, all sorts. Sam Cooke . . .'

'That's nigger music,' interrupted Dawn.

'So's Elvis's,' said Dan.

'You're not allowed to say "nigger" in this house,' I snapped. It

107

was none of her business what sort of music my brother played.

'We're going to write our own stuff, too,' said dan. 'Kind of R and B cum blues cum rock 'n' roll.'

'You don't need a singer, I suppose,' said Dawn. 'I wouldn't mind singing with a pop group,' and she turned round and snapped her fingers, wiggled her hips, tapped the toe of one crocodile-nosed shoe, looked at Dan with black eyes all big and stupid like a cow's and sang in a foul, nicotine-croaky, warthog-flat voice a song about loving me do.

How *could* she behave like that with Dan when she was engaged to Albert? If Dawn thought Dan had animal magnetism, did Dan think *she* had? Surely he *couldn't*. He had already said she wasn't his type, preferring the *au naturel*, Melanie Pratt sort, and if *I* thought she was the most hideous woman in the world, surely he would, too. He was, after all, my brother, and we always agreed on such things (Petula Clark prettier than Karen Kay, Sophia Loren more beautiful than Elizabeth Taylor, Alan Bates more handsome than Albert Finney).

And surely he couldn't possibly be impressed with her singing. Our voices were a hundred times better. I bet she'd never been in the school choir. Come to think of it, she'd probably never even been to school.

'Or how about this,' said Dawn, and wiggling her vulgar pink hips like an African tribeswoman sang, *'You ain't nothin' but a hound dog, a cheatin' on me.'*

'It's a boy's own group, isn't it, Dan,' I shouted, drowning her din.

'Yeah,' said Dan. 'Sorry, Dawn.'

'Oh, well, suit yourself,' said Dawn. 'What are you going to call yourselves, anyway?'

Dan said they hadn't decided.

So again we suggested names. I thought of Desperate Dan and the Cow Pies, which I thought brilliant but Dan said was too Billy Bunterish, Ronald and the Rhythm Men, Champion and his Wonder Horses, Robin Hood and his Merry Men, William Tell and the Apples, and Clifford and the Cliffhangers. Hattie thought of Captain Pugwash and the Pirates, Spotty Dog and the Woodentops, Dan and the Daredevils, Basil and the Blackbirds, and Teddy and his Singing Bears. Dawn thought up really silly ones like the Flaming Firecats, Teddy Boy and the Brothel Creepers, and the Mad Bad Three (even though Dan had said there were four of them).

Infuriatingly, Dan seemed to like Dawn's better than ours, and he said none quite hit the nail on the head. He wanted something angrier, more rebellious.

'How about Harry and the Headmasters,' said Hattie. 'They're always angry.'

'Or Sam Snake and the Hissing Vipers,' I said.

'Or something simple like the Wildcats,' said Dawn.

'Yeah, that's more the sort of thing.'

'It's got to be something and the Wildcats,' I said. 'Like Gerry and the Pacemakers. How about William and the Wildcats.'

'William! You're kidding! For a *pop group*,' screeched Dawn. 'That's a toff's name. You'll be suggesting Henry and the Higgenbottoms next.'

'How dare you speak to my sister like that,' Dan should have said. *'Kindly show some respect,'* But needless to say he didn't.

'No, I won't,' I said. 'I bet the next one you come up with is Gorblimey and the Guttersnipes.'

'Oh, it's like that, is it?' said Dawn, narrowing her black eyes at me. 'Well, how about Sarah and the Toffee-Nosed Brats?'

If there'd been a bread knife handy I would have sliced off her head. Instead I said, 'How about Dawn and the Smelly Dustbins? Or Dawn and the Common as Mucks? Or Dawn and the Above Her Stations? Or', and I'd just hit on a much better, more subtle idea, 'Virgil et Agricolae?'

'Or,' said Hattie, cottoning on, 'Les Monsieurs et les Rouges Chats.'

'What's the point of having a foreign name for an English pop group?' said Dawn. 'No one would know what it meant.'

'*Some* people wouldn't.'

'Stop bitching, all of you,' said Dan. 'It's worse than a flaming henhouse.'

'Don't you mean dog kennel if we're bitching?' said Hattie.

'What we're after,' said Dan, and his hair looked so funny if I'd been in a laughing mood I would have roared, 'is something wild and untamed.'

'How about the Roaring Leopards?' said Hattie.

'Or the Snarling Sabre-toothed Tigers?' I said.

'Or simply the Wild Ones,' said Dawn.

'I like it,' said Dan, and slapped his thigh. 'The Wild Ones. Yeah. I like that a lot.'

'But wild makes you think of forests or unbrushed hair, mentioning no one in particular,' I said.

'And men who live in the wild and have no table manners,' said Hattie.

'That's why it's spot on,' said Dan.

I was about to say I thought it a most unsuitable name when Dawn said. 'Thank you, Dan,' and put her head on one side and gave him a stupid pouty aren't-I-clever smile, and she tried to say with her eyes 'We're both grown-ups and understand things these two children never will,' but I was pleased to notice she failed dismally and just looked stupid, like a painted sheep. And if, at that moment, a pair of headlights hadn't shone weakly like blind cats' eyes through the gloom and doom, I might have said, 'Actually, servants normally wait to be collected in the *kitchen*, you know.'

'Oh, it's him,' she said as uninterestedly as if he was the baker or Kleeneze man. 'If he was a real gent he'd come and get me and escort me back to the car with an umbrella over me head. As it is, I'm going to get bleeding drenched.'

'Can I do something?' said Dan standing up, but Dawn said she couldn't possibly take his dressing gown, why, she bet he didn't have anything on underneath and gave the foulest witch's laugh in the world, and said she'd just bung her jacket over her head. 'What's the betting me mascara ends up round me chin?' she said. 'See ya later. Ta-ta.'

The car drove off into the night and we sat in silence, listening to the wind, that sounded like twenty lions roaring through loudhailers into the trees, and the rain, lighter now like fairies in ballet shoes dancing on the glass roof. A faraway door was bang, bang, banging like a Chinese torture. If you listened hard you could faintly hear Albert changing gear. I pictured his large red butcher's hand on the gear stick. Was it at this very moment brushing accidentally on purpose against Dawn's thigh?

Gradually, like a classroom when an evil teacher has just left it, the conservatory returned to normal. It took a while for my face to turn cool again, for my heart to return to its normal gentle pace.

Hattie and I sat on Dan's lap, one on each knee, and he put his arms round us and stroked our hair. He smelt of Wright's Coal Tar Soap and clean damp dog and ever-so-slightly of a public house.

'You really mustn't be beastly to poor old Dawn,' he said.

'Poor old *Dawn*? Poor old *us*, you mean, having to put up with her.'

'Yes, Sausage, but she doesn't know any better. She hasn't had the education you're getting. She's just a silly girl who doesn't know how to behave.'

'And doesn't know her place,' I said. 'I mean, she's only a servant so why should she be in here choosing a name for your pop group as if she was one of us? She should be in the kitchen darning socks

110

listening to *Mrs Dale's Diary* and minding her own business.'

'Yes, and why should she eat with us and use our bathroom and fill it with her foul old pongy muck,' said Hattie. 'Her surname isn't Hillington, is it, though you'd think it was the way she carries on.'

'No, but she is kind of part of the family – or that's what Granny would like,' said Dan.

'Part of the family!' I screeched. 'Never, in a million years.' And Hattie muttered, 'Over my dead body.'

'I think you should turn the situation to your advantage and learn as much as you can from her. You two don't often get a chance to meet people like her. As Aunt L said, everything's on the verge of change. Once old Macmillan and his ex-Eton-riddled cabinet are out of the way and new blood is in power, people with our sort of background will be right out of fashion. We're heading towards egalitarianism, you know.'

'What's that when it's at home?' I said, realising too late late I'd already picked up one of Dawn's foul expressions.

'A classless society. When everyone is treated equally.'

'But they are already,' I said. 'I mean if, for example, a farm-worker's son was very clever he could go to university if he wanted.'

'In theory yes, but in practice no, because the farmworker wouldn't be able to afford to keep him there. The grant's a joke. And he'd *never* get to Oxford or Cambridge – unless he was genius level, and even then he wouldn't fit in.'

'I don't see why he should fit in,' I said. 'Someone who was at Cambridge wouldn't fit in with a group of football supporters, would he? Is that what ega . . . thingamy is? When everyone mixes with everyone else?'

'Kind of,' said Dan.

'You mean, Lords will have lunch with dustmen, and tractor drivers' daughters will marry judges.'

'In an ideal world, yeah if they wanted to,' said Dan.

'It doesn't sound very ideal to me,' I said. 'I don't want to marry a road sweeper or bus driver who picks his nose at the table. Is that what you mean?'

'Not entirely,' said Dan. 'Anyway, a road sweeper wouldn't want to marry you, you're such a snob. Come the revolution . . .'

'What revolution? There'll never be one, not in England.

'Personally, I'd like things to stay just as they are,' said Hattie. 'Then when I grow up I can paint all day and have babies but have a servant to do all the boring things like washing up and mending and polishing the silver.'

'You'll still be able to,' said Dan. 'The only difference will be that

111

everyone will have the chance to do that. And there won't be any servants. Everything will be done by robot.'

'I don't see how a machine could set the table,' I said. 'How would it know whose table napkin went where, or whether it was breakfast, lunch or tea?'

'You'll be amazed at what computers can do already,' said Dan.

'Anyway, I think the Wild Ones is a foul name for a pop group,' I said. 'Desperate Dan and the Cow Pies is much better. It would make people smile which is more than can be said for the Wild Ones.'

'We don't want to make people smile,' said Dan. 'We want to make people think, maybe, and dance, and get angry even.'

'Why do you want to get people angry?' I said. 'There are enough angry people about already. Why don't you want to make them happy?'

'We do,' Dan said. 'happy and a bit angry at the same time.'

'I still don't see what you've got to be angry about,' I said. 'Granny says you've had a privileged upbringing and should be grateful.'

'I am,' said Dan. 'In one sense.'

'And what about in the other?'

'I'd like to kick the whole damn lot in the teeth,' said Dan. 'Now, who's for a game of Champion No Wonder Horse?'

He jiggled his knees and neighed, and Hattie as Rebel woofed and I said 'See 'em off, Champ', and we sang at the tops of our voices, *'You'll hear about him everywhere you go the name of Champion, No Wonder Horse.'*

Normally I had no trouble turning myself into Ricky, the room we were in into Wild West country, Dan's knee into Champion's sleek chestnut back. But not that night. Try as I might, I remained me, Dan's knee remained Dan's knee and the conservatory remained the conservatory, with Dawn swaying in the corner like a repulsive pink ghost.

CHAPTER ELEVEN

My mother said, I never should, play with the gypsies in the wood, I dreamt to the tune of the storm. *If I did, she would say, naughty girl to disobey.*

In my dream the gypsies were large rats with sideboards and leather jackets, laughing and lolling with Dawn on the kitchen table. *'You ain't nothin' but a toffee-nosed brat,''* they sang and Dan, half-man half-beast, joined in. 'Shoo, shoo, little dirty feet!' cried Granny like Miss Tittlemouse, clattering her dustpan, but they were there to stay, and though I implored Dan to get rid of them – *'They ain't nothin' but a pack of vermin'* – he just howled with Howlin' Wolf laughter. The revolution had come, the Wild Ones had taken over and Hattie, Granny and I were cast into the dark and stormy night that was fit for neither man nor beast.

By morning the raging had ceased and the world, slightly the worse for wear, was at peace again.

Beneath sky as grey as an elephant's eye we squelched across the lawn, our Wellingtons leaving sinking footsteps in the soggy grass. Branches and twigs and flotsam and jetsam were strewn everywhere, flowers hung their petal-less heads in shame and a yellow fertiliser bag lay spreadeagled in a bush. The runner beans were all at sixes and sevens and so were the raspberries.

The black summerhouse's roof hadn't blown off like a bristly wig, and the pitch had kept out all traces of the storm. The head hung like a rough-shelled, giant goose's egg from the rocking chair.

'You do the nose and mouth,' I said. 'You're the artistic one.'

'I can't remember what a ram's nose looks like,' said Hattie and drew an upside-down V with a black felt-tip. 'Shall I do a smiling mouth or a sad one?'

'One in between. He's not going to smile or be sad. He's not that sort of person.'

We wrapped aluminium foil round pipe cleaners and threaded shiny blue beads onto the ends. Then we curled them up and glued one to each side of his head.

After breakfast, a scowling, stinking and bone-riddled bloater affair, when I managed to slip into an otherwise boring Profumo-dominated conversation between Dan and Dawn that it was my birthday tomorrow, Hattie and I walked round the barbed-wire fences to collect damp sheep's wool which we dried in the Aga.

'We wouldn't make very good hairdressers,' said Hattie, back in the summerhouse.

'Don't you mean wool dressers?' I said.

'Look from the back view,' said Hattie. 'He looks like a moth-eaten old grandfather.'

I had chosen the eyes with great care. They were a pale cabbage green with black middles. As soon as I saw them in amongst the gentle doll and teddy ones in the toy shop I knew they were destined to be Snuff Mull's.

'We must get them in the right place,' I said, gluing the backs of them. 'If they're too close together he'll look stupid.'

'And if one's higher than the other he'll look as though he's asking a question,' said Hattie.

'And if they're too far apart he'll look mongl ... like a mongrel. How's that?'

'Higher. Left one lower. Right one in a bit.'

I pressed them into place.

'How does he look?' I whispered, standing back. His flat face was more like a bull terrier's than a ram's, and the mouth wasn't quite right and his hair was a bit tufty, but overall he was perfect.

'He reminds me of a cross Humpty-Dumpty,' said Hattie and I told her that once he was christened she must never make fun.

I gently put him into Granny's old hat box, and we set off down the red brick road which was more of a river than a road. If anyone asked us what was in the box we'd say it was a dead bird we'd found drowned in the storm and we were taking him to the churchyard for his funeral.

The tiny church had a thatched roof and a short stumpy steeple like a docked tail or a sawn-off shotgun. Inside there was room for only seven pews and four horseboxes, as we called them, inside which you could play cat's cradle without the vicar seeing. A family of house martins lived in the eaves, whose squealing and squabbling competed with the vicar's sermon.

Some of the gravestones, buried under lichen and moss and brambles and nettles, were very old; you had to stretch your imagination a long way back to picture what a 250-year-old dead body looked like. The churchyard had a corner set aside for Hillingtons so they could rest in peace (or 'rust in peace' as Dan said) under the speckledy yew trees. The grass there was lusher than elsewhere

114

in the churchyard. Hattie had said it was because Hillington blood was richer than other people's and I said blood didn't get into the ground unless the coffin leaked, and it was probably because the sheep didn't like eating grass under yew trees, and Hattie said they wouldn't, would they, like eating themselves, you know, *ewes*. We had asked Granny, and she said there was nothing very special about Hillington bodies, why a body was a body.

'But there must be something special about them, Granny, or they wouldn't have a whole corner of churchyard to themselves,' I had said.

'Ah, that's a different matter. They had power and influence, once upon a time. In the old days when the estate was much larger, they provided employment for almost everyone in the village.'

'So it's right that they shouldn't be buried next to the villagers,' I had said. 'After all, they wouldn't have slept in the same bedroom as them when they were alive, would they.' But Granny just said everyone was equal in the eyes of God.

'I reckon there's room for two more graves in the Hillington Corner,' I said. 'The great aunts will die first. They're ancient. Or perhaps Granny. Or Aunt Lynette. Her liver will pack up or she'll kill herself in her sports car.'

'Daddy drives fast, too. Just think. Perhaps at this moment they are lying in a bottomless French ditch ...'

'Belt up.'

Mrs B had been the last person to die in the village because she was at the end of the row. We put the scattered red and yellow roses back in their silver urn on her grave and arranged the wild flowers we'd picked in a discarded Seven-up bottle.

Winifred Butterworth, beloved wife of Jack, died in her sleep on March 3, 1963. May she rest in peace.

'I never knew her name was Winifred,' I whispered. 'That's Granny's name.'

'I wonder if she's wearing her hat.'

'Don't be daft. Dead bodies don't wear hats. They don't wear anything.'

'I wonder if her body's a skelington yet,' Hattie whispered. 'And if it is, where does all the fat go? Would the worms have eaten it or what?'

'Shhh,' I said, though I wouldn't have minded knowing myself.

We said a little prayer for her and I took Snuff Mull out of his box and placed him on Mrs B's grave, about where her tummy would be, and knelt in the soggy grass.

Oh, most powerful of beasts and king of kings, upon whom we

115

put our trust in order that you will protect us, the Hillington family
. . .'

'And Jack,' hissed Hattie.

'And Jack, and all those we love, be they in human or animal form, from evil er, great and small. And now, oh wondrous one, we would like to christen you . . . Snuff Mull,' and I licked my finger and painted a cross on his forehead. It was unfortunate that I'd been sucking a strawberry-flavoured sweet, but Hattie said a pink cross didn't matter, in fact if anything it was better because it made him more religious and less witchcrafty.

Back in the summerhouse, we placed Snuff Mull on the mantelpiece and lit the candle on either side.

'It's got to be in rhyme from now on.'

'Why?' said Hattie and I said it was all part of the magic, and if she laughed I would never speak to her again.

We knelt down and I said:

'Please, Oh Mighty One, get rid of the wicked winter once and for all,

So that Clifford and Granny can return to nor-mal.'

I ignored the clucking sound coming from Hattie's throat, got up, parted Snuff Mull's wool and posted one of Granny's straight hairs and one of Clifford's short ones through the hole.

'And please could Dawn Potts be not evil but good,

And stop any more animals being killed in the wood', and I posted one of Dawn's yellow hairs and a sparrow's feather.

'Can you think of anything else?' I whispered, and Hattie said, 'Something about Dan – and the parents.'

And even though he's in a pop group please help Dan,

behave less like, er, a rough and rude angry young man.

And please could Mummy and Daddy have a lovely Second Honeymoon,

And be safe and sound and come back very soon.

We remain, Oh Mighty One, your most faithful of followers. Amen,' and I made the sign of the cross in the air to show it was white magic, not black.

Coming out of the summerhouse felt a bit like coming out of church, when you've done your praying for the day so you know nothing too dreadful can happen. And then Hattie said, 'By the way, I've got a confession to make. I'm going painting with Aunt Lynette this afternoon.'

I asked if I could come and Hattie said they'd be discussing light and colours and perspectives and things and might be a bit boring; anyway they had to buy my birthday presents.

116

I have to spend a whole afternoon on my own with her. I would write. *I feel ill at the thought of it. Without Snuff Mull to give me strength, goodness know's what will happen* ...

'Okay, kid, it's just the two of us. What do you fancy doing?'

Lunch was over (if you could call sardines on toast followed by stewed plums with no cream or custard lunch; in my book it would be a snack). Dan was in Shotestead being a Wild One, Hattie and Aunt Lynette had roared off to paint a windmill, Granny had retired to her room. That left Dawn and me washing up in the scullery with the kipper-coloured Elvis Presley and the mousetrap for company. Things didn't look promising.

'We could go for a bike ride, I suppose,' I said flatly, eyeing her short, tight pink skirt. At least if we were on bicycles I wouldn't have to talk to her. A woman on the wireless was singing about it being her party so she could cry if she wanted to. I agreed with her.

'Blimey, I haven't ridden a bike since I was a kid. Okay, anything for a laugh,' and she joined in with the song.

'I liked that song until you joined in.' That was one good thing about Dawn, I supposed. You could be as rude to her as you liked and not be told off. Even with Hattie and Veronica you could only go so far. It gave you an unfamiliar, liberated sort of feeling. 'How come you always wear pink?'

'Pink makes the boys wink,' said Dawn. 'Surely you've heard that one.'

'No, I haven't, actually,' I said, vowing never to wear pink in my whole life.

The bikes lay in a corner of the coach house alongside tins of paint and creosote and a tray of mouldy, maggoty apples.

'Blimey, they look as though they've come out of the ark. And look at the saddles! You could do yourself a mischief with one of those – as the actress said to the bishop, ha, ha, ha!'

We brushed off the cobwebs and I pumped up the tyres and squirted oil on the rusty chains. Dawn had the man's black bike that used to be Daddy's and I had the one which was once green but was now rust and whose front brake didn't work.

'Haven't you got a looser skirt?' I said. 'That one's not very suitable for cycling. Especially on a man's bike.'

'It'll have to do,' she said. 'I won't be showing any more leg than what you're showing in your shorts, will I?'

It wasn't the same thing, but I couldn't be bothered to argue.

'How do you get on to the bleeder?' she said, lifting one leg over the saddle to reveal, exactly as predicted, a black pair of knickers. (I supposed I should be thankful she was wearing any at all.) She bumped off over the wobbly cobblestones, the front wheel twisting and turning as if it was taking part in a Slow Bicycle Race. 'This must be what's known as giving oneself a cheap thrill,' she screeched and her laughter would have woken the dead, let alone Granny. 'Gawd, I can't reach the flaming pedals. What are you trying to do – ruin me sex life?'

We found a spanner and after a lot of effort on my part because it had all rusted up, I lowered her seat.

'Where shall we go?' I said. 'How about Framlington Heath?'

'I thought we might go into Shotestead,' Dawn said. 'Treat you to a coffee.'

'Granny doesn't let us cycle there because of the traffic.'

'Well she needn't never know, need she,' said Dawn. 'Not unless someone, mentioning no names, tells her.'

'What if someone she knows sees us?' I said, and someone was bound to with Dawn attracting so much attention. Except – if they did see us and tell Granny, she might sack Dawn! ('Honestly, Granny, I did everything I could to persuade her not to go, including saying you didn't allow it, but she still insisted. And she was in charge of me so I had to do as she said, didn't I.')

'I'll take the stick,' said Dawn. 'Your gran's got a real soft spot for me.'

Only because she pities you.

'Anyway, I don't like coffee.'

'Okay, a milk shake then.'

So off we set, bump-squeak-splashing down the red brick road, Dawn's bottom bulging round the seat like a squashy pink cushion, wisps of yellow candy-floss hair waving against wisps of white candy-floss clouds, her screeches sounding like a large, colourful bird who's just learnt to fly.

'It's like being a kid again,' she shouted, lifting her spindly white legs out straight to avoid getting sprayed by the puddles. And then, as we turned into the road she said, 'This is the life, eh? Cycling down country lanes without a care in the world. Phew. I'm puffed out already.'

'That's because of all those foul fags you smoke. Race you to that oak tree.'

As expected, it was like the fastest racehorse in the world racing an out-of-condition donkey.

We had just turned into the main road when a passing lorry hooted.

'What's he doing that for?' I said crossly. 'If we go any nearer the side we'll wobble into the ditch.'

'Ner, he was hooting because I'm showing so much leg,' said Dawn. 'That's a pleasure you've got in store when you're older.'

'I can't see any pleasure in jumping out of your skin,' I said and wanted to add, 'How do you know he wasn't hooting at *me* showing so much leg,' but I didn't.

Then a man in a van leant out of his window and wolf-whistled and shouted 'Cor' vulgarly. A man trimming his hedge stopped in mid-snip to stare, and another quite old man taking his dog for a walk muttered 'Lummy'. Then we came to some men in jeans and no shirts building a red monstrosity. They all looked round and one, as blond and handsome as Adam Faith, with a nice, strong, golden-haired chest, put his hands on his hips and shouted, 'Give us a lift, Dawn love,' and Dawn shouted 'What, on my crossbar? You might do yourself a mischief,' and he shouted that was why he wanted a lift and what was she doing tonight, eh? and everyone laughed except me. Was it simply the amount of leg Dawn was revealing that was causing all the attention, I wondered. Or was it this strange thing called animal magnetism that fools grown-ups but not children?

We came to a wobbly, squeaking, swerving stop at the entrance to the recreation ground. We were going there because Dawn was dying for a 'fag'.

'Coo-er, me bum's never going to be the same again,' she said, rubbing it in full view of anyone who cared to look.

We leant the bikes aginst the railings behind a bench, and Dawn said wouldn't they get nicked?

'Of course not. People don't steal things round here.'

'Where I used to live in London you'd leave an empty milk bottle on your step and it would be gone by morning.'

'No!'

'Yeah, straight up. They'd smash them over the road to puncture car tyres.'

'How can people be so foul?'

'I could tell you a lot worse things than that an' all – but I won't because I mustn't warp your innocent young mind, must I?'

'It's too late – you've already warped it.'

Sitting on the bench in opposite corners was an elderly couple. Both stared over the hills and far away at some private place. The woman wore a hat and the man didn't. Dawn nudged me and nodded at them. 'I hope that's not how Albert and me'll end up – miserable as sin with nothing to say. What a thought, eh?'

119

'I can't imagine you ever not having anything to say,' I said and did a cartwheel on the grass.

She laughed. 'I suppose I am an old gasbag.'

'Anyway, maybe those two weren't married,' I said, walking ahead so that people wouldn't think we were together.

'What, you mean they're living in sin?' Dawn said, and her cackle caused a couple walking their dog to look round as sharply as if there'd been a car accident.

'It must be so lonely to be old and not married,' I said.

'What makes you think married people are any less lonely?' Dawn said. 'From what I've seen, marriage is no guarantee of happiness.'

'It must be the sort of people you know,' I said. (Rough and rude who yell and fight and smack their children in public and get drunk and smash each other over the head with rolling pins.) 'All the marriages I know are happy.'

'That's what you think,' said Dawn. 'You don't know what goes on behind the net curtains. You toffs are good at hiding it all under the carpet. There could be God-awful ding-dongs going on for all you know.'

I felt a vague uneasy feeling, as if a small secret I'd pushed into a far corner of my mind was gently stirring in its sleep.

We sat on a damp bench. In the distance beyond the cricket pitch two small, carefree girls played on the swings. I watched them swing towards, then away from, the cloudy sky.

Dawn delved in her plastic handbag for a packet of cigarettes. Piccadilly, they were called. The packet was empty. Although there was a litter bin within throwing distance, she dropped the packet to the ground.

If I'd been a dog I'd have taken a chunk out of her ankle. Instead I jumped up, picked up the packet and flung it in the bin. 'Honestly, Dawn, what do you think the bin's for?' I said, for in my book there was nothing worse than a person who dropped litter.

'Oh, sorry, I forgot,' she said, obediently putting the silver paper from her new packet into the bin. She lit a cigarette and slipped her feet out of her muddy-heeled shoes. Her toe nails were painted pink, and I noticed a foul corn.

'You shouldn't wear pointed toes,' I said. 'You'll get bunions soon, too.'

'Ain't we the Little Miss Bossy-Boots. You have to suffer to be beautiful, you know. Can you imagine me plodding along in brogues? It wouldn't suit my image.'

'Why, what is your image?'

'A mixture of Marilyn Monroe, Brigitte Bardot and Grace Kelly.

Ner, only kidding. That's how I'd *like* to look, given half the chance. Well, we can all dream, can't we.'

Like me and Black Champion. 'I suppose men wouldn't whistle at you in brogues. Why's it a *wolf*-whistle, by the way?'

'Because men are wolves. Or like to think they are, anyway.'

'Albert's not a wolf, is he, he's more of a ginger tom, I'd say. A friendly ginger tom.'

'He can be like a wolf at times,' said Dawn. 'All men can be.'

The two girls shrieked with excitement as they swung higher and higher. If I had the choice between having a swing and talking to a coarse maid, I knew which I'd choose. Even though when she wasn't showing off she was almost bearable, you couldn't depend on her.

In front of us two dogs sniffed at each other's rear ends. 'Blimey, don't dogs have disgusting habits,' she said loud enough for their frowning female owners to hear. 'And look at that poodle's balls. They look like shiny black conkers. Bloody obscene if you ask me.'

Then, blowing smoke into the already-stale afternoon air, she added, 'By the way talking of Albert, I was wondering if you could do me a small favour.'

'Not if you're going to show me up in public like that.' I said, biting on a grass stalk. It tasted as sweet as chocolate.

'Would you take a message to him?'

So that's why she wanted to come to Shotestead. I should have guessed.

'Why can't you?'

'Because I'm not in the mood for making small talk with his parents. They don't approve of me. Tell him I'm sorry but I can't make it tonight.'

I felt a small thistle near my heart stirring itself. *'Why* can't you?'

'Oh, I dunno,' she said, shrugging. 'You can have too much of a good thing, can't you. He'll come to expect it every night, won't he.'

'But when you're married to him you'll see him every night so you might as well get used to it now.'

'Yeah, but you can look at it another way. Precisely because of that I should be making the most of being a free agent while I've got the chance.'

'But you love Albert, don't you? I thought if you loved someone you want to spend every minute of the day with them.' (I wouldn't say no to spending every minute of every day with Mr Richards.)

'Yeah, well,' she said, flipping ash on to the grass. 'That's what the fairy stories say.' And she paused. 'Course I love him. It's just that sometimes I think I'm too young to settle down. It's a big world out there, you know. I want to have adventures, a bit of excitement.'

'But you can have adventures with Albert,' I said.

'Ner. It's not the same,' said Dawn. 'It's that feeling of freedom you get when you're on your own, of being able to do anything you like. It's like when I was cycling just then, with the wind in me face, the sun on my thighs, and those blokes whistling at me and not a care in the world.'

I agreed that they wouldn't have whistled if Albert had been there.

'It's the difference between wearing a tight corset and wearing nothing underneath, not a dicky bird.'

'What is?'

'Being married and not being married.'

For a second I pictured a row of women balancing on a telegraph wire wearing underwear made out of dead birds.

'But being whistled at isn't everything in life. If I had the choice of being whistled at or being married to someone nice, I know which I'd choose.'

'Yeah, I know I should count my blessings,' said Dawn. 'It's just this thing of wanting to *be* someone. Okay, so Albert says he'll try and raise the dough for me to open a boutique in Shotestead but it's hardly going to get me name in lights, is it?'

'You'd get into the local paper. And nice men like Albert don't grow on trees. If you don't marry him you might end up old and lonely like that woman on the bench.'

'Yeah. It's a toss up, ain't it. I know my type should be happy just to settle down and have kids, but I'm not like that. I wish I was. It would make life much simpler. The thing is, I'm not convinced about this marriage lark. I think there's something a bit unnatural about spending your whole life with the same person. Animals don't, do they. They have a different mate ever year.'

'Swans mate for life,' I said. 'And lions, I think, or is it gorillas. Anyway, we aren't animals.'

'We're not that far off,' said Dawn. 'Hey, even though you're only a kid we seem to be on the same wavelength, yeah?'

That's what you think.

'If you want someone on your wavelength, why don't you work in a factory?'

'I did for a while. In Buntings, and guess what I did all day. Looked out for duff spuds. Spuds, spuds, spuds swimming before my eyes. It nearly drove me potty. The money wasn't bad, mind.

Six pounds nine and six, and they took you there and back in a coach.'

'At least you could chat with other girls of your age.'

'Yeah, but what about? Babies and nappies and Hoovers and recipes and stuff I'm just not interested in. One day, maybe, but not now. Not when I'm in me prime, sort of thing. I know it's a dead-end job working for your gran but I can learn more from her and your aunt than I ever could in a factory. I thought – and don't laugh – they could educate me, teach me to speak proper, act like a bit of a lady.'

'Like in *Pygmalion*? Why do you want to be a bit of a lady? You'd make Albert feel uncomfortable.'

Dawn ground out her lipsticky cigarette end with her pointed white toe. 'Yeah, that's the thing about Albert. He's not what you'd call classy, is he.' And she slumped back, crossing her arms and stretching out her legs. 'I mean, even if you saw him in the first-class carriage of a train in a three-piece whistle reading *The Times,* you'd still know he was a butcher.'

'There's nothing wrong with being a butcher. It's a very respectable thing to be.'

'I suppose so. Anyway, it still does no harm to know how to behave proper. It would be nice to know that if I were ever taken somewhere posh I wouldn't make a complete prat of myself.'

'For a start, you would have to improve your table manners,' I said. 'I bet Brigitte Bardot doesn't talk with her mouth full.'

'Okay,' said Dawn, sighing. 'While you're about it, you might as well tell me what else I do wrong.'

My golden opportunity had arrived. 'One. Not using your table napkin. Two. Calling it serviette. Three. Being far too greedy with the butter. Four. Cutting it off at the corner. Five. Using your knife instead of a spoon in the marmalade. Six. Slurping your tea. Seven. Putting your elbows on the table. Eight. Pretending your fork's a spoon to eat peas. Nine. Using a piece of bread to mop up your gravy ...'

'How the bleeding hell else are you meant to mop it up?'

'You're meant to ask your hostess whether she minds you using your spoon, or else leave it. Ten. Taking the last piece of toast without asking the others whether they want it. Eleven. Putting salt on your food without tasting it first.'

'Blow that for a game of soliders,' said Dawn. 'If I've cooked it I know exactly how much I've put in – usually none because I forgot.'

'Don't ask and then argue,' I said. 'Twelve. Talking about anything connected with stomachs, feeling sick, going to the lavatory, dead animals, having babies, spots on chins, et cetera. Thirteen. Leaving the table without excusing yourself. Fourteen. Not using your fork for second course. Fifteen. Calling second course pudding, or afters. Sixteen. Not ...'

'Hang on a minute. I'll never remember this flipping lot. I reckon it's easier staying common as muck, and I'll just have to accept the fact I'll never be invited to dinner at Cliveden. You know, that's Lord Astor's place where Profumo first clapped eyes on Christine Keeler – naked in the swimming pool.'

'Oh yeah?' I said, forcing my voice to sound flat and uninterested.

'You see she let both Profumo, who was Minister of War, and a Russian geezer called Eugene Ivanov, who was the Russian Embassy Naval Attaché, have their wicked way with her. That's what all the scandal's about – a breach of security. And because Profumo said in the House of Commons he hadn't slept with her, which was a dirty great lie, he had to resign.'

'I don't see why any of that's a breach of security.'

'Because Profumo may have told her things that she then passed on to the Russian bloke. You see, when a geezer's in bed with a woman he's likely to divulge top secrets.'

'Why?'

'Because if he doesn't the woman could refuse to let him have his end away – you know, play hide the sausage. And in the words of someone or other, an erect prick has no conscience.'

The two girls were now swooshing down the slide, head first. 'Weeeeee,' they screamed without a care in the world.

'Did Christine Keeler pass on top secrets, then?'

'Ner. She's not that way inclined. That's why the whole thing's such a farce. She was just interested in having a good time. She's not a prostitute, by the way. She's what's called a good–time girl.'

'What do they do?'

'Have a good time, of course.'

Talking to Dawn was like talking to a character in *Alice in Wonderland*. The caterpillar, perhaps, or the March Hare.

'They go to posh parties, meet lots of interesting people. Sleep with men, too, but not for money. Maybe for presents – you know, fur coats and diamond necklaces and that but not for money.'

'Does she want to have a baby, then?'

'Who? Christine Keeler? You're kidding. You don't just go to bed with a man when you want a baby. You do it for pleasure, too, you know.'

This was news to me. The Family Doctor booklet Mummy

124

had given me hadn't mentioned pleasure. Nor had Miss Crowe in biology when telling us about the reproductive system of the rabbit. Did rabbits do it for pleasure, too, I wondered. Was there such a thing as a good-time rabbit?

'Well, strictly speaking,' continued Dawn, 'it's more pleasurable for the man than the woman. That's why it's the man who gives the presents. Actually, it can be a bit bloody boring for a woman – or so I've heard. The woman just lies back and thinks of England and lets the man get on with it,' and she sighed. 'I sometimes wish I was a man, actually. Not only for that reason. Men have an easier time of it generally. And they don't get pregnant. There's this new contraceptive pill women can take, but I've heard it makes you fat.'

Mary pondered all these things in her heart. That was my favourite expression in the Bible, and that's what I did then.

'But I thought,' I said treading cautiously the way you would in an old house with a few rotten floorboards, 'that unless you were a prostitute you only er, went to bed with your husband.'

'That's what Society says you should do, so in theory yeah. In practice they're all at it.'

All? I thought of a few of the unmarried women I knew. Miss Rose and Mummy's bridge friend Gillian, and Sally Anne, Daddy's secretary, and Aunt Lynette, and Hilda in the underwear department.

'Not *all,* surely,' I said.

'Well, not the squares and the prudes and the ugly ones. But all the others, I reckon.'

That cut out everyone on my list – except for Aunt Lynette and Sally Anne.

'So how come only married women have babies?'

'Oh, we are little Miss Innocent,' she said. 'Unmarried women have them, too, but it's all kept hush-hush, and when the baby's born it's usually adopted. There's a stigma attached, you see. You can have an abortion done by one of those dodgy back-street quacks who's just after your lolly. But it's illegal and it can make you sterile.'

The girls were now riding the seven-seater pre-war rocking horse called Billy. 'Giddy-up,' the older one shouted, and Billy obligingly bucked then reared. 'Go faster,' shouted the younger one, beating Billy's old wooden flank with a make-believe whip. If it had been this time last year, it would have been Hattie and me riding on Billy.

'When I grow up I'm never going to sleep with a boy unless he's my husband.'

125

'That's what they all say,' said Dawn. 'Say you meet a Cliff Richard lookalike who can't marry you for ten years. What would you do then?'

'I'd wait. Patience is a virtue.'

'Yeah, but *he* might not think so and go off with someone else.'

'Well, maybe if we were engaged, and I was wearing a ring . . .'

'There's a good example of hypocrisy,' said Dawn, lighting another cigarette.

'What is?'

'Society's attitude to unmarried mothers. There's a film called *The L-shaped Room* showing at the flicks at the moment, right? And the review in the local paper said a young French girl 'in her condition'. No mention of her being pregnant. I mean, 'in her condition' could mean she had acne or a hump back, yeah? But they couldn't print 'a single pregnant girl'. On, no, they'd get bloody judges and vicars and retired civil servants writing in their droves about the decline in moral standards. And yet I bet every single one of that lot has slept with an unmarried girl at one time or another. And of course if the girl gets pregnant, the toff doesn't want to know.'

'I bet they haven't *all*.'

'Bet they have. Take your dad, for example.' And she stabbed my arm with her pointed finger nail. 'Bet he's had a few on the side.'

If I was the Red Queen or the duchess in *Alice* I would simply have screamed 'Off with her head' and that would have been the end of that.

'How *dare* you. Anyway, you don't even know him.'

'No, but I know about men.'

'Just because you know about foul, rough, common men, it doesn't mean you know about my father. I'm not going to waste my breath talking to you,' and I got up and stumped towards the gate.

'Hey, don't get the hump,' she said, running up behind me. 'I just say things off the top of my head sometimes. I didn't mean it, honest.'

'It's too late,' I said. 'And I'm certainly not going to take the message to Albert.'

'Oh, please.'

'No. You'll just have to see him tonight then, won't you.'

'Oh, go on. I'll do you a favour in return. Tell you what. I'll make you a dress.'

'Get lost.'

She said I should be flattered she trusted her to do something so important and I said *important?* In my book, saving children from dying in earthquakes was important. So was Daddy's job, and passing exams and doing the harvest. But how on earth could telling a butcher his fiancée couldn't meet him be considered even remotely *important?*

'Yeah, all right, point taken. Just say to him Dawn can't make it because it's Amami night.'

'What's Amami night?'

'He'll know.'

'I don't. How can I give a message I don't understand? If he says "What's that?" I'll have to say I don't know and look stupid.'

'He won't. He'll know.'

'Anyway, *why* can't you see him tonight? There won't be anything much happening at home. You'll be bored stiff.'

'Don't worry, I've got a million and one things to do, including, by the way, wrapping up your birthday present. And if I get bored, I can always see what you lot are up to.'

Why was she giving me a present, as if she was a member of my family? I'd only know her a day and a half (though it felt like a hundred and a half).

We walked out through the gates and past the big red sleeping Seconday Modern with its hundreds of glass eyes where poor children who failed the 11-Plus went.

'That reminds me of one of the schools I went to,' said Dawn. 'I can smell the disinfectant and sweaty changing rooms from here.'

'How many O-levels did you get?' I asked cruelly. 'Not cookery, by any chance?'

'Ha, bleeding ha. My sort don't go in for O-levels. My favourite subject was British Constitution.'

'We don't do that at our school.'

'You learn how the Government and all that works.'

She studied British Constatution so that when the Revalution comes she will know exactly what to do.

And in the joke section: *Why were Dawn's schools good? Because they were approved schools!!!*

We walked along Pedlar's Lane. On one side there used to be scrubland where an anti-social white billy goat glared gruffly at you out of the corner of his double-crossed eye. Now there was a bevy of bungalows who glared gruffly at you out of the corner of their double-glazed eye. I was about to say I preferred the goat any day when Dawn said, 'Albert and I are thinking of buying one of them. That end one. What do you think? It's got a utility room where you

127

do your washing and that, and it's double-glazed.'

I couldn't think of one nice thing to say about it. But I had to say something. 'It must be strange not going upstairs to bed.'

'You can tell you've never lived in a council flat.'

Why is Dawn like a council flat? Because they're both cheap, ugly and don't have anything upstairs!!! I found this so funny I laughed out loud.

'Let's hear it.'

'No fear. I have secrets too, you know.'

What could Amami night mean? Was it code for saying she wasn't in the mood for playing 'hide the sausage'? Was it another way of saying she had her period? Or was it something darker and altogether more sinister?

'Tell you what,' I said. 'If you tell me what Amami night means I'll give Albert the message.' For she was, after all, giving me a birthday present, even though it would be foul.

Apparently, it was just an expression which meant you didn't want to go out.

'Is that all?' I said. 'I don't think much of your secrets.'

'All right then, guess what us cockneys call the male private parts? Wedding tackle.'

'Wedding tackle! It sounds like fishing tackle! Honestly, if Dan or anyone mentions anything to do with fishing I'll *explode!'*

We turned into White Lion Street and my stomach gave a nervous churn. Just say when I got into the butcher's I thought of wedding tackle and laughed? Just say when I gave Albert the message he went red and had to fight back tears? I didn't want to be the bearer of bad news, only good.

'Look, I don't want to take your silly mess . . .'

'I'll meet you at the Rimmel counter in Woolworths, okay?'

That summed her up nicely.

CHAPTER TWELVE

Through the curtain of lambs' legs and white sausages and goose-bump chickens, I could see Albert chopping and chatting to a customer. I lurked outside pretending to study the meat display. I didn't want to be served by his father.

Seeing all that flesh and skin lured my mind towards Albert playing 'hide the sausage' while Dawn lay back thinking of England. Did she talk while he did it? Did she look lovingly at his red face, or did she have her eyes closed so that she could pretend he was Cliff Richard or Elvis Presley? Did Albert *suspect* it could be a bit boring for the woman? Where did they do it? What did his wedding tackle look like exactly? Then suddenly he was there at the window reaching for the stewing steak so I could do nothing but grin and wave and go in.

Just my luck he hadn't finished serving the customer, so I was stuck with Mr Thirtle. He looked up from wiping blood off the counter and said, "Hello, ducks. Your granny forgotten something? My, you're a grown-up girl to do the shopping on your own.'

Fancy going into a shop with no intention of buying anything! It was like going to the doctor and telling him there was nothing wrong with you. I went scarlet. I had precisely threepence in my pocket.

'I just came in to say hello, really,' I said. 'And, er, I was wondering if you could spare another bone for Clifford. He buried the other one and because he's so old and absent-minded he's forgotten where it is. I've got threepence.'

Mr Thirtle grinned with his mouth but not with his eyes. 'That's all right, ducks. Clifford's bones are on the house.' He didn't go 'Ha, ha' this time.

He bent down behind the counter and I managed to catch Albert's eye.

My words ran together like a string of sausages and there was no time to study his reaction or soften the blow by adding that she sent her love, because Mr Thirtle had bobbed up from behind the counter.

129

'Going to let me in on it or is it a secret?' he said, grinning with just his mouth again.

'Er – I was just telling Albert it's my birthday tomorrow,' I said.

I was worse than that Mr Profumo. Twice as bad, in fact, for he had only lied once!

'Oh, lovely,' he said, wrapping up Clifford's bone in the *Daily Sketch*. 'And what will that make you, if you don't mind me asking a lady her age.'

'Eleven,' I said.

'Ah. A prime age, that. You make the most of it, ducks. Before you can say Bob's your uncle you'll find yourself turned into a young woman. Anyway, many happy returns for tomorrow,' and he smiled, this time with his eyes, too, and handed me the parcel and without even a glance at Albert, I fled.

Everything cost one and nine at the Rimmel counter where Dawn was trying out lipsticks.

'I hope you realise you made me lie – twice,' I hissed at her. 'First to pretend Clifford had lost his bone . . .'

'You what?'

'I had to have a reason for being in there.'

'Why? 'Ere, do you think this colour's *me* – or do you prefer this one?'

'And then when Mr Thirtle asked what I was whispering about to Albert I had to say I was telling him about my birthday.'

'I don't see why you . . . Oooh, this one's nice.'

'Because you said Mr Thirtle didn't approve of you.'

'Oh, it wouldn't have mattered. He's got to get used to the idea sooner or later. Look, I want your honest opinion. Which . . . ?'

'Never mind your foul lipsticks, I've just been through a vile experience because of you and you aren't even sorry. Lying might come naturally to you but it doesn't to me. That's the last favour I ever do you. And you haven't even thanked me.'

She looked round, surprised. 'Oh, sorry, Sarah. And ta very much. You aren't half a worry guts, though. I mean, if I only went into a shop to buy something, I'd hardly ever go near one.' Then she peered into a small mirror on the counter and smeared her mouth in chicken-pox-scar pink.

'You can't do that. You haven't bought it.'

'What do you think a tester's for if it isn't for testing? What do you reckon to the colour?'

'But it could be smothered in germs. You don't know where it's been.'

'It's hardly likely to have been up a dog's bum, is it. I can't decide

130

whether to go for the pale pink, pouting image like Brigitte Bardot, or bright red like Marilyn Monroe or your Aunt Lynette. I mean if you were a boy, which would you find most irresistible, this ...' and she pouted her lips into an O, 'or this ...' and she wiped it all off with a tissue and smothered her mouth in a livid measles red.

'If I were a boy I'd prefer no lipstick at all. Then it wouldn't get all over *my* mouth or my collar.'

Dawn put her head on one side and narrowed her piggy black eyes. 'How come an innocent kid like you knows about lipstick on collars?'

Stupid, daft, nosy woman.

'I saw it in a film. And for the last time, don't call me kid.'

'Which film?'

'None of you business.'

'Oh, pardon me for breathing.'

'Anyway, aren't you interested to hear what your fiancé had to say?'

'Go on.'

'He didn't say anything because he didn't have a chance. He looked quite crestfallen though.'

'Yeah? I'm wondering whether to be daring and get some green eye shadow. Oh, maybe not.'

And then, in the middle of Woolies, in full view of everyone, she got out her foul pink plastic comb and backcombed her hair in the little mirror, before powdering her nose and spraying her foul vile scent behind her ears, clouds of it as if it were fly spray.

What's the difference between Woolies and a public lavatory? As far as Dawn's concerned, nothing!!!

I looked round, fully expecting a puce-faced manager to be striding towards us. 'You can't do that here,' I said. 'Not if you aren't going to buy anything.'

'Why not? It's a free country, innit?'

'Not where we're standing. We're standing on ground belonging to Mr F. W. Woolworth.'

'God, you're so middle-class,' said Dawn.

Upper middle, actually. 'And you're so ... *ignorant*,' I hissed.

We walked out of poor old Woolworth's empty-handed, and just say all their customers were like her; they'd go bankrupt in a week. I supposed I should be grateful she hadn't stolen anything.

'I want to go home now,' I said, but Dawn said I hadn't had my milk shake yet.

'I don't want one, thank you.'

'Oh, come on,' said Dawn. 'I'll be taking you somewhere I bet

131

you ten bob you've never been before.'

The Top Spot was down an alleyway off White Lion Street, and you passed it if you were going to the library or Eileen the hairdresser. Like a public house or a tramp or a child being sick in a gutter, you normally averted your eyes.

Even though it was a warm day and even though everyone inside appeared to be smoking, the steamed-up window was tightly closed. Leather-jacketed boys were hunched round a juke box that had a row of crash helmets on top, and pale, bored girls sat at orange formica-topped tables drinking Coca Cola smoking and talking to a man with sideboards and a shiny black coxcomb, who was offering them blue sweets. The place looked about as inviting as the waiting room of a station where all the trains go to Hell.

'I'm not going in there,' I said.

'Oh, come on,' said Dawn, waving at the man with the sideboards. 'I'll buy you an ice-cream soda. It's your birthday tomorrow, for Christ's sake. It's only a coffee bar. It won't *bite*. Where's your spirit of adventure?'

Like an autumn leaf deciding whether or not it was time to drop off, I wavered. But Black Champion stepped in and advised me strongly against it.

'I've got someone to see, actually,' I said. 'I'll meet you at the bikes.'

Hilda was alone, folding girdles. 'Hi,' she said, her round face beaming.

'Er – hi,' I said. 'Has the Old Dragon been any nicer to you since my speech?'

Hilda turned a pretty milk-shake pink. 'To be honest, not really, though it was ever so nice of you to say what you did. The truth is your granny and your aunt aren't that valued as customers by her no more. Your granny never spends much and your aunt's a bit, well, cheeky.'

'Oh,' I said, suddenly feeling extremely fed up. It wasn't long ago that Hillingtons were prize customers wherever they went. 'Well, I'm afraid I won't be spending much either, but I was wondering – would you mind quickly telling me what Amami night means?'

She didn't go any pinker so it can't have been too rude.

'You say, "Sorry, it's Amami night" to a boy when you don't want to go out with him. Amami's one of them hair-setting lotions, see. The idea is you want to stay in to wash you hair, but clued-up blokes know it's just an excuse.'

'Oh, I see. Thank you,' I said, wondering whether Albert was clued up.

'What do you want to know a thing like that for?' she said, narrowing her eyes. 'Blast, shouldn't you be out climbing trees and riding ponies and stuff? There'll be plenty of time to worry about them things when you're older.'

'Yes, right. Thank you, Hilda,' I said. 'See you soon.'

'There's something I've always wondered about bicycles,' I said as we pedalled past a field of bashed-about barley beneath a blank, birdless sky.

'What's that then?'

'Why is it that men's bikes have a crossbar and women's don't?'

'Dunno. Never thought about it.'

'The only reason I can think of ...' and I paused to savour the moment. Dawn wouldn't fail to be impressed by this clever bit of logic '... is that men need a crossbar for balancing their, er, you know, wedding tackle on.'

Dawn jammed on her brakes, and if my reactions hadn't been sharp as razors I'd have crashed straight into her. She threw back her head and cackled so loudly and for so long that both Jack in his cowshed and Albert in his butcher's shop could hear. I pedalled off into the washed-out old afternoon, all my fury collecting in my legs and making them whizz round faster than egg whisks.

' 'Ere, wait for me. I'm not laughing *at* you. I'm laughing *with* you,' she shouted. But she would no more catch me than a bubble car would a Mercedes Benz.

If, as the duchess in *Alice* believed, there is a moral in every story, the moral in this one was; Sulking never pays, or She who cycles off in high dudgeon is in danger of missing out on something more interesting. For as I pedalled furiously along I heard a deep, rich, lion's growl and then a sudden screech. I looked over my shoulder. Then tugged on my non-existent brakes. For an enormous American pink car had stopped beside Dawn. It was taking up the whole road, and just say an ambulance or a fire engine needed to get by?

Dawn and the car went together like love and marriage; both stuck out like sore pink thumbs in the dull green, dingy yellow, earth-brown rural setting. Dawn sat on her saddle, an acre of leg showing, her hands on her hips, her bosoms thrust forward. She said something and laughed. Two of the Americans were leaning out of the windows. The third was stretching across so he could get a good view.

Then they hooted again and drove slowly towards me, rocking

133

roll crashing through the open windows, and I felt like Ratty, Mole and Toad when they saw their first motorcar: ... *The magnificent motorcar, immense, breath-snatching, passionate, with its pilot tense and hugging his wheel, possessed all earth and air for a fraction of a second ...*

The American in the back was a negro. He was laughing, which made his teeth look very white. The passenger in the front had a crew cut and a thick bull's neck. The driver had dark-brown hair and see-through hazel eyes. He chewed gum and far from being 'tense and hugging his wheel' was very relaxed; clearly, driving gigantic pink cars through the English countryside came as second nature to him. He smiled at me in a very casual sort of way, and although he didn't hoot or squeal to a halt he did raise his strong brown bare arm in a wave, smile and shout 'Hiya, kid!' Then he put his foot sharp down on the accelerator and with a massive surge of power like a rocket, the pink car was off.

Like Ratty, Mole and Toad I watched the car dwindle to a speck in the far distance. If I'd been a horse in this 'new raw situation', I'd have done what Toad's old grey horse did and simply abandon myself to my natural emotions by rearing and plunging. Instead I thought about what it would be like to be sitting in the front seat between the Americans, laughing and joking and travelling very, very fast ...

'Blimey, them Yanks have something, don't they,' said Dawn puffing up. 'Such style. So flash. So polite. So *casual.* They're something else,' and she shook her head in wonder.

If I had been speaking to her, I would have agreed.

'What did they want?'

'Oh, just trying to chat me up. Do I look a fright? Me hair ...? Cor, the driver was better-looking than James Dean. Did you notice his *eyes?* Can you blame me having doubts about old Albert when temptations like that cross my path. And have you ever seen such a flash car? It was a Cadillac. Boy, that driver wasn't half tasty.'

'He looked tough and stringy to me,' I said, and managed to keep my mouth in a still, straight line all the way home.

I described the Top Spot to Hattie later and she said she wouldn't have gone in there for all the sugar beet in Norfolk. 'You might have picked up some vile disease, or more bad language,' she said.

Even so, I thought, my spirit of adventure, as Dawn called it, had temporarily forsaken me and I'd let a possible diary-worthy entry slip through my fingers. I'd have to make sure it didn't happen again.

I told Hattie, too, about Woolies, and about lying in Thirtle's, and Dawn's thighs attracting so much attention, and the joke about Dawn and the council flat and the Americans in the pink car. I didn't tell her about Amami night, though, or about lying back and thinking of England, or unmarried mothers or good-time girls or wedding tackle. I'd save those for Mr Richards; he was bound to be broadminded.

'I feel so guilty you've had such a vile time,' said Hattie. 'Specially as it's the day before your birthday.'

'What birthday?' I said, as gloomy as Eeyore. 'The way things are going it's not going to be much of one.'

'Of course it will. And I know what Aunt Lynette's giving you. I wish I was getting one.'

'It doesn't *feel* like the day before a birthday,' I said, nevertheless pleased by this piece of news.

After tea I followed Granny into the garden. She was wearing her old mac, lace-up shoes and the dreaded straw hat. I passed Clifford gnawing on the bone he was meant to have buried.

I told her about lying twice to Mr Thirtle. 'Was it very wicked, Granny?'

'Not necessarily, darling,' she said though you could tell she was thinking about something else. I wished she would look at me instead of her storm-battered roses; no wonder I hadn't yet found the right time to tell her about Mr Richards. 'Sometimes one has to lie a little to spare people's feelings. It's what one calls a white lie, and is quite forgivable.'

I thought of the song about the night having a thousand eyes for those who told white lies.

'But, Granny, Dawn's been telling me about Mr Profumo, who had to resign from his job as War Minister because he lied.'

Granny didn't say, 'Oh dear, Dawn really shouldn't be telling you about such things', but, 'Ah, that's a different thing altogether. Mr Profumo held a position of great responsibility, and the country's defence system could have been put in jeopardy. Personally, I think it was all a storm in a teacup. He lied in the House of Commons, you see, and that will never do. Your little white lie to Mr Thirtle hardly comes into the same category.'

'But I don't see the difference,' I persisted. 'Whether you lie in the House of Commons or a butcher's shop, it's still a lie. I mean, perhaps Mr Profumo started with a little white lie in the butcher's when he was my age, and just got worse and worse as he got older.'

'I hardly think so, darling. Mr Profumo is basically a good man

135

who happened to give in to temptation and get caught up in an unfortunate incident. His lie was probably a one-off.'

'Granny, I don't think Dawn should tell me, well, some of the things she does, do you? I don't think they are really suitable for someone of my age.'

Instead of answering, Granny looked deep into the heart of a yellow rose, as if it were her own private looking glass.

I turn to my grandmother for morral guidance, I would write. *I seek but I do not find . . .*

'Granny?'

'Oh, I dare say it won't do you any harm,' she said with a start, and why couldn't she look at me instead of that foul rose? 'One finds out about such things sooner or later. And you're becoming such a big girl now.'

I hovered like a dragonfly. Was she referring to my size or the fact it was my birthday tomorrow? Had she, indeed, remembered it even? Whichever, shouldn't I point out that even though I was big for my age, I was still a child and childhood, as Mr Thirtle and Hilda had said, should be made the most of?

'Anyway, we'll have a lovely day tomorrow because it's my birthday,' I said.

'That's right, I'm sure we shall,' she said, snipping off a deadhead and tossing it into the trug. 'Darling, I've been meaning to ask you. Would you care to write a play again this year? Aunt Daphne and your cousins are coming over next Saturday and last year's was such a success.'

Yes, it was. It was called *The Blue Rose*. Dan played the prince. I was the princess and Hattie played the plum fairy and the queen. 'Certainly,' I said. 'Er – as long as Dawn doesn't have to be in it.'

'As you wish darling. Just look at these broken stems.'

I wandered off, vaguely thinking I would have a chat with Aunt Lynette. I crossed the courtyard and looked through her window. She was lying on her *chaise-longue,* a gin and tonic in her hand, listening to some loud jazz. I couldn't tell whether her eyes were closed or not perfectly like Tommy Brock's.

Aunt Lynette had looked rather sad and lonely lying there like that. In fact come to think of it everyone round these parts seemed lonely: Granny, Aunt Lynette, Jack, Hilda, Dawn, even possibly Brian 'Ogre of the woods' Pike. I was a bit, too, I supposed, and as for this lying back and thinking of England lark – no boy was ever going to do that to me and so what if I was accused of being square or ugly or a prude. Why, I had better things to do with my time. If I wanted to lie back and think of England I could do it perfectly well on my own, thank you very much.

'All in all, I feel a bit fed up,' I said out loud.

Once on the red brick road I galloped as fast as a mighty cannon ball seemed to fly, as an arrow from a bow, not even flinching at whirly-bird pheasants or a scuttling rabbit. On and on, thrash, thrash through puddles, clinkety-clinkety across the road, and squelch-suck up the edge of a ploughed field, where I had to slow to a canter. Then I was back on the straight and narrow – a green path between pheasants' cover and blackcurrant bushes – and holding my breath I galloped through a dancing curtain of midges, rounded the corner ... and, as controlled as a Lipizzaner horse, I stopped dead in mid-gallop.

Hanging upside-down, its little pink feet nailed to a branch like St Peter on the cross, was a small, stout hedgehog. His black beady eyes were open and a bluebottle was exploring his cheek. He was a young hedgehog who would have been looking forward to falling in love, maybe, and having babies and dreaming of finding the fattest slug in the world ... He had been killed in his prime, and for a moment I saw not the hedgehog but Dan hanging upside-down, his grey eyes staring blankly, a bluebottle crawling over his cheek ...

Of course, a brave, well-bred horse like me wouldn't shy from such a thing. So, I tossed my head to frighten away the bluebottle, pawed the ground, whinned loudly and galloped away.

On the way back I called in at the black summerhouse to say a little prayer. One of Snuff Mull's horns had dropped off. It made him look silly, like a girl with one pigtail. I stuck it back on, my hands still hot and pounding from the gallop. Then I found some paper and a biro, sat on the veranda and wrote a letter to Veronica.

Dan wasn't at supper, nor was Granny – not in mind, anyway. She ate only two mouthfuls of watery cabbage, one of mashed potato and one of pink-middled sausage. I didn't blame her but still, one had to eat. I asked her if she wasn't hungry and she said as you got older you need less food and then Dawn crashed on about how important it was for old people to keep their strength up or they'd just fade away.

Suddenly a chilling icicle raced up my backbone; one of two things could be happening: a) Dawn was cooking foul food on purpose so that Granny literally would just gradually fade away; or b) Granny suspected Dawn was slowly poisoning her which was why she wasn't eating. And the reason Dawn wanted Granny to die was because she had used her animal magnetism on Granny

137

and persuaded her to change her will so that she would inherit the estate. Or if not the estate, at least lots of money. *That* was why she had taken this job rather than one in a shop or a factory where she would be with girls on her wavelength. This was turning out to be like one of Mummy's Agatha Christies – and I was in the thick of the plot! I would address Mr Richards directly on the matter.

You told us, Mr Richards, to play detective this summer. Well, I don't have to play *at being one: I've* got *to be one, because only I, and possibly Granny, know what is really going on round here. I shall be a cross between Hercule Poiro, Miss Marple and Sherlock Holmes minus moustache, knitting needles and deer stalker!*

My first move would be to speak to Mr Allcock the solicitor, to find out whether she had changed her will recently. I also had to find out whether the sausages were poisoned. But if they were, how come Dawn was eating them with such gusto? Perhaps she put the poisoned ones furthest away from Granny so Granny would end up eating them. It was risky, because she could always turn the dish round at the last minute, but it was possible.

As we cleared away, I sneaked Granny's uneaten sausage into my shorts pocket. Just as I was doing it Granny said, in a louder than usual voice which made me jump, 'I must have a word with Dan. He's treating my home like a hotel.'

'Don't you mean a B and B, Mrs Aitch?' said Dawn.

'What's that?' said Hattie.

'It's a bed and breakfast place where people who can't afford a hotel stay on holiday,' I said. 'There are lots in Blackpool.'

'And Clacton,' said Dawn. 'That's where we went once. And if the one we stayed in was anything to go by, B and B stand for Bedbugs and Bugger-all-else.'

'We sometimes stay in a hotel called Queen's, and each bedroom has its own bathroom,' said Hattie. 'So I suppose that would be a B, B and B – Bedroom, bathroom and breakfast.'

'No, it would be a B, B, B and B,' I said craftily. 'Bedroom, bathroom, breakfast and bidet.'

Dawn fell into my trap as easily as a weasel into Brian Pike's snare. 'What the flaming heck's that when it's at home?'

'Ah-ha,' I said, nudging Hattie. 'And anyway, it's never at home. It's only something posh hotels have. And maybe Christine Keeler,' I added, even more craftily, because that would really get her curiosity going.

'Oh, go on,' said Dawn. ''Ere, by the way, what have you got in your pocket, Sarah? You haven't turned into a geezer all of a sudden, have you?'

My face turned the colour of a hot plum. Trust her to notice. You couldn't even have something private in your pocket without her sticking her nose in.

'There's no steam rising from her shorts, so she can't be a *geyser*, exactly,' said Hattie.

'If you must know it's, er, a sausage for Clifford,' I said.

'Ah, playing hide the sausage already, are we,' shrieked Dawn, and lucky for her that Granny had gone into the kitchen or she'd have been sacked on the spot. 'And there was me thinking you were a *nice* girl,' and she had to crash down the pile of plates because her hands were shaking so much from her laughter.

Ignoring her was the best – and only – policy.

'How do you play hide the sausage?' said Hattie. 'I've never heard of it.'

'It's a bit like hide the thimble,' I mumbled.

'Anyway, why do you want to give Clifford a sausage?' said Hattie. 'You don't want to poison him, too, do you? What's the betting we've already got tapeworms growing in our tummies that will grow until they're fifty feet long and will run out of space so they'll end up popping out of one of our ears or nostrils – or our bottoms.'

'You're having me on,' Dawn said.

'She's not, actually,' I said. 'That's what happens when you eat pink sausages. The tapeworm absorbs all the goodness so you end up starving to death while the tapeworm lives happily on munching your insides.'

'All right, I take the hint,' said Dawn. 'Next time I'll make sure they're burnt to a bloody crisp. I still think it's a funny place to keep a sausage. It makes you look as though you've had a sex change.'

I looked at her as if she was a piece of chewing gum stuck to a Wilton carpet.

'Is that why your family calls you Sausage, by the way? Because you like keeping sausages down your shorts?'

'Come on Hattie, let's play racing demon.'

'I can't stand that game,' whined Dawn.

'Tough,' I said.

CHAPTER THIRTEEN

I was woken the next morning by laughter belonging to the Great,
Long, Red-Legg'd scissorman from *Struwelpeter*. He was dancing
down a dark back-street alley, his straight mad hair streaming
behind him, and I just knew, the way you do in dreams, that he
and his giant scissors were on the look-out not for thumb-sucking
children but unmarried girls having babies ... He stood behind a
bloodstained wooden butcher's counter, grinning but not in a
friendly way. 'How about a nice string of hide-the-sausages,
Madam? On the house, ha, ha, ha ...!'

Thankfully, daylight was beginning to filter through the chrysanthemum curtains, and despite my dream, I still managed to
drum up that dancy, prancy, can't-lie-still-a-moment-longer feeling
children always have on the morning of their birthday.

I got quietly out of bed, slipped a clean blue T-shirt and shorts
over my unwashed skin and crept downstairs.

Clifford stared sleepily at me from his box by the Aga.

'Hello, Clifford, I'm eleven today.' He stepped out of his basket
like an old man climbing out of the bath, and stretched his legs.
'I'm in my prime,' I added and he looked at me through uncomfortable blue eyes and whimpered as if to say "It's all right for
some".

'Walkies?' I said and Clifford thumped his tail on the bricks like
a tired walking stick.

The sky was as grey as a storming elephant with a few white
tusks dotted about, but who cared about the weather when you
were in your prime?

I was cantering down Holly Tree Loke – Clifford had found an
interesting scent in the hedge – when round a bend I almost collided
with Brian Pike.

'Well, fancy bumping into you, Miss,' he said in his soft, sing-
along voice and he tried to make his eyes twinkle, the way adults
do with children, but they just looked hard and sly, and made me
feel shy and uncomfortable. The Yellow Dog stared at Clifford
snuffling among deadnettles, and grinned but not in a friendly way.

140

"That there dog should be on a lead at this time of year," said Brian Pike. 'I wouldn't like to see no harm come to him.'

'Oh, you needn't worry about Clifford. He wouldn't hurt a fly.'

'It's not the flies I'm worried about,' said Brian Pike, also grinning but not in a friendly way. 'He can hurt as many of them buggers as he likes. No, it's them young partridges and pheasants that be a-bothering me.'

'Clifford's too old to chase after them,' I said.

'You show me a dog young or old that wouldn't chase after a partridge, given half the chance, and I'll show you – er, a hedgehog that doesn't like slugs.'

'I can show you a hedgehog that doesn't like slugs,' I said, because it was, after all, my birthday; devil-may-care day. 'That one you killed and hung up by the blackcurrant bushes. By the way, Mr Pike, why *do* you hang the animals you kill up for the world and his wife to see?'

Mr Pike rested his gun on his leg and got out his tobacco. This was the Yellow Dog's signal to sit down. He didn't take his eyes off Clifford. 'Well now, it's partly so as Mr English can see I'm doing my job properly, but mainly as a warning to other animals to keep away from my pheasants.'

'But how will the other animals know you mean that?' I said. 'They could think you mean keep away from the hens or the bullocks or the corn, even.'

'That they could, I suppose. But where I hangs the bodies is always near the pheasant feed, so they should take the hint sooner or later.'

'I think it's unkind,' I said bravely. 'It makes fools of the animals. Dangling there so everyone can laugh at them. They should be buried discreetly. It's like . . .' and I was going to say it's like people watching you have a bath, but Brian Pike wasn't the sort of person you could say things like that to. 'Anyway, I think the hedgehog was the saddest one of all, even sadder than the barn owl. They're very nice animals. And that one was in his prime.'

'We have been snooping around, haven't we,' he said, narrowing his eyes. 'Look, it's not a part of the job I relish, believe you me, but it has to be done.'

'I don't see why,' I said, and why was it only on one's birthday one could be so brave? 'Hedgehogs eat worms and mice and slugs, not pheasants.'

'They eat their eggs like nobody's business.'

'But just imagine if *you* were a hedgehog killed in your prime . . .

141

By the way, I'm in my prime today, too. It's my birthday. I'm eleven.'

'Well, fancy. Many happy returns of the day, Miss,' he said and the Yellow Dog, bored now the conversation had moved on from killing animals, lay down, though his head remained alert. 'A very fine age to be, eleven. Here,' and he burrowed in his pocket, causing the Yellow Dog's ears to prick up, and thrust a crumpled bag of sweets into my hand. They were sherbet lemons.

'Are you sure? All of them? Oh, thank you very much, Mr Pike. They're my favourites.' I said. Later, I would try one out on Clifford to make sure they didn't have rat poison in them. One couldn't be too careful round these parts and sherbet would be ideal for concealing a poisonous taste.

'By the way, there is another present you could give me if you don't mind me asking,' I said. 'Could you not kill any animals today – seeing as it's my birthday. Or tomorrow, because it's Sunday.'

'Ah, you drive a hard bargain,' said Brian Pike, trying to twinkle his eyes again. 'Oh, go on with you. How can I say no to a pretty young lady on her birthday? I'll have to check the traps, mind.'

'Oh, *thank* you, Mr Pike,' I said. As for Monday, Tuesday, Wednesday, Thursday and Friday, I'd cross those bridges when I came to them.

'Now, in return I'd like you to do a small favour, if you'd be so kind.'

'I can guarantee Clifford won't go within a mile – well, several yards, anyway – of a pheasant.'

'No, it's something else,' he said and the Yellow Dog pricked up his ears. 'Something we'll keep between ourselves, if you get my meaning.'

I felt almost flattered he should trust me, a stranger practically, with a secret. I'd been told a few times I had a trusty face.

'I'm good at keeping secrets,' I said.

Mr Pike looked over his shoulder. 'I want you to deliver a little something for me,' he said, pulling out from his breast pocket a crumpled white envelope. 'I was going to deliver it myself, but seeing as how I've bumped into you ... It's for that there girl your gran's got working there. Dawn Potts. But be discreet like, if you follow me.'

My mouth didn't drop open in amazement because my new motto was 'Nothing can surprise me'. But even so....

'Righty-ho,' I said cheerfully, taking the envelope and putting it down the waistband of my shorts and covering it with my T-shirt.

'And don't worry, I promise not to read it.'

'I'd be much obliged,' he said, touching the peak of his cap with his forefinger. 'Have a very happy birthday, then, Miss. Cheerio.'

'Er – cheerio. Come on, Clifford.'

As I walked back my brain buzzed like a hive of frenzied bees. The plot was thickening by the minute. What was Brian Pike's connection with Dawn? When she'd said 'I wouldn't fancy meeting him down a dark alley', had she in fact meant the opposite? Perhaps they were brother and sister! Under all that yellow dye she was bound to have black hair, and if Brian Pike shaved off his beard they might look quite similar. Except Dawn had a cockney accent and Mr Pike a Norfolk one. Perhaps they were cousins. Yes, that was it! Then they could be in love, too, and that was why Dawn hadn't wanted to see Albert last night. The letter would be full of foul soppy things like *Darling, I can still taste your sweet kisses on my lips*. Perhaps they were in love and plotting to overthrow Mr English and Granny, and Dawn had just been pretending to be revolted by the dead animals! Clearly, neither liked their job much, so why else would they be doing them unless they had an ulterior motive – that one day they would take over the house and estate! 'When the revolution comes . . .' Perhaps that was what they were waiting for.

How tempting to open the letter. But that would be cheating. Mr Richards might never forgive me. 'Sarah, only one thing marred an otherwise superb diary . . .'

I was so busy thinking about all this as I walked up the drive that when I heard voices sing 'Happy Birthday' for a second I wondered whose birthday it was!

I ran up to the dining-room window and there, sprawled across my mat was a great mountain of presents and cards; more than last year, and more than Hattie got on her birthday.

I raced through the front door and skippity-jumped across the hall.

'Happy birthday, darling,' said Granny smiling, and Dan picked me up and swung me round and they all sang Happy Birthday again, and Hattie and Dan sang 'Happy birthday, dear Sausage' which made Dawn look silly because she sang 'Sarah'. She was wearing a leaf-green shiny shift dress and a silly matching bow in her hair.

They all sat down to watch me open my presents.

'Goodness, there's so much I don't know where to begin,' I said, just for something to say.

Daddy's card was a photograph of a chestnut horse with a white blaze. Inside it said 'Lots of love to my grown-up birthday girl' and three kisses. Mummy's, of Little Grey Rabbit washing up, said, 'We'll be thinking about you every minute of today. Love and kisses to my precious one', and no kisses because she'd included them in her message. Their present was smart white skating boots and a short pink pleated skirt. There was a note tucked inside that said, 'Sorry, darling, Christmas would have been a far more apt time for these'. Yes, it would, I thought, a dull disappointed ache creeping through me, the way it always did when I opened presents from my parents. 'What do you want your own pony for?' said Black Champion inside my head. 'You've got me, haven't you?' Yes, but ... between now and Christmas I'd have to drop some heavy hints.

'Ooh, dig that skirt,' said Dawn. 'Dare you to wear it down White Lion Street.'

'It's for skating, stupid,' said Hattie, and Dawn said. 'Watch it. You're treading on thin ice, calling me stupid. Thin ice – skating ... Geddit?'

Dan gave me a pair of very grown-up sun-glasses that had tiger's stripes round them, the sort Aunt Lynette might wear and, typical boy, no card. I put them on and Dawn said 'Blimey, you look like Ava Gardner with brown hair and no bust.'

Hattie gave me *Dr Dolittle's Circus* and a home-made card of me looking rather stout riding Champion. The steam from his nostrils read 'Happy Birthday'. Inside she had written, 'To a real Champ (NB not chump!!) Love Hattie' and three kisses. 'PS There's something else to come later, fingers crossed.' Veronica gave me *Jill Has Two Ponies* by Christine Pullein-Thompson and a card with a pony on, and a letter which I put on one side to read later. I got another horse card of a Stubbs horse from Aunt Daphne and Uncle William and the cousins, plus a children's encyclopeadia. Granny G gave me a red hand-knitted cardigan and a Racey Helps mouse card. The great aunts gave me Scrabble and a card of a Norfolk scene in watercolours with just their names written inside in old-fashioned weeping-willow writing. There were cards, too, from Sheila Page and Miriam Poole, our daily help Mrs Smith and Daddy's secretary Sally-Anne. Then I came to Dawn's present. You could tell it was hers a mile off, by the cheap paper with horseshoes and little girls on it, and the card's envelope which was as rough as blotting paper. I wished she hadn't bothered. Now if she had a birthday coming up I'd have to buy *her* something.

The card had a 'teenager' with a yellow ponytail talking on the telephone and it said on it: To tell you on your birthday you're a really super kid'. Inside it said in babyish unjoined-up writing,

'Love Dawn'. The present was *Alice in Wonderland*. It was, of course, a cheap, rough-papered version that smelt musty even though it was brand new and, unlike my copy at home with the proper Tenniel ones, had vile modern illustrations that would have felt more at home in a comic and made the March Hare look like Joyce Grenfell and the duchess like Charlie Drake. Alice was on the cover in a bright pink dress with yellow bouffant hair just like Dawn's (and I was sure there was a joke there somewhere about judging books by covers). Even so, considering she probably didn't have two pennies to rub together it really was very kind of her, and clever to have thought of a book – and a classic, to boot – rather than a piece of plastic jewellery or something.

'Thank you very much, Dawn,' I said (because yes, it *did* warrant a 'very much'). 'It's one of my favourites.'

'You mean you've already read it?' she said, looking crestfallen.

'It doesn't matter. It's the sort of book you want to read again and again.'

'Oh good,' she said. 'Well, I ain't read it once yet so I might borrow it sometime.'

Granny's card of a smiling sheep said 'Lots of love, darling, Granny' in small, shy, wooly writing.

Her present made you believe once and for all in magic. It was just too much of a coincidence to be a coincidence. Clearly, she too was aware there was something fishy going on and had chosen *me* to sort it out. Why else would she have given me a brilliant detective set? It contained a deerstalker, a magnifying glass, some powder to sprinkle around for fingerprints, a notebook and pencil and a pair of handcuffs.

'Oh, Granny, *thank you*. What a perfect present,' I said. 'I'll find lots of uses for it round here,' and I smiled at her and she half-smiled back, and it was a very special, private moment between the two of us.

I was so flattered that she had picked me to be her detective. What an excellent choice! I wouldn't fail her. I put on the deerstalker and looked at the burnt toast in the rack through my sun-glasses and magnifying glass. 'I deduce that this toast is at least twenty minutes old and, judging my the yellow strand of hair, a woman by the name of Dawn Potts is the culprit,' and everyone laughed and Dawn said 'Ooh, you are rotten. By the way, how are we going to celebrate this happy occasion?'

We? I longed to say. *What makes you think you're going to have anything to do with the celebrations?*

We looked out at the sky, and Dawn said, 'Looks as though it's going to piss d... whoops, sorry, Mrs Aitch, bucket down.'

'Just because the sky's grey doesn't mean it's going to rain,' said Hattie.

'Good point, Hat.'

'If you must call me Hat, I'd rather you called me *Chapeau*, if you don't mind.'

'I read in the local paper something about a new bird sanctuary opening,' said Granny.

'But if it's raining they'll look all bedraggled,' said Hattie.

'I think it's cruel, keeping birds in cages,' said Dawn.

'What would *you* like to do, Sausage?' said Dan. I was hoping someone would say that. Except I didn't know. Going to the sea was my first choice, except it would take forever to get there and the thought of Dawn hogging the limelight in a bathing costume – or even worse, a bikini – made it out of the question.

'How about the pictures?' said Dawn. 'There's *Summer Holiday* on at the Gaumont. That should cater for all tastes. There's singing for Dan, lots of nice scenery for you to gawp at, Mrs Aitch, Cliff Richard for *me* to gawp at, a red London bus to keep you two kids amused.'

'What makes you think a red London bus would keep us amused?' I said. 'Frankly, I find buses boring, don't you, Hattie?'

'Exceedingly,' said Hattie. 'And for the last time, we aren't baby goats.'

'It's had good reviews,' said Dan.

'Is it suitable?' said Granny. 'If it has pop singers in it ...'

'Dan's a pop singer and he's suitable, isn't he Granny?' said Hattie, and I muttered 'That's a matter of opinion.'

'It's only a U,' said Dan.

'Yeah, it's as tame as a church mouse, so I've heard,' said Dawn. 'Even the Pope wouldn't turn a hair, if he's got any to turn, ha, ha, ha!'

Dan seemed to find this amusing, too, and there was something intensely irritating about them laughing at the same thing that wasn't the slightest bit funny. Dan and Dawn – only the w stopped them having the same name.

'What do you think, then, Sarah? Do you fancy it or what?'

'Only if Granny does,' I said.

'Oh, I don't mind, darling. I haven't been to the pictures for years. The last time I went was with your grandfather to see *Brief Encounter* and he disgraced me by snoring all the way through it. So yes, if that's what you'd like to do.'

I said yes please and I promised not to snore and everyone

146

laughed, and I asked if Aunt Lynette and Jack could come, and Albert too to keep Dawn company. I watched her closely when I mentioned Albert, but her dumb sheep's face gave nothing away. If I gave her the letter before she'd asked Albert there was a danger she might ask Brian Pike instead, and I certainly didn't want a murderer coming on my birthday outing. But Granny solved the problem by saying she was going into Shotestead so she'd ask him.

'*We're all going to the cinema ha-ha*,' sang Hattie, though we weren't supposed to sing at table.

'*No more working for an hour or two*,' sang Dawn in her warthog voice. 'Oh, I do like a birthday,' she said.

'Don't you mean, "Oh, I do like to be beside the seaside"?' said Hattie.

'Yeah, that an' all that,' said Dawn, and I just hoped Dan could hear her slurp her tea like a lorry driver with false teeth.

After breakfast I followed Dawn into the pantry.

'This is for you,' I said, handing her the envelope. 'It's from Brian Pike.'

'Oh,' she said, looking no more surprised than if, say, the milkman had given her a Christmas card.

'Aren't you going to open it?' I said and then, as cunning as a fox, added, 'I've never seen a gamekeeper's writing.'

But Dawn wasn't fooled. 'Who's a little Miss Nosy Parker then?'

'No, I'm not. I could have read it any time but I didn't.'

'More fool you,' she said. 'I have to have *some* secrets.'

I was about to say if all her secrets were as tame as Amami night they weren't worth knowing, when Dan peered round the pantry door.

'Who's got a secret?' he said coming in, and Dawn slid the letter under the George the Fifth tin.

'All girls have secrets, don't they, Sarah?' she said looking at Dan in her stupid way and giggling.

'*You* might. I haven't got any from my brother,' I said.

The smell of Dawn mingled with stale cheese and mouldy strawberry jam and ages-old custard and mustard powder and mint sauce made my throat feel sick. But I didn't want to leave Dawn and Dan alone in there. I felt in my bones it would be tempting fate, like leaving a rabbit alone with a fox, even if the rabbit was very old and had myxomatosis and the fox had just had a large breakfast.

'Where is everyone?' shouted Hattie.

'In the pantry,' said Dan. 'It's what's known as a Pantry Party.

Right, as we're all here I suggest someone volunteers to put their head in the Dried Egg tin.'

'And I suggest it should be the only man present, don't you Hattie?' I said.

'Or the only blonde woman present,' said Hattie.

'You rotten little tinker,' said Dawn.

'Lummy, what's going on?' said Aunt Lynette, opening the door wide. 'Are you playing sardines? Have I given the game away? Or are you raiding the larder?'

'Oooh, Miss Aitch, you makes us feel as though we're up to no good,' said Dawn.

'Speak for yourself,' I said.

We came out and Aunt Lynette kissed me loudly. 'Happy birthday, darling,' she said. She smelt of powder and peppermints and cigarettes. She wore a white blouse with red and black splodges, and red trousers and red lipstick to match.

'You look nice,' I said.

'It's not every day my niece is eleven,' she said. 'Now, if my present doesn't suit, no matter. I can always take it back.'

Suit – was that a hint it was a boring old piece of clothing? But no, it was small and hard and square. It didn't rattle, or smell. I ripped off the paper. It was a Brownie camera, in a case with a strap that went over your shoulder!

'Oh, *thank you*, Aunt Lynette,' I said, kissing her. 'What a simply super present.'

And it was. Hattie was a painter and Dan was a pop singer. Now I could be something – a photographer!

'This will be a great asset when I'm doing my detective work,' I said and told her about Granny's present.

Aunt Lynette laughed. 'As long as you don't come snooping round with it when I'm in the bath.'

'Nor me, neither,' said Dawn, and why wasn't she getting on with the washing up? 'Mind you, they wouldn't print a nude photo, would they, not even in this day and age. They'd tear it up. An ex-boyfriend of mine works for a processing lab and they're always having a good old laugh about some of the things people take photos of. He was telling me how some bloke took a whole film of horses' backsides.'

How come she had to have a finger in every single pie going? Now I couldn't even take photographs without worrying her stupid ex-boyfriend would develop them and warn her I'd unravelled her plot.

'Why would anyone want to do that?' asked Hattie.

'Because they're a bit odd,' I said before Dawn had a chance to speak. 'Would you like to see *Summer Holiday* with us this afternoon, Aunt Lynette? It's got Cliff Richard in it. It's meant to be very good.'

'Why not,' she said. 'Yes, I'd love to, darling. A bit of light relief will do wonders. Is everyone going?'

'Yes,' I said, adding 'worst luck' with my eyes, and I think Aunt Lynette understood.

'By the way, when can we start your portrait, Dan?' she asked. 'I'm simply itching to get going.'

'Er . . .'

'You don't need to do one now, Miss Aitch,' said Dawn. 'Not now Sarah's got her camera. You could just take a snap of him. Much less of a fag.'

'Dawn, dear,' said Aunt Lynette, and gave her a look that would have withered a row of healthy cabbages. 'A black and white photograph taken with a cheap camera is hardly *art*.'

'*How much is that doggy in the window?*' sang the transistor radio.

Dawn was upstairs hoovering, Granny was in Shotestead, and Dan, Hattie and I were lying on the lawn listening to *Children's Favourites*. Hattie had insisted we listen to it, and I didn't let on that I'd seen her postcard to Uncle Mac. I hadn't meant to read it, but I reasoned that if the postman could read it so could I. *Dear Uncle Mac* it had said. *Please, please play Champion the Wonder Horse for my sister Sarah, whose 11 years old on Saterday. Champion is her favrite programe on television. Its mine to. We both know all the words to the song of by hart. Thanking you in advanse. Love Hattie Hillington (Miss). PS When Sarah was younger she thought it was Champion no Wonder Horse! It has now become a famly joke. PPS Sometimes Sarah pratends she is Champion!!*

'I hate this song,' said Hattie. 'I bet whoever sings it looks just like Dawn.'

'She certainly doesn't sing like Dawn,' I said. 'By the way, Dan,' I said, hardly daring to ask, 'are you going to play in your pop group today?'

He looked up from *The Times*. 'Course not,' he said. 'Not on my sissy's birthday. Actually, the real reason is Rick Benton's a drover at Norwich Cattle Market on a Saturday.'

'Dan, honestly. You needn't have said that,' said Hattie.

Uncle Mac announced he was going to play *The Laughing Policeman* next, for someone called Ian Bradshaw who lived in Birmingham.

149

'I wish we could take it in turns to have a birthday every day,' said Hattie. 'Then we'd see more of you and less of the foul, vile Dawn.'

'I can be foul and vile too, you know,' he said. 'Shall I give you an example? I'm going to tickle you two little shrimps until you're begging for mercy.'

We screamed as Dan tickled us and the Laughing Policeman laughed and we laughed, and then we heard: 'Is this a family orgy, or can anyone join in?'

'Just ignore her,' I said, but it was hard to laugh and be yourself when *she* was looking down her nose at you from your grandmother's bedroom window.

Uncle Mac played *Little White Bull* and *Please Please Me* and *The Ugly Duckling* and *There's a Hole in my Bucket*.

'And now for our last request this morning,' he said, and Hattie held her breath. 'Dear Uncle Mac, could you please play *Messing About on the River* for my grandson Graham . . .'

Hattie was furious. Apparently she'd written to Uncle Mac three times. 'How dare he ignore me? Especially as your birthday is on a Saturday. The next time it's on a Saturday you'll be too old for *Children's Favourites*.' I told her it didn't matter; it was the thought that counted and she said what was the point of thoughts if they didn't come to anything; for all I knew she hadn't sent the postcards, and I turned red and said don't be daft, I knew she wouldn't lie.

'Goodbye, children, everywhere,' said Uncle Mac.

'And good riddance,' said Dan. 'Silly, smug old bugger.'

'Dan! He's very nice.'

'How do you know? How do you know he's not an old perv on the side?'

'Because he wouldn't be doing the job he's doing if he wasn't nice.'

'Oh, the innocence of youth,' said Dan, sitting up with his hair in his eyes like a Highland steer. 'Let's play a game. I'll be an escaped convict and you, Sarah Holmes, with the assistance of Dr Hattie, have to find me. I'm on the run, starving and thirsty, so I'll be looking for refuge. Your first clue will be under the dustbins. Give us ten minutes.'

'You've got escaped convicts on the brain,' muttered Hattie.

It was a brilliant clue hunt. The first clue read, *Fink I'll see if I can find a hen to sink me teef into*. At the henhouse we found a footprint in the mud facing the wood. Then a cigarette end and a match and then a clue on the fence that said, *Fink I'll just see if there's a trakter wot I can make my getaway on*. In the tractor shed we found some ash. I studied it under my magnifying glass. It didn't tell us much expect that he'd been there. Then Dr Hattie said, 'Holmes, is this an arrow that I see before me?' and it was a chalk one pointing at the calf shed. There we found a clue attached to the feeding trough that said, *Fink I'll saddle meself with a set of wheels.* Under my bicycle basket was a clue that said, *Fink I'll try and find a bit of classy transport to keep me in the red,* which of course was Aunt Lynette's sports car, and on it went, to the last clue which simply read, *I'm alrite.* 'Elementary, my dear Watson.' I said. 'I'm all right, Jack. He's at Jack's, bet you ten bob.'

'Sherlock Holmes would never have had said ten bob,' said Hattie. 'He'd have said a florin or a guinea. Come on.'

Our escaped convict, cowering behind Jack's raspberries, didn't put up much of a fight, and I managed to get the handcuffs on with no trouble.

'So you got your man then,' said Jack, rounding the corner. He wasn't wearing his cap which made him look like a shorn sheep. 'Making arrests on your birthday. Whatever next. Here you are, my booty,' and he handed me what could have been his sandwiches wrapped in greaseproof paper but turned out to be a box of Meltis Fruits.

'Oh, thank you, Jack,' I said. 'We can eat them in the cinema. The prisoner has invited you, I presume?'

Jack said it would be a fair old treat, that would, he hadn't been out on a jaunt since Mrs B passed on. 'Now, who would say yes to a spot of elevenses?'

As we walked down the drive, full of digestive biscuits and orange squash, I had the nicest surprise of my whole birthday. It was like going back in time, to summers before the advent to Dawn and Brian Pike and pop groups and sex scandals and buggers of winters. Snuff Mull must have already got to work. For there stood Granny in her heathery jumper, tweed skirt and smart grey shoes. But the real miracle was her hair: it was no longer white and long and witch-like but in neat waves coloured a discreet shade of blue and held in place by an almost invisible hair-net. The bald patch hardly showed because a wave was covering it.

'Thank Christ for that,' muttered Dan. 'She's stopped looking gaga, tra-la.'

'Oh, Granny,' I said, running up to her and throwing my arms round her thin as a twig body. 'Your hair looks lovely.' Close up I could see powder – slightly too orange – on her cheeks and a smidgen of lipstick on her lips. She'd smartened herself up because

151

it was my birthday. What a brilliant compliment!

'It was high time I pulled myself together,' she said and even her voice didn't sound gaga any more. 'And what better day than today?'

I took one hand and Hattie took the other and Dan walked on ahead and did pretend cricket bowls which was a mistake as it prompted Granny to say that she hoped Dan wasn't going to leave organising the cricket match till the eleventh hour, and I added, 'Or the eleventh man.'

We told Granny about tracking down the villain, and she must have been listening properly because she said 'Good gracious' or laughed in all the right places.

She even had second helpings of fish pie at lunch.

'It's funny that, ain't it, Mrs Aitch,' said Dawn, 'How a new hair-do can give you an appetite. I've noticed that with meself.'

Hattie said don't talk tommy rot and Dawn said, 'No, honest. Straight up.' So Hattie said 'In that case you must have a new hair-do every day,' and Dawn said 'Watch it,' and I told them there'd be no arguing on my birthday and to belt up.

Oh, if only I could be like this every day!

Granny drove Dan, Jack and me to the cinema. The others went in the MGB.

Jack wore a brown trilby with a small pheasant feather tucked into the brim, and a checked sports jacket and shoes the colour of polished conkers.

What a nice couple they made from back view, Jack in his trilby and Granny with her neat waves curling round her navy hat. I made a face at Dan expressing this but he thought I was grinning at Jack's hat.

'That's a smart hat you've got there, Jack,' said Dan.

'Hasn't seen the light of day, this old hat, for ooh I don't know how long,' he said. 'Only comes out on special occasions.' And he looked round and grinned and winked at me, and I hoped Granny was concentrating so hard on being the slowest driver in the world that she hadn't caught sight of his dodgy teeth.

'And Granny's had her hair done specially, too,' I said, prompting Jack to say, just as I'd hoped, 'Yep, I was thinking, Mrs Hillington, how grand you were looking. Back to your cheery old self again,' and how easy it was to get adults to do or say whatever you wanted. My next move could be to say 'Granny, as it's my birthday, could Jack call you Winifred?' but decided that would be pushing my luck. Instead I said, 'I believe the film's got a bit of romance in it.'

'Has it now,' said Jack. 'I'm partial to a bit of romance – on the silver screen that is,' he added and I bet he had gone as red as a beetroot. 'Look at that there black old cloud,' he said, quickly changing the subject.

'Yes, just the sort of afternoon to go to the pictures,' I said, 'I hope it rains and rains so we won't have to feel guilty about being indoors.'

'Now don't you be a-saying that,' said Jack, 'or the old harvest'll never get done. You'll be giving us a hand again this year I expect, Master Dan?'

'Er,' said Dan and I nudged him. 'I hope to, Jack. That is, if a record company doesn't snap us up. I've formed a pop group, you see.'

'Fancy yourself as a bit of a Frank Sinatra, do you? Or should I say *Adam Faith*?' Jack said Adam Faith the way Granny would say 'bowling alley' or 'supermarket'.

'No, more like the Beatles, actually,' I said.

'Come again?' said Jack, which made me feel really cross, and how on earth could I have even considered someone so square to be Granny's husband?'

'Actually,' Dan said to me, 'more like the Rollin' Stones than the Beatles.'

I was about to ask who they were when they were at home when Jack said, 'That won't be the same if you don't help out with the harvest. That'd be like Christmas with no turkey.'

We sat in the front row of the circle and I was allowed to do the seating plan. It went Jack, Granny, me, Dan, Hattie, Aunt Lynette, Albert, Dawn. I passed round the Meltis Fruits and then the lights went down. 'Ooh, er,' said Dawn so loudly that the whole cinema, including the usherette, the ice-cream lady and the projectionist, could hear. 'And keep your paws off, Albert, I want to concentrate on the film.'

I am sorry to say that both Dan and Aunt Lynette laughed.

'Shhh,' I hissed and there wasn't another squeak out of anyone until the film was over.

In the cinema car park, I took a photograph of everyone grouped round Aunt Lynette's MGB. 'Smile please,' I said and everyone did. Jack with his mouth closed so his teeth didn't show, Granny politely, Aunt Lynette haughtily, Hattie sillily showing her gums as well as her teeth, Dan lazily, Albert lop-sidely (perhaps he was trying to look like Cliff Richard), his shiny-blue-suited arm round Dawn who, with her hands on her hips and one knee bent on the

153

bonnet so an acre of thigh was showing, entirely dominated the photograph.

'Can we have one on the cinema steps with me in it, please?' I said because it had just occurred to me that standing under the 'Summer Holiday' sign would make a good cover photograph for my diary. I stared hard at Dawn in the hope she would be the one to drop out and take it, but instead she had the nerve to ask the cinema manager, and maybe it was something to do with the way she thrust her bosoms at him, but he didn't mind at all.

'Watch the birdie, ladies and gents,' he said.

'What birdie?' said Hattie, and Dawn said 'Maybe he means my brooch,' and just as we all looked round at her silly bird brooch he took the photograph. She had managed, yet again, to be the centre of attention – and she was the least important person there!

Jack and Albert came back for tea. Granny's house made their feet and their hands look too big. Jack shot all the scones off the plate and Albert bumped into the tallboy and apologised to it, causing Hattie and me to rush into the drawing room and weep with laughter.

It didn't matter at all (well, not much, anyway) that my birthday cake came out a Mr Kipling packet and there was only enough for one thinnish slice each. It had no icing on top and a thin layer of jam sandwiched it together. Compared to last year's giant one, made by Mrs B and iced by Mummy, it was a sad little shrimp of a cake, the sort you would rather die than let your schoolfriends see. But the candles were, after all, the important thing, and this year I was allowed to light them myself which I did, using only one match. '*Happy Birthday to you*' everyone sang in an assortment of farm animal voices.

My wish, as I blew out the candles, was that we could always be this happy and also, in passing, that my diary would be ten times better than anyone else's.

After tea we played charades in the conservatory, which produced gales of laughter.

Dawn really showed herself up, proving once and for all that her head was riddled with rubbishy television programmes and had less literary knowledge than a mosquito; she kept saying 'What's that when it's at home?' and when Hattie was trying to do *Dr Dolittle* she kept saying *Emergency Ward 10* and *Dr Kildare*. Even so, she was terribly funny trying to do *That Was the Week that Was*, and

154

as for Albert doing *Muffin the Mule* – we were all in fits!

Dawn and Albert weren't at all soppy and lovey-dovey with one another. They were more like a brother and sister, being rude to each other in a joky, friendly way and having pretend playful fights; they were obviously well suited. That's how I would like to be with my fiancé, I decided. Much better than being like Rosie Alton's elder sister and her fiancé who sat holding hands staring adoringly into each other's eyes.

After charades, Dan wedged his cigarette in between the strings of his guitar (which I thought very stylish) and played a nice song called *That'll be the Day* by someone called Buddy Holly. I particularly liked the bit when his voice went deep and he sang 'That's some day when I'll be true'. The words were a bit silly and American, of course, about loving and turtle doving and the man dying if the woman left him. But it was a good tune. Dawn and Aunt Lynette snapped their fingers, and Albert and I beat time with our feet.

We clapped loudly at the end, even Granny and Jack, and Dawn shouted 'Encore'. So he played *Champion No Wonder Horse* to make up for Uncle Mac not playing it and Hattie and I sang at the tops of our voices. Then he sang *Johnny B. Goode* by someone called Chuck Berry. I could see what Dawn meant about rocking roll making you want to get up and dance. I didn't, of course, though my *heart* did. Needless to say she did though, her hips wiggling like a bulging snake, her head nodding like the dog in the back of Rick Benton's car, but I wasn't watching her; I was watching Dan. In fact I couldn't take my eyes off him. He was like a different person when he played his guitar. His eyes sparkled like the sea and his face no longer looked tense and angry but relaxed and at peace with the world. His voice didn't shout like in the car but was gentle yet strong and had a sort of quiet authority. If Mr Richards had sung to us in class, that was how I imagined his voice to have sounded. His long relaxed fingers made playing a guitar look the easiest thing in the world, and he could play even the complicated bits without looking. I was close to bursting with pride, and I think Granny, Hattie and Aunt Lynette were, too.

Afterwards, Dawn went to change into her 'glad rags' (a tight shiny gold dress that looked far from glad to have her body squashed into it) because she and Albert were going to a dance in the town hall, which prompted Dan to play *Let's go to the Hop* and Hattie said why, are they going to turn into rabbits? They dropped Jack off on the way, and Aunt Lynette went to the Rat-catchers to meet some friends. That just left the four of us.

155

'It's been my best birthday ever,' I said – and later wrote in my diary – as we played beggar my neighbour. But a few days later I was to add in brackets: *and by the looks of things, the last happy day of this summer.*

PART TWO

CHAPTER FOURTEEN

Outside the house martins squabbled and inside we cleared our throats and sang, '*Praise my soul, the king of heaven*'. On the second to last line of the hymn, Mr Rackham always strode over to the pulpit, singing in a loud voice without his hymn book. One day, perhaps, he would get his timing wrong and find he was still standing at the lectern when the hymn was over or, even better, not realise there was another verse over the page and have to stand in the pulpit humming foolishly because he didn't know the words. Today though, his timing was impeccable. He hadn't, I noticed, set the pulpit's hour-long egg timer. Did this mean he was going to speak longer than an hour?

We waited for the organ to grind to a halt, and set down.

'It was Oscar Wilde who said, "I can resist anything except temptation",' boomed Mr Rackham and paused like an amateur comedian for his audience to smile. It was a promising start but, like an interesting-looking chocolate that turns out to have a hollow middle, it soon meandered into boringness, and my thoughts began to drift. My eyes, however, remained fixed on Mr Rackham's face, and every now and then I blinked so they wouldn't look too glazed. It was quite an art to adjust your face so it appeared to be listening to a sermon even though your mind was in the show ring or the Arizona desert or, as mine was then, back at Gressenham Hall picturing what Dawn and Dan were getting up to. With practice, you could even smile or look concerned or repentant at the right moments. Perhaps when I was older I would write an article entitled 'The Art of Looking as Though You are Listening'.

It was just Hattie, Granny and me in the Hillington Horsebox. Aunt Lynette was an atheist and only went to church for weddings and funerals. Dan had said did Granny mind awfully if he didn't come but he had to help a bloke fix his car, and Granny shrugged and said she supposed he was old enough to make up his own mind about such matters. Dawn had one of her 'heads' coming on. I was half-glad because we would have had to listen to her foul, foghorn voice, and half-sorry because that meant we'd left her alone in the house with Dan.

159

Aunt Lynette's words about Dawn keep haunting me, like a medal-some ghost, I had written in my diary that morning. *'Watch out, Dan, she has an eye for a pretty face ... She has her sights set on higher things ...' I just hope and pray that 'higher things' means running a bootique or having a bungalow with a utility room rather than marrying someone from a higher class, and that Dan won't be tempted to do anything stupid and that his good breeding will win the day.*

'We have all been tempted in one way or another, at some time,' thundered Mr Rackham, and for a moment his butter-wouldn't-melt-in-the-mouth eyes flashed like lightning over me.

Suddenly something diary-worthy occurred to me; that the world could be divided into two: those who went to church and those who didn't. And, come to think of it, those who went to church and didn't smoke and those who didn't and smoked. Dawn, Aunt Lynette, Dan, Brian Pike, Daddy, Mr English, Maurice the Mole Man, versus Granny, Hattie, me, Jack, Mummy, Mrs English and her two children Michael and Mary-Anne, Reggie and his wife Doris, Major Smedley and his wife, Mr and Mrs Allcock. The two sides were fairly equal, but if I was forced to choose, if it was a matter of life or death. I would be tempted to go for the non-church-going smokers.

'Let the Profumo Affair, which has rocked the nation, be a lesson to us all,' roared Mr Rackham, and my mind snapped back to attention like a soldier. 'If nothing else, it has demonstrated that no one is free from temptation, be they cabinet minister or carpenter, peer or postman, lord or lavatory attendant ...' and Hattie nudged me the way children do when a rude word is mentioned in church '... viscounts and, yes, I'm afraid to say on occasion, vicars,' and Mr Rackham paused while a gentle titter fluttered round the church like the wings of a small, embarrassed sparrow. Was he talking about himself by any chance? He hadn't gone red, but vicars didn't as a rule. 'As the Lord says ...'

When the service was over, the congregation queued up to shake Mr Rackham's squishy hand in the porch. 'So nice to see you looking well again,' he murmured to Granny, his eyes peering via her eyes into her soul. He held her hand longer than anyone else's, either because of who she was or because she always put a one-pound note in the collection box. He greeted us as if we were long-lost children – at least he greeted Hattie that way because of her smallness and prettiness and leg and pink glasses, but vicars were, after all, meant to pay special attention to the blind, the halt (whoever they were) and the lame.

160

'We enjoyed your sermon, Mr Rackham,' she said politely to suck up, but what she really meant was she liked it because he had said 'lavatory attendant'.

'Splendid, splendid,' said Mr Rackham vaguely. I stared at his round face that even close up didn't look as though it needed shaving, and tried to picture him cassock-less, having his wicked way with a good-time girl, or even the plump Mrs Rackham whose petticoat always showed under her dirndl skirt, but it was way out of reach of my imagination. Yet he must have done it at least once, because they had a son called Toby. Just as I was thinking this, Michael English, who had grown at least a foot since last year, looked round and winked at me, and I turned crimson.

Out of the corner of my eye I could see Mr Allcock moving up the church path, his hands clasped behind his back like Prince Philip, deep in conversation with Mrs Smedley. 'Excuse me, Mr Rackham,' I said. 'I must have a word with someone.'

I ran up behind him. He, too, was talking about the Profumo Affair. He was saying it could be the downfall of the present Government. When there was a lull in the conversation, I said, 'Excuse me, Mr Allcock, could I have a word with you – er, a quiet word?'

'Oh, hello, Sarah. Yes, certainly. Shall we go over there, then we can pretend we're studying the gravestones – or that sheep's rear end!'

What was the world coming to – first a vicar talking about lavatory attendants in church and now a country solicitor mentioning a sheep's bottom!

Mr Allcock wore a tweed suit and polished brogues with small holes that looked like woodworm. When he wasn't smiling he looked as stern as a guest at a Royal wedding. He was what an American would call a perfect English gentleman. If I had come from a humbler background, he would have made me feel very shy.

He took out his pipe and tapped it on a gravestone. 'Well, I'm sure, er,' and he peered through the lichen, 'Jeremiah Lambert won't mind. Now, what was it ...?'

'This is all top secret, Mr Allcock.'

'I swear, on Jeremiah Lambert's gravestone, I won't breathe a word,' he said and you couldn't quite tell whether or not he was 'taking the mickey'.

'What I want to ask you, Mr Allcock, is whether Granny has changed her will lately. Since April, to be precise.'

Mr Allcock studied the holes in his shoes and I could tell he was thinking of a polite way to say Mind Your Own Business.

161

'I know you aren't supposed to tell people things like that, it's just that ...' and I looked behind me. 'You see, I think Granny's life may be in danger.'

Mr Allcock's eyebrows appeared over the top of his spectacle frames. They were a mixture of grey, white and brown. The tobacco he put in his pipe was burnt amber, Albert's hair colour. I told him about Dawn, and how I thought she was either stealing from Granny or trying to poison her, so that when Granny died she would inherit lots of money. 'That's why I need to know about the will, you see. If Granny has included her in it that would give her a motive.'

I also told him about Granny giving me a detective set so she obviously knew something was up, and that Dawn believed in astrology so maybe she was a witch on the quiet.

His eyebrows still raised, Mr Allcock struck a match and sucked on his pipe. It sounded like our central heating system starting up. I wondered in passing whether he was long- or short-sighted. Either way, it would be amusing to watch him light his pipe without the help of his spectacles.

'Brian Pike the gamekeeper is in on it, too,' I said. 'He hangs dead animals round the farm like washing. My theory is that they're cousins and in love.'

'I thought she was engaged to that butcher chappie,' said Mr Allcock. 'That's why, I was led to believe, your grandmother employed her – and I agree with you, she was an unlikely choice – because she'd be, er, steady.'

This was new to me. 'Yes but just because you're engaged to someone doesn't necessarily mean you're steady, does it. Granny must have had plenty of steady village girls to choose from. No, I believe that Dawn used her, er, animal magnetism on Granny.'

Mr Allcock coughed, but he couldn't fool me. I knew a disguised laugh when I heard one. I was tempted to stump off in high dudgeon, but now I'd got this far ... 'But the really curious thing is, Mr Allcock, *why did someone like Dawn Potts pick Granny*? Why didn't she choose to work in a factory or a shop or a boutique with girls her own age instead of being stuck in an old house with an old lady? She's not the solitary type at all, in fact she never stops talking. She's fashion-mad, too. Maybe she's already stolen things and has a criminal record, and Granny was the only one kind enough to employ her.'

Mr Allcock scratched the side of his nose with the stem of his pipe.

'You don't think I'm being silly, do you, Mr Allcock? If you were in the house I'm sure *you* would sense something fishy was going on.'

But would he? Mr Allcock didn't strike one as being a 'senses' sort of man. He studied the bowl of his pipe, inside and out, as if checking an insect hadn't alighted on it. 'I think, Sarah, if I may say so, you've been reading too many Agatha Christies. We're talking about real life, you know, not St Mary Mead. Maids simply don't go round poisoning their employers in this day and age.'

'Why not?' I almost shrieked. 'Or if not poison, a tripwire at the top of the stairs, or a rug on a polished floor or something. She wanted to know exactly how Mr Pike disposes of dead animals' bodies, perhaps in the hope of picking up a few handy hints.'

Mr Allcock smiled. 'I'll tell you this much. Although, as you know, I'm not allowed to talk about other people's wills, I can assure you that Dawn stands to inherit very little. Certainly not enough to warrant, er murder.'

'But she will get something? She might think it's a lot more than it actually is. Or she might be trying to get things out of Granny while she's alive. She's already got her television and her sewing machine.'

The smoke from Mr Allcock's pipe went straight up into the air in an elegant stream, not in circles like Popeye's.

'Honestly, Dawn Potts is up to no good. Children can sense these things.'

'I'm sure they can,' said Mr Allcock. 'In fact I must congratulate you on your remarkable powers of observation, er, Holmes. But don't get yourself in a state about it, Sarah dear. We don't want it to spoil your holiday, do we? As far as I can see, Dawn Potts is just a straightforward, rather simple girl who wants a job to keep her ticking over until she marries the butcher and has children.'

'*If* she marries the butcher,' I said. 'She has her sights set on higher things. And what about Brian Pike? He writes her letters, you know.'

'Ah, perhaps he's just a flash in the pan,' said Mr Allcock. 'A pretty young lady like her probably wants to make the most of being single. As they all seem to want to do these days.'

'Pretty? Do you think she's *pretty*? With all that foul black eye stuff and foul yellow hair?' I said, trying to keep my voice on an even keel.

'Well, er, perhaps not. Rather a tarty little piece, I'd say. In fact come to think of it, let's delete "pretty" and simply leave it at "young lady", shall we?' said Mr Allcock, his brogues fidgeting near a sheep's mess. 'Now, I'll tell you what we'll do. We'll meet

163

up in a week's time, same time, same place, and you can give me another report.'

'All right. Thank you, Mr Allcock. And if in the meantime something awful happens, like the house burns down or we're all murdered in our beds, you'll know what to tell the police.'

'Now you are being fanciful,' he said smiling, and if only his left foot would move just a fraction ... But people like Mr Allcock didn't step in sheep's messes. 'Now, I think you should stop taking the world on your shoulders. Sarah dear, and start enjoying your holiday.'

After I'd talked to Mr Allcock, the world on my shoulders felt more like just Europe, I wrote later. *I could tell he wasn't taking me seriously, but at least now it's not just me who knows.*

'What on earth were you talking to Mr Allcock about? You both looked very serious,' said Hattie in the car on the way home.

'Oh, this and that,' I said.

'I must have a word with him,' said Granny more to herself than us.

'Who, Granny, Mr Allcock?'

'No, Dan. He is forever using my telephone without asking and he hasn't even thought about the cricket match.'

'Perhaps he's using the phone to sort out the team,' I said.

'If the telephone conversations I've overheard are anything to go by, I think that's highly unlikely,' said Granny.

Dawn was sitting in the kitchen reading the *News of the World* with her feet on the table and smoking a cigarette. When she saw us she sat up, stubbed out her cigarette, covered the ashtray with the paper and sliced a runner bean.

'Nice service, was it?' she said.

'Ripping,' said Hattie.

'Spiffing,' I said.

'I'll do the beans, Dawn dear. It is your day of rest,' said Granny.

'Oh, ta, Mrs Aitch,' she said and went back to reading the paper. ''Ere, according to this, Christine Keeler ...'

'Thank you, dear, we've already heard quite enough of that topic from Mr Rackham.'

'In church? What did he say?'

'You should have come, then you'd know,' said Hattie. 'Instead of being a wicked sinner.'

'Like I said, I had a bad head.'

'It can't have been that bad or you wouldn't have been smoking a foul cigarette,' I said.

164

'You telltale tit,' said Dawn, sticking out her tongue. 'And you've just come out of church.'

'I haven't completely lost my sense of smell,' said Granny. 'I don't mind you smoking if you must, dear, but preferably not over our lunch.'

'Has Dan gone?' I said as casually as asking after someone's health.

'Yeah, ages ago,' said Dawn. He's funny, your bro. He's so wrapped up with his pop group he hardly gave me the time of day.'

'What, you mean he wouldn't tell you the time?' said Hattie.

'He promised he'd be back for the dinner party this evening,' said Dawn.

'I should think so too,' said Granny with a sniff. 'Rupert is, after all, *his* friend.'

In order to be alone with her, I helped Dawn set the lunch table.

'Did Brian Pike have anything interesting to say in his letter?' I asked. I had checked it wasn't still under the George the Fifth tin.

'Ner. Not really,' she said and didn't turn red but perhaps, like a sun behind dense cloud, it was unable to penetrate through the layers of make-up.

I tried another tack. 'Was he at the dance last night, by the way?'

'Yeah. Yeah, he was, come to think of it. He's not a bad little dancer, surprising though it may seem. Not as good as me but a bloody sight better than Albert. God, I love dancing. It's like nothing else in the whole world. You feel free as a bird. Like cycling, only better. You kind of lose yourself. Nothing else matters except moving to the music. The music last night was really crappy, though. James Jones and the Big Five, they called themselves. Talk about square. I hope the Wild Ones will be an improvement. I'll have to teach you to dance. Then you can be my partner at the Shotestead Show dance.'

So she'd be coming to that, would she. Did she honestly think I'd be seen dead dancing with her with the whole county watching?

'Did you dance with Brian Pike?'

'Yeah. Just once, while Albert was in the Gents. *Can* I teach you to dance some time? I bet you've a good sense of rhythm.'

'Yes. Maybe,' I said, putting the bent fork accidentally on purpose at her place. 'Why do you wear so much make-up on a Sunday when it's just Hattie and Granny and me to see you?'

'Because you never know who's going to turn up. Besides, I look a complete bloody fright without it.'

165

'But if you don't mind me saying, you look a bit of a bloody fright *with* it.'

'I look more of a bloody fright without it, believe you me.'

'Do you take it off when you go to bed?'

'Course I do. I'm not a complete slut. And talking of sluts, you and Hattie haven't had a bath since you've been here, have you? I thought you top-drawer lot were meant to be so hygiene-conscious.'

'It's none of your business,' I snapped, bending down and pretending to pick something off the carpet so she'd think my red face was the blood going to my head. 'By the way, you're not related to Brian Pike, by any chance?'

'Are you kidding?' she screamed and unless she was a brilliant actress with three Oscars under her belt she must have been telling the truth. 'My relations might be on the dodgy side, but they aren't murderers.'

'Just wondering. He used an expression you use, and expressions run in familes, don't they?'

'You're as daft as a brush,' she said. 'That's like saying I'm related to Mae West because I say "Come up and see me some time".'

'I've never heard you say that.'

'Give me a chance, I was just about to.' And she put her hand on her wiggling hip and said in an American accent, 'Come up and see me some time. The telly's up there, you know. You're always welcome to watch it. Or don't posh kids like you watch telly?'

'Not in summer,' I said. 'We have better things to do.'

'Ooh, get you,' said Dawn cheerfully.

To our delight, Hattie and I had the afternoon to ourselves. Dawn was going to 'knock up an outfit', and after her snooze Granny planned to visit Mr English to discuss the Shotestead Show's entertainment programme in the main ring. Dan, needless to say, hadn't returned.

We decided to go for a ride on Snap Dragon.

Like Miss Haversham's wedding cake, the saddle and bridle were covered in cobwebs. We rubbed the leather with saddle soap, washed the bit and carted them, along with some dusty old grooming implements, to the park.

'I bet we have a bugger of a time catching him,' I said.

'Bugger is a swear word, you know,' said Hattie.

'It's not in Norfolk and when in Rome . . . Come on, you bugger,' I shouted, holding out a handful of grass. Snap Dragon looked round at us, snorted, lifted his tail and farted!

'Of all the cheek,' I said.

'That's because you called him a bugger,' laughed Hattie.

'All right. Watch. Come on Snap Dragon, darling, sweety-pie, lovey-dovey sweetheart.' But he just stuck out his nose and shook his head aggressively, swished his tail and walked away.

'See,' I said.

'He knew you weren't being sincere,' Hattie said.

Eventually, with much stamping of feet and gnashing of teeth, we coaxed him into being tied to the gate where we brushed a year's supply of autumn leaves and winter tangles and spring mud from his matted, wild horse of Borneo coat.

Even Mr Allcock wouldn't call Snap Dragon a pretty pony. He was a colour of an unkempt farm rat with a fat, fox-coloured tummy. He had short legs, a squat body, a thick brutish neck, a bristly, scrubbing-brush mane that Dan referred to as his Joe Brown haircut, dull toad-like eyes and yellow smokers' teeth.

Compared with the clipped, dainty, well-bred ponies at the riding stables at home, Snap Dragon was like a caveman pony. He had belonged to a coal merchant who paid Grandpa rent to let him eat his grass. But the coal merchant emigrated to pastures new, leaving Snap Dragon behind in pastures old, and Grandpa decided to keep him on as company for Smiler and for us to ride.

When you were out in public with Snap Dragon you just hoped, the way you did with Dawn, that you wouldn't bump into anyone important you knew.

We had a devil of a job getting the bit past his barred, nicotine-coloured teeth, and when we put the saddle on his back he groaned like the laziest furniture remover in the world.

If your dream was to gallop over hill and dale on the back of a fiery, fearless stead, Snap Dragon wasn't the one to make it come true.

As soon as Hattie was on his back he made it plain he would rather be lazing in his field than taking us for a ride – or perhaps he was 'taking us for a ride', as Dawn would say, for all the way up Holly Tree then Shady Loke he kept trying to turn round and head for home. On Cow Parsley Lane, I trotted alongside him, my head held high, whinnying cheerfully, picking up my feet to set a good example, but it didn't wash with old Snap Dragon. Getting him to walk in a straight line was a major achievement, let alone trot. As for cantering – the word simply didn't exist in his book.

'Come on, you lazy beast,' said Hattie, kicking his hairy belly, and he just stopped dead, jerked his head down into the hedge and started to eat, and Hattie ended up round his neck.

167

Cautiously, we crossed the main road and went down a grassy track. We passed Brian Pike's lonely little cream-coloured cottage on the edge of the big bad wood that in winter tried to huff and puff and blow the house down. It had smoke coming out of the chimney, and reminded you of a witch's cottage in a long-ago fairy story. It was surrounded by tumbledown outhouses which were probably full of ferrets and bullets and gin traps and rabbit skins and squirrel skeletons.

Brian Pike was painting a hencoop with creosote. Without his deerstalker he looked more like a trumpeter in a jazz band than a gamekeeper. His shirt sleeves were rolled up and his thick arms looked as though they were covered in hairy black spiders. The Yellow Dog was gnawing a bone on what should have been a lawn but was in fact bare earth, which you didn't look at too closely in case you saw unpleasant things lying about that had much better have been buried. The Yellow Dog stopped gnawing to growl, and Brian Pike waved at us with his paint brush.

'Your turn on Speedy Gonzales,' said Hattie when we were out of the cottage's sight, sliding off him and narrowly avoiding a nip.

I had made myself a little switch like old Mr Benjamin Bunny's. As far as I was concerned. I was boss round these parts. I mounted him and his back sagged and groaned like a bad-tempered old armchair – an extremely hard armchair, for the saddle was like a rock.

I was just lengthening the stirrups when suddenly, out of the blue, an American jet screamed by. It flew so low it was a miracle it didn't slice through the telegraph wires and tree tops; if it had had a glass bottom you could have seen the pattern on the pilot's soles. And it was so piercingly, screechingly, deafeningly loud it made your ears ache and your insides shudder; it was as though it had pierced through your *heart*.

This was the excuse Snap Dragon had been looking for to abandon himself to his natural emotions. His ears twitched back against his head like two flat caps, and beneath me I could feel every muscle in his body harden. Then, with a great thrusting surge as powerful as the pink Cadillac's, powerful enough to launch a rocket to the moon, he was off like a bat out of hell.

I jerked backwards and almost slithered down his tail. For a second I looked up at sky and tree tops with a bouncing hot bottom as my pillow and then, mustering together every ounce of tummy-muscle strength, I righted myself and grabbed hold of the flying reins. I dropped the switch; under the circumstances it was unlikely

I'd be needing it. 'Whoa, you bugger, whoa,' I gasped but if anything it spurred him on.

'You're not wearing your hat! Your feet aren't in the stirrups! Grip like mad! Oh, blimey O'Reilly,' cried Hattie, who'd be growing smaller and smaller like Alice, her face white and worried under her hard hat, already picturing my gravestone in the Hillington Corner.

'Whoa,' I said, losing my balance and banging my nose on his hard jerking neck which brought tears to my eyes.

We galloped like the swiftest arrow from a bow past Woodman's Cottage and for a split second I saw Brian Pike's mouth fly open, the Yellow Dog leap to attention. Then they were gone, maybe for good, maybe they would be the last two living beings I would ever see.

I bent low over his pounding neck to avoid being knocked out by overhanging branches, my cheek scritch-scratching against his prickly scrubbing-brush mane. My life was in his hooves which cracked like pistols on loose stones, the wild stirrups bashed and crashed every which way, his strong shoulders rippled rhythmically on and on, my bottom bouncing like a demented yoyo on the rock-hard saddle, my thigh muscles gripping like crazy, my back and my eyes streaming with sweat and tears.

We careered across the main road without looking left or right, and just say there'd been a ... but there hadn't been, I was still all right Jack, and if only I could trust him not to buck or rear or shy or trip on a tree stump or jump over a gate or crash into a car. I might just survive to tell the tale. Trust. That was the name of the game. But how could one possibly trust a mad surging beast who didn't know about lorries and main roads and highway codes and hadn't even had the decency to wait until I'd put my feet in the stirrups?

Then sharp as razors, without a moment's pause, without a by your leave, we turned left into Shady Loke and boy, if I hadn't been bracing myself for this change of direction I would have sailed clean over the hawthorn hedge. And now more overhanging branches lay in wait and teenage pheasants ran for their lives to avoid being churned to a feathery pulp by flashing hooves, and surely he would tire soon? Surely his strength knew some bounds? It didn't appear to. For with the bit well and truly between his teeth now he was on softer ground, he pushed his neck forward and went at full gallop, his powerful muscular body forging away beneath me. We were going faster than Black Beauty galloping to save his mistress's life, faster than Champion on his most urgent mission, faster even than

169

Aslan taking Lucy and Susan to the witch's house. Perhaps he was Aslan himself, in disguise, who didn't need to be guided and never grew tired, who rushed on and on, never missing his footing, never hesitating, threading his way with perfect skill between tree trunks. . . .

Living dangerously; even Dan wouldn't dispute that that was what I was doing. And then, as the red barn loomed closer and we swished right at the sweet-and-sour silage that I had fully expected to end up in head first, something happened that can only be described as a miracle; I stopped being rigid with fear and tugging like grim death on the reins; suddenly it had become the most exciting feeling in the world, galloping like the wind on not a foe but a friend's hot bumpy back, and I almost wished he'd go even faster – take off, even! Boy, this was the life; if only it could always be this exhilarating, and he could go to Timbuctoo or Tipperary for all I cared – where he went I went; we were in this together!

Ahead of us, lying in wait like a sly brown tiger, I could see between bobbing ears the five-bar gate. Oh God/Snuff Mull please don't let him jump it, he'll never make it, his hooves will catch and we'll go flying. 'Trust,' a voice said, louder and richer and stronger than mine. 'Trust and the world trusts with you. Fear and you fear alone.'

It loomed closer and closer as we went headstrong, headlong, towards it.

With just inches to spare, he jammed on his brakes, jerked down his head to inspect the grass and I ended up round his neck. For a moment or two I stayed like that, breathing in his bristly hot sweat, listening to the thump-thump of our hearts, weak with relief we were back safe and sound. Then I slithered off his hot, heaving, lathery back and landed on the ground, shaky but standing and still in one piece.

'You're a very bad boy,' I said, panting.

He looked round and pushed forward his white foamy face and bared his grassy teeth as if to say, 'I got you back safely, didn't I? What more do you flaming well want?' I winked at him and he blinked back, and I suddenly felt a warm strong rush of affection for this ugly, unloved, uncouth brute with whom I'd just shared quite an intimate experience. I reached to stroke his hairy nose but he batted my hand away and that was one thing you couldn't accuse Snap Dragon of: hypocrisy. Unlike riding-school ponies, he didn't even attempt to humour us loathsome humans.

My legs felt like a sailor's as I led him through the gate and took off his saddle and bridle. His back steamed like a Turkish bath. I smacked his hot, damp hindquarters and he meandered off, blew through his nose a few times, sniffed a magic circle, lay in it and rolled on to his back displaying his wedding tackle for the world and his wife to see while making snuffly grunting noises of enjoyment through his mouth. I was just thinking that I wouldn't mind a good roll, too, when Hattie, Brian Pike and the Yellow Dog came huffing up.

'Oh, thank goodness,' puffed Hattie. 'All the way back I was expecting to round a corner and find you dead in a ditch or hanging from a branch by your hair. You beastly boy, Snap Dragon.'

'Yeah, he ought to be put down, that one,' said Brian Pike, and the Yellow Dog wagged its tail.

'You'd like to put everything down if you had your way,' said Hattie and quickly laughed so that he'd think she was joking.

'Hmmmmmph,' said Snap Dragon, stood up, shook himself vigorously like a brown dog after a bath. Then, with his back towards us, he calmly started to eat as if bolting with a girl on his back was part of his everyday routine.

'Talking about the Galloping Major. Are you sure you've nothing broken, Miss?' said Brian Pike and I said I was just a bit shaky that was all, and thanked him very much for his concern.

'It was lucky it was you and not me,' said Hattie. 'I'd never have been able to grip so long with my leg,' and she hugged me. 'Coo, your T-shirt's wringing, and your hair,' she said, and forgetting Brian Pike was there added, 'It'll be interesting to see whether Granny tells you to have a bath.'

I don't know about Brian Pike's, but the Yellow Dog's ears certainly pricked at the word 'bath'.

Granny did tell me to have a bath, not because I smelt but because otherwise I'd be as stiff as a board in the morning.

'Poor darling,' she said, and stroked my damp hair. 'Perhaps we should have the wretched useless animal put down.' But I said she couldn't possibly, it was the Yanks' fault, not Snap Dragon's.

'Don't call them Yanks, darling, it's so vulgar.'

'Dawn does,' I said as a sort of challenge.

'Dawn isn't my granddaughter,' said Granny, which was exactly the answer I'd hoped for.

Hattie had a bath with me to keep me company. Between us we left a beauty of a black ring.

'Shall we leave it for You-Know-Who to clean?' said Hattie. 'It is her job, after all.'

I told her not to be so mean.

171

Afterwards, I wandered into the kitchen garden to help Dawn pick runner beans. I planned to drop into the conversation that I'd just avoided, by a whisker, a bloody death, and she'd actually stop whatever she was talking about and listen for once.

The bath had left me feeling all glowing inside. If I could survive a ride on a bolting pony, I could survive anything!

I stayed on the other side of the beans so I didn't have to look at her while I talked. Or be jabbed by her finger. I could still smell her, though.

'Hello, old bean,' I said. 'Want any help?'

'Oh, it's you. Hi.' she said, handing me a basket over the twisted green curtain. 'Beans for lunch, beans for bloody supper, beans coming out of our ears . . .'

'Is that why we're all full of beans?'

'Speak for yourself. Personally, I hate the buggers. I keep telling your gran to get herself a freezer, then we could space them out through the year, but she just says she's trying to get rid of possessions, not acquire them. I suppose you do when you get to her age. After all, you can't take it with you, can you.'

'Talking of buggers, you know Snap . . .' but before I could get any further Dawn said. 'I'm looking forward to this evening.'

'Why? Are you seeing Albert?'

'Nah. Meeting this Rupert geezer. And apparently your aunt's bringing some of her home-made wine, so a jolly time should be had by all, yeah? It's bloody lethal, so I've heard.'

Lethal . . . What a mercy Granny didn't drink alcohol. And the thought of Dawn – and come to that Aunt Lynette and Dan – drunk (even Mummy had got a bit squiffy on Château Hillington last year) didn't bear thinking about. I could see it now; they would get louder and sillier and Granny would get quieter and smaller, and as for Rupert, he'd go home and say to his parents, 'Honestly, they've gone to the dogs, that Hillington family.'

'Oh,' I said and then added, 'that's good.'

'You don't sound very pleased,' said Dawn. 'Don't you like your aunt or something?'

'Course I do,' I said. 'She's just a bit . . .' and I was going to say over-powering but that would have put her in the same category as Dawn, '. . . eccentric.'

'That's why I like her,' said Dawn. 'I think she's brilliant. A real laugh. Intelligent, too. There are too many boring old gits in this world, she's like a breath of fresh air. Mind you, I feel bloody sorry for her.'

'Why?' I said, surprised. She was quite rich and clever and

talented and had lots of friends and a sports car. If anything, Aunt Lynette should feel bloody sorry for Dawn.

'Well, for a start she ain't got a bloke.'

'So?' I said, 'Lots of women haven't, and they're quite happy. It's not the end of the world, not having a ... bloke.'

'It is if you want a baby, I mean, someone with your aunt's background couldn't have a baby unless she was married, could she.'

'Aunt Lynette doesn't want a baby,' I said. 'She wouldn't have the time to look after it, and can you imagine her changing nappies?'

'Actually, she's desperate for one.'

'How do you know?'

'She told me.'

Despite my new motto, this piece of news was still as surprising as, say, Granny wanting to keep a gorilla for a pet, or Jack going for a cruise on the *Queen Mary*.

'The tragedy is, of course, that she's leaving it all a bit bleeding late. She's forty any minute now, ain't she, and once you're forty the chances are you'll have a mongrel, or die in childbirth, that is if you get pregnant at all. Because the older you get the less fertile you are. And all those fags and Vera Lynns – gins, to you – won't help much, neither. The baby'd probably come out with a smoker's cough and hiccups,' and she laughed. 'Anyway, unless she finds herself a man pretty damn quick she can say ta-ta to having a baby.'

I thought about this. 'It's a shame humans can't be artificially seminated like cows, isn't it,' I said. 'I suppose if the worst came to the worst she could adopt a baby.'

'Come off it,' said Dawn. 'Do you think they'd allow an unmarried artist who drives a sports car and has a Ban the Bomb sign in her window to adopt a baby, when there are hundreds of boring, square, normal couples on their list? I suppose she might just get away with a nig-nog baby, but it'd stick out like a sore thumb round these parts, and people would talk.'

'No they wouldn't. They would know it was adopted because a white woman can't have a black baby.'

'Course they can. If they've been knocking off a black Yank from the air base. No, the only answer is to find her a suitable white bloke – and quick.'

I thought and thought of suitable men. But all the ones I could think of were either married, ugly or stupid, and Dawn said all the ones she could think of were half her age and thick as two short planks. 'I suggested we spend an evening in the Horse and Groom, where the off-duty Yank officers go, but she said she was past the stage of going to pubs to pick up men, it was too sordid for words. Even though she doesn't approve of them setting up their air bases over here, she's got a soft spot for Yanks.'

'How do you know?'

'Because all English women who lived through the War have. Mainly, I guess, because they splashed their money about. I bet it was some jealous English bloke who thought up that expression 'Over-sexed, over-paid and over here'. The other one going round at the time was "One Yank and they're off".'

I thought about this. 'Does that mean that if a Yank appears it frightens the British men off?'

'No, silly. It means a woman only has to see a Yank and she yanks her knickers – or bra, I suppose – off for him.'

'Oh, I see,' I said, my mind boggling. 'By the way how come every conversation I have with you revolves round s-e-x?'

'Because it's a big part of our lives, ain't it? I mean, if it weren't for that we wouldn't be here, would we. It's what makes the world go round.'

'It might be what makes *your* world go round . . .'

'The Yanks, see, had something the British blokes hadn't. Style. It was the way they swaggered about the place ever so casual in their tight uniforms, and the way they looked you straight in the eye and gave you a knowing 'I've been around, lady' look. Confidence, that's what it all boils down to. I suppose. And they were bigger-built than the weedy old half-starved Brits, and I'm not just referring to their chest measurements. I don't know if they actually were but that's the impression they gave. You know what I mean – well hung.'

'No. I don't know what you mean. You make them sound like pheasants.'

Dawn cackled. 'You're a card, blimey. Well hung means the geezer has a big cock.'

Her voice could be heard by the wood pigeon in the trees and the worms in the ground, and no doubt by young, innocent Hattie, too.

'That makes them sound even more like pheasants,' I said, refusing to stoop to her level. (*Why should Dawn's mind be underground? Because it's a sewer!!!*) 'Everything seems to revolve round pheasants these days. Pheasants and s-e-x.'

'You see, not only were the Yanks better paid than our lot – five times better, so I've been told – they weren't on rations either, so they were much better fed.'

Did that mean if a man ate a lot his . . . wedding tackle got bigger? Certainly, Snap Dragon ate a lot and his was quite big. From now

174

on, whenever I saw a boy eating a big meal that's all I'd be able to think about.

'Show me a weedy Yank and I'll show you . . .' and Dawn paused '. . . an English girl who secretly doesn't hanker after a Yank.'

'Well, I don't, for a kick off,' I said. 'I hate the way they chew gum the whole time and laugh at things that aren't funny.'

'You ain't old enough to count . . .'

'Yes, I am. One, two, three, four . . .'

'What about the hunk in the Cadillac? You found him sexy, I could tell.'

'Do you realise you're warping my mind? After this summer it'll never, ever be the same again.'

'Yeah, sorry. Mind you, you are eleven. A teenager, practically. Or are you toffs slower developers than us lot?'

For a while we picked beans in silence. Then I said, 'She must know lots of men in the art world.'

'Yeah, but most of them are gingers. The thing is, a bloke her age would probably want to marry someone a lot younger. My age, say.'

'Why?'

'Because that's the way men are. In the words of Ena Sharples, "A man isn't going to choose mutton when he can have spring lamb", yeah? So she'd have to go for someone a lot older than her, and then there'd be the risk of him not being able to get it up.'

'Get what up?'

'His wedding tackle, of course.'

Suddenly, I had the perfect solution: Mr Richards! Even though I would have liked to have married him myself one day, at least he would be my uncle which was better than nothing. I pictured the wedding. Aunt Lynette, who had given up smoking and gin, would be smiling under her white veil and would look far younger than forty, and Mr Richards in his speech would say it was all thanks to a certain young lady, the chief bridesmaid, alias Emily Pepys, in fact, that he'd found true happiness. I would have to cross out all references to Aunt Lynette in my diary and start again. *My aunt is beautiful, witty, talented – and dreams of marrying a tall, dark, handsome man*, I would write.

'I've just thought of someone who's witty, clever, artistic and very tall, dark and handsome – and he's an ex-RAF pilot.'

'Where, where?' cried Dawn. 'Seriously, though, do you think he'd be interested in your aunt? If he's *that* great shakes, don't you think he'd go for, well, a Brigitte Bardot type? I'm not saying your aunt is ugly or nothing, it's just that . . .'

175

Perhaps she was right. Mr Richards obviously liked pretty girls or he wouldn't have mentioned the ones in Bangkok. Meanwhile, I'd had another idea.

'How about if we could persuade the Yan ... Americans they needed a picture painted of their commander or a plane or something. Then she'd be on the base surrounded by thousands of handsome pilots and one of them, who would be interested in art, is *bound* to show an interest in her.'

'That's a thought,' said Dawn. 'We'll give them a ring tomorrow, yeah? We'll go to the village because your gran's got a bit twitchy about the phone. All old people get twitchy about something. With my gran it was hairs in food.'

'By the way, what's a ginger?'

'Ginger beer, queer, of course. Blimey, I thought everyone knew that.'

CHAPTER FIFTEEN

'A thorn between two roses, what!' said Rupert as he sat down between Hattie and me at supper.

Although Rupert's face wasn't quite unusual enough to inspire Aunt Lynette to paint it, it was a nice friendly face, and being a Rugby player like Dan he had a decent figure. I wasn't sure whether he had animal magnetism or not, I'd have to ask Dawn later. If it hadn't been for his age, he would have definitely been a candidate for Aunt Lynette's hand in marriage.

Apart from an angry spot on his chin that you planned not to look at while you were eating and hoped Dawn wouldn't comment on, he hadn't changed a bit. Even though he was the same age as Dan, he didn't seem to be going through a difficult phase at all. He wore a sports jacket and a blue silk cravat and had short neat nut-brown hair. It was freshly washed, his face was freshly shaved, and all in all put my brother's pulled-through-three-hedges-backwards rats' tails and whiskers to shame.

Dan's behaviour wasn't much better than his appearance. For he had greeted his best friend whom he hadn't seen for a year with 'How are ya, old son?' in a broad cockney accent, and was now, instead of making polite conversation, drumming on the table-cloth with his knife and fork and making a 'Tch-tch-tch' noise with his tongue. This left Hattie and me to ask Rupert all the boring questions you're supposed to ask a guest, like what they've been doing and whether they've been fishing and how their parents and sister and farm are.

'I hear you've formed a pop group, Dan,' said Rupert, laughing nervously, and Dan actually deigned to stop 'Tch-tching' for two seconds to say 'Yeah', leaving me to explain that they were called the Wild Ones of all things, and that they planned to play rocking roll cum rhythm and blues, whatever that was.

And then Dan stopped his 'Tch-tching' altogether and said, 'I say, Rupert old man, you're on the Shotestead Show's dance committee, aren't you?' Now that it had occurred to him Rupert could be of use he had dropped his cockney accent like a hot brick, and how devious could one get? 'Any chance we'll be able to do a

177

turn? We're going to be bloody good.'

Rupert said they were pleased to support local talent, but it was a decision for the whole committee.

'Put in a good word for us, there's a good chap,' said Dan as pompously as a colonel, and I just hoped Rupert was so used to talking to colonels that he hadn't noticed.

At the first opportunity I would explain to him that Dan was going through a tricky phase which would end as soon as he arrived in Cambridge, and to bear with him for the time being; he was just at that no-man's stage of being half-man, half-boy, and had temporarily gone slightly off the rails: if Rupert said that was the stage he himself was at and he hadn't gone off the rails, I would say it was Dan's artistic temperament rearing its ugly head.

Despite this minor setback, I was feeling very cheerful. This afternoon I'd lived dangerously and defied death, and as soon as there was a lull in the conversation I would recount my adventures word for word as I had done in my diary. I would say to my spellbound audience whose mouths, even Dan's, would drop open, 'While between my legs the beast's muscular body surged on like a thing possessed, I grimly gripped on for dear life.'

Before supper I'd marked the fullness of the weed-killer bottle and sprinkled fingerprint dust on the cap, and checked all stairs for trip wires. Clifford had eaten the suspect sausage with no ill effects so far, and now Granny was almost back to her old self and in charge of the food I didn't have to worry so much there. She was wearing her lilac Liberty-print dress and I hoped she'd stay seated all evening so Rupert wouldn't spot the ladder in her stocking.

Aunt Lynette was very cheery because of something to do with a Nuclear Test Ban Treaty between Britain, Russia and America, and even Dawn seemed on her best behaviour. She was wearing a pink nylon dress with black spots and a pink bow in her hair which she'd puffed up to the size of a beach ball. The dress was far too short, of course, but at least it didn't make her bosoms look as huge as some things I'd seen her in. Even so, it still didn't stop Rupert having a quick peek at them.

The table looked more like the counter of an off-licence than a dining table. On the wine-bottle labels was a pen and ink drawing of Gressenham Hall, and written underneath, in neat italic handwriting, *Château Hillington. Pomme de Terre. 1960.* The contents were an unusual colour for wine, and you knew it was only a matter of time before Dawn would comment. And sure enough ...

''Ere, you are positive that's wine, Miss Aitch. Looks like a you-know-what sample to me.'

'Dawn, dear,' said Granny.

(That was something else I'd have to explain to Rupert: that due to the winter, Granny was temporarily gaga when she employed Dawn. 'Isn't she *frightful*,' I'd say and Rupert would reply, 'Ya, she is rather.'

'Trust you to lower the tone – and you haven't even had a drink yet,' laughed Aunt Lynette. She looked quite pretty, too, and if you ignored the strands of grey in her dark bouncy hair and a few thin lines around her eyes she could get away with being thirty-seven or even thirty-five.

Dawn said she was only trying to crack a joke and sorry if it was in poor taste and I said, 'How do you know, you haven't tasted it yet,' and everyone laughed, especially Rupert but that was probably because he was nervous.

While Aunt Lynette poured the wine, Dan sharpened the carving knife gaily in the air with the steel, and Dawn said he reminded her of Errol Flynn. He gave Rupert one slice of beef more than anyone else, and Dawn a fatty piece. Granny served the vegetables, and gave Dawn the one burnt roast potato.

''Ere, Rupert,' said Dawn and the way her eyes were darting round his face like small blackbirds, you knew what was coming, and apart from fainting or pretending to have an epileptic fit, I couldn't think of any way to stop her. 'If you don't mind me saying, that's a nasty-looking spot you've got there. Have you tried Medac? It'll dry it up nice. I've got some in my room.'

Rupert's cheeks turned the colour of his spot; perhaps that was Nature's way of camouflaging it. Aunt Lynette said, 'Oh, Lor', and Dan said in a silly northern accent, 'She's nothing if not blunt, is our Dawn,' and Granny looked at her in despair, the way you would if your daughter has just vandalised a phone box or failed the 11-Plus, and Hattie mumbled, 'Honestly, some people,' and Rupert cleared his throat and said, 'Thank you, er, Dawn.'

Was this Dawn's way of saying to Rupert 'Come up and see me sometime'? It would be interesting to see whether she brought the Medac down or invited him up to her room. That was another thing to add to the list to tell Rupert – that Dawn made everyone go red, including Dan, it was just the foul way she was.

'Have I said something wrong?' said Dawn, looking round in her wide-eyed pretending-to-be-innocent way. Little did she realise that it didn't fool anyone.

'Are you looking forward to going to Cirencester, Rupert?' I asked politely, trying to bring some dignity and repose to the dinner party.

179

'Oh, rather,' he said, his face still flame coloured.

'What's that when it's at home then, Rupert?' asked Dawn, and Rupert said, 'An agricultural college. Some say the best in the country, actually.'

'Oh, *naturally*,' said Dawn, putting her elbows on the table, cupping her chin in her hands and staring at him very intently. 'I didn't for one moment assume you'd be going to the *worst*.'

The cheek of the woman! How I longed to say to her you're only a servant, a nobody, whereas Rupert belongs to one of the oldest, most distinguished titled families in the county. 'She simply doesn't know her place,' I'd tell him later. 'Ignore her, if I were you.'

'Well, cheers, chaps and chapesses,' said Aunt Lynette, raising her murky glass that could have had a few tadpoles lurking in it. 'To us all.'

'Mmmm,' said Dawn, gulping it down as if it were Corona. 'It's not half bad.'

'No. Jolly good, actually,' said Rupert, clearing his throat.

I asked Granny if I could have just a taster, seeing as how I was eleven, and Dawn said yeah, in France all children have a glass of wine with their meal, and Granny said we weren't in France but in England, where customs were different.

'Yes, that's like saying because they eat horse in France, we should be eating it for our supper,' said Hattie. 'I wonder if that's where Snap Dragon will end up – in thin slices in a mushroom sauce on a Frenchman's plate.'

'Hattie, *please*,' I said looking down at my thin slices of roast beef and thinking of Snap Dragon rolling happily in his magic circle.

'He'd be far too tough and gristly,' said Dan. 'You'd need a hacksaw to carve through his muscly old flesh.'

'*Darlings*,' said Aunt Lynette, throwing down her knife and fork, 'I've been considering going vegetarian for a while, and that just about settles it.'

'Same here,' I said looking daggers at Dan.

'Granny said Snap Dragon should go to the slaughterhouse after what he did to Sarah, didn't you, Granny?' persisted Hattie.

'He'll probably end up as dogfood,' said Dawn. 'Just think, Clifford ...'

'That's quite enough,' said Granny sharply. 'In polite circles one doesn't discuss what happens to animals in general and ponies in particular when they go to slaughterhouses.'

'Ugh. The whole thing reminds one of Jews being shunted off to death camps,' said Aunt Lynette. 'Seventy to one cattle truck. Can you imagine?'

'Yeah, that's what I was thinking,' said Dawn, though I bet she wasn't. 'And just one bucket for a lav. The Nazis didn't eat the Jews, though, did they?'

'I wouldn't put anything past them,' said Aunt Lynette who, like Dawn, had almost finished her second glass of Château Hillington.

'Course they didn't eat them,' said Dan who *had* finished his second glass. 'They saw them as vermin and Germans wouldn't eat vermin.'

'I bet Brian Pike does,' said Hattie. 'I bet he's eating stewed stoat at this very moment.'

'I know they made lampshades out of . . .'

'Will you kindly *stop*,' said Granny in her Duchess voice, though it was a pale, thin shadow of how her Duchess voice used to be. 'What must Rupert think?'

'Yeah, what *do* you think, Rupert?' said Dawn.

'Er, sorry, what about exactly?'

'Anything you like,' said Dawn. 'Whether you think Stephen Ward is guilty of living off immoral earnings for example.'

'Or your view on the unemployment figures being the highest since 1947, or the colour bar in universities in Alabama, or Chelsea boots,' said Dan. 'Or candy-stripe shirts or E-type jags or the latest copy of *Private Eye*.'

'Or whether you're considering voting Labour at the next general election because they will discontinue the Polaris programme,' said Aunt Lynette.

Rupert took a mouthful of roast potato in order to give himself time to consider his answer. I came to his rescue. 'Wouldn't it be hilarious if you, Dawn, decided to become a vegetarian. Getting married to a butcher, I mean.'

'Yeah, I suppose it would,' said Dawn. 'I'd be tucking into a nut cutlet every night and Albert a bloody steak. That wasn't a swear word by the way, Mrs Aitch.'

'I reckon that would be grounds for divorce,' said Dan. 'Can you imagine the headline? *BUTCHER GIVEN CHOP!*'

'Or *MARRIAGE BUST-UP A JOINT DECISION!*' said Aunt Lynette.

'Or *ONE MAN'S MEAT IS HIS WIFE'S POISON!*' I said, pleased that was the best so far.

'Or *MARRIAGE AT STEAK!*' said Hattie.

'Or *BUTCHER GIVEN COLD SHOULDER!*' said Dawn.

'Or *BUTCHER LEFT TO STEW!*' said Dan.

'Or *BUTCHER COOKED HIS GOOSE!*' ventured Granny.

'Or *BUTCHER'S MARRIAGE IN OFFAL MESS!*' I said.

'Or *BUTCHER'S MARRIAGE NOTHING TO BEEF ABOUT!*' said Hattie.

'Or *BUTCHER HAS A LEAN TIME!*' said Aunt Lynette.

'Or *BUTCHER'S MARRIAGE TOUGH!*' I said.

'Or *BUTCHER'S MARRIAGE FOULS UP!*' said Dawn.

'Or *VEGETARIAN CARVES UP MARRIAGE!*' said Dan.

'Do you mean "calves" or "carves"?' I said.

'Carves,' said Dan, sawing his knife in the air. 'Calves are veal in butchery terms. Oh, that's another one. *BUTCHER TELLS WIFE: VEAL NEVER MEET AGAIN!* Come on, Rupert old chap, you haven't come up with one yet,' he added, which I thought very unkind of him.

'Er – not much cop at this sort of thing, I'm afraid,' he said, clearing his throat. "Er – how about, er, *BUTCHER MADE TO LOOK A CHUMP!* You know, chump chop. No? Never mind. Well, er, how about, *BUTCHER OUT FOR A DUCK!*?'

I laughed politely and Dawn said, '*Pardon*, Rupert? Oh, *duck*! Blimey, I thought you said something rude there for a moment. I don't get it.'

'Out for a duck's a cricket term,' said Dan.

'So? What's that got to do with a marriage splitting up?'

'Maybe the butcher was a cricketer,' I said.

'The nearest Albert's ever got to a bat is to have them in his belfry!' screeched Dawn.

Rupert's cheeks were matching his spot again. He had hardly touched his food.

'Actually,' he said, staring at his plate, 'I jolly well hope everyone doesn't become vegetarian because we'd go bankrupt – as would your, er, fiancé, er, Dawn.'

'Why's that then?' said Dawn, narrowing her eyes to two black spiders. 'Don't tell me you're a butcher, too – actually?'

'No, I'm a cattle farmer, actually. Or will be one day.'

'A ruddy wealthy one,' said Dan, more to himself.

'Ah. Bullocks you mean.' said Dawn. 'Oh blimey, I've just thought of a brilliant one. Close your ears, Mrs Aitch, it's a bit rude. And you, too, kids. How about this: *BUTCHER'S WIFE SAYS BULLOCKS TO HER MARRIAGE!*'

There was a deathly hush and Dawn said, 'Blimey, have I gone too far?' and then Aunt Lynette's laughter pealed out like church bells on a quiet winter's morning and Dan's roared like a man in a public house and Rupert went 'Ha, ha, ha' in a forced sort of way, and the thing was, my tummy was laughing fit to burst, and if Granny and Hattie and Rupert hadn't been there I would have roared. As it was I pulled a disapproving face at Hattie, and vowed to write later: *Thanks to Dawn, I have become a terrible hypocrite. Let's hope it's only a phase.*

When the laughter had died down, Rupert said, 'I say, Sarah, do tell us what happened to you and Snap Dragon today.'

'Oh, yah, *do*,' said Dawn in imitation, and Dan the vile traitor that he was because only a week ago he was talking just like Rupert, actually sniggered.

'And go on, Ma, let her have just a glass,' said Aunt Lynette. 'It'll spice up the story.'

'The story's spicy enough already, thank you,' I said. 'Though I wouldn't mind just a taste.'

Granny nodded, and Dan poured me just over half a glass. It tasted a cross between vinegar, Veno's cough medicine and a mouldy carrot, but I managed not to pull a face. Hattie did, though, and said 'Ugh', and that must be the difference between an eight-year-old and an eleven-year-old. Or perhaps it was simply that Hattie wasn't a hypocrite like I was.

'Watch out – it's got a kick like a mule,' said Dan.

'Or Snap Dragon,' said Hattie. 'Go on, Sarah.'

So I began my story, about calling Snap Dragon a bugger as Norfolk people do and him snorting at me (I left out the farting bit because Rupert was there), and I'd just got to the aeroplane bit when Dawn said, 'Yeah, I heard that one. Made me row of stitches go wonky. I call it a diabolical liberty.'

'Frankly,' said Aunt Lynette, 'I don't know who the hell they think they are terrorising our countryside and disturbing the peace. I suppose, Sarah, you're going to say that Snap Dragon bolted, and you can't blame the old love. Now, just say you'd fallen off and broken your neck. Would you have been able to sue the American Government? Would you heck! The way farmers aren't allowed to sue when their cows abort and their eggs won't lay ...'

At last Hattie and I found something to laugh about, and even Granny smiled.

'Don't you mean *hens* won't lay, Aunt Lynette?'

'I say, I think you're being a bit tough on the poor old Americans,' said Rupert, quite bravely really considering it wasn't his birthday. 'I mean, if someone's got to do it, it might just as well be them using up their fuel rather than our boys.'

'Do what, though, Rupert?' said Dawn with her mouth full. 'Why do they have to fly so flaming low and make such a blinking racket?

It's as if they're spying on women sunbathing in the nude or something.'

'They have to fly low to avoid radar.'

'Yeah, but why do they have to fly the things at all? It's not as if we're at war or nothing is it.'

'They have to practise – check everything's ticking over for if there's a real war,' said Rupert.

'*When* there's a real war, you mean,' said Aunt Lynette. 'With these ruddy air bases littered all over our country like caravan sites, we'll soon be littered with their nuclear weapons, too.'

'But I thought the Americans are our friends,' I said. 'They sent all that vaccine to Bradford when there was the smallpox scare. And came to our rescue in the war. I thought if anyone the Russians were our enemy.'

'No one's our enemy – at the moment, darling,' said Aunt Lynette. 'But just say the Americans fall out with another country – an Arab country, for example. They'll use British soil as a launch pad for their nuclear missiles. And where will that leave *us*? Slap bang in the middle of it all. Mere pawns on the chessboard of war.'

'That's right,' said Dawn. 'That's good, Miss Aitch, mere pawns on the chessboard of war. Poetry in motion, in the words of Johnny Tillotson. Oh, let's not talk about war no more, it gives me the creeps.'

'That's why it's vital to ban all bombs now,' continued Aunt Lynette, drumming her fist on the table like a politician, and I wished she'd shut up. I wanted to get on with my story. 'Because once this arms race gets underway there'll be no stopping them. It'll only need one idiot to press a button and bompf – we'll all go up in smoke.'

'President Kennedy would never allow that to happen,' I said.

'Right,' said Rupert.

'I wouldn't be too sure,' said Aunt Lynette. 'Look what happened over Cuba. That was touch and go. Now, no doubt someone like you, Rupert, would say the reason that was all over so quickly was because both sides were petrified the other would press the button first. But what I say is, why have the bally things in the first place?'

'I say, you aren't a member of CND are you, Miss Hillington?' said Rupert.

'Actually, Rupert, I am,' said Aunt Lynette, putting her head on one side and staring at him very hard. 'In fact not only am I a member of CND but also . . .' and she paused to give her statement more impact ' . . . the Committee of 100.'

Whatever it was it must have been quite serious because Rupert's jaw dropped open, and even Dan looked surprised.

'I say,' said Rupert. 'Aren't they law-breaking Communists who boo at the Queen?'

'They are a group of artists and intellectuals, Rupert, such as John Braine, Vanessa Redgrave, John Osborne and Lindsay Anderson, whose one and only aim is to bring about peace on earth and goodwill to all men.'

'Take no notice of Aunt Lynette, she's on her high horse,' I said quietly to Rupert.

'But *you* aren't, Sarah, you're on a short, fat pony,' said Hattie. 'Go on with your story.'

'So anyway, I was just lengthening the stirrups when out of the blue ...'

'I forbid any more talk of war in front of the children – or for that matter, in front of me,' said Granny in a startlingly loud voice, her eyes fixed on an unopened bottle of Château Hillington. 'I've lived through two and that's quite enough thank you. I cannot even tolerate the thought of another one.'

'But you can't bury your head in the sand, Granny,' said Dan, and Dawn nodded and said, 'That's right.'

'Well said, Mrs Hillington,' said Rupert, holding up his glass.

'Really, Rupert, so far the conversation's been nothing but wars and gloom and doom. What must you think of us,' said Granny vaguely.

'Well, er ...'

'Yeah, what do you think of us, Rupert?' said Dawn, putting her elbows on the table and gazing into his eyes.

I knew exactly what he thought of us. I could picture now what he was going to say to his parents, Sir Eustace and Lady Margetson, and his sister Fiona, who we all secretly thought would one day make the perfect wife for Dan. 'Honestly, they've turned into Labour-voting extremists, Communists even, obsessed with war and politics – apart from Sarah, who seems to have her head screwed on the right way. Dan's turned into a pop-singing yobbo – and to think he was once my best friend. Tragic, isn't it, to see a once-decent farming family go to the dogs.' And Fiona would cross Dan off her list of possible husbands, and his parents, muttering about it being a sign of the times, would pass on the news to all their friends who would never invite a Hillington to a drinks party again.

'Well, er, I'm afraid I must disagree with you on the question of defence,' said Rupert. 'I firmly believe that every country should defend itself.'

'But not with *nuclear* deterrents, Rupert,' said Aunt Lynette. 'Do you realise they could contaminate whole areas of the earth with radioactivity for hundreds of years? Have you ever heard of nuclear fallout, Rupert? And we will be sitting on the monsters' doorsteps, practically. Think of your bullocks. They'd all have to be slaughtered – if there were any left to slaughter.'

'Yeah, don't forget your *bullocks*, Rupert,' said Dawn, giving him one of her big-eyed looks.

'There won't be another war, will there, Granny?' said Hattie. 'I couldn't bear it if we were all taken off in a cattle truck to a gas oven.'

'There won't be any cattle trucks or gas ovens,' said Aunt Lynette. 'They'll all have been blown into smithereens.'

'We'd be all right, we aren't Jewish,' I said. I too found the prospect of gas ovens and seventy to a cattle truck and one bucket for a lav far more worrying than bombs. You couldn't picture a bomb the way you could a cattle truck.

'I thought I said there would be no more talk of war?' said Granny but she didn't, I notice, suggest a new topic.

Later, I would explain to Rupert that it was one glass too many of Château Hillington that had made everyone so political; they weren't normally like this.

'The thing is, Granny,' said Dan who, judging by the colour of his cheeks had had one *bottle* too many, 'I think children should at least be *aware* of the possibilities. I mean, when I was their age I had hardly heard of Adolf Hitler, let alone Auschwitz or Belsen.'

'Hear, hear,' said Aunt Lynette. 'One can shield children far too much from unpleasantness and it all comes as a far greater shock to the system when they find out for themselves the world isn't all sweetness and light.'

'I agree with Mrs Aitch,' said Dawn. 'I saw things when I was a child that could have turned me off the human race for life.'

'But they didn't, did they?' said Aunt Lynette, her voice raised. 'I think children act as their own censors. They retain what is relevant to them at the time and discard the rest like a sieve.'

'With respect, Lynette, considering you've never had children I fail to see why you've suddenly become an expert on the subject,' said Granny.

Dawn and I looked at each other, and Aunt Lynette looked down at her plate. For a moment I thought she was going to cry, or walk off in a huff. Instead she said, 'With respect, Ma, Dr Beeching has probably never ridden in a train in his life, yet he's in charge of the railways.'

'Ya, and look at the botch-up he's making,' said Rupert. 'He's planning to close half the stations and a third of the tracks.'

'That's because everyone's got a motor these days,' said Dawn. 'We've got to move with the times, you know, Rupert.'

At the same time as I said, 'I'd like to get on with my story now, if no one objects', Dan said, louder, 'Look at Sarah, for example. When she was younger, whenever the parents read her *The Tale of Peter Rabbit*, that bit about not going into Mr McGregor's garden because their father had an accident there; they always left it at that and missed out 'he was put in a pie by Mrs McGregor' because they thought it would upset her. Then later when she read the book to Hattie, she couldn't believe her eyes when she came to that line.'

'You thought it was a mistake, didn't you, Sarah,' said Hattie.

'Yes, I thought the printers had played a joke. Talking of stories . . .'

'And how did you feel about not being told the real truth about Peter Rabbit's unfortunate papa, Sarah?' said Aunt Lynette, her eyes squinting like someone who has just taken off their spectacles. 'That you had, near as dammit, been lied to.'

'Er . . .' I didn't want to be disloyal to my parents, nor did I want to take Aunt Lynette's side. In fact I didn't want to talk about this at all. 'I was just surprised, that's all. I don't think it was a lie.'

'Excuse me,' said Aunt Lynette, 'I think it was. Omission of the truth is just as bad as lying. It wouldn't stand up in a court of law.'

'Yeah, but a lie would be if her mum had told her the rabbit's dad lived happily ever after,' said Dawn. 'Just missing out the pie bit isn't a lie.'

'I'm sorry but I'm afraid it is, Dawn,' said Aunt Lynette. 'A murderer could say in court he'd picked up a gun and then conveniently miss out the part about pulling the trigger.'

'Yeah, but it's still not a lie, like, say, Mr Profumo's in the House of Commons. 'Ere, that reminds me', and she looked at Rupert and put her head on one side and you knew something unsuitable was brewing. 'Have you ever met any girls like Christine Keeler, Rupert – just out of interest?'

Rupert's face had stopped bothering to turn back to its normal colour between each embarrassing incident. Like a faulty traffic light, it was stuck permanently on red.

'Don't be beastly to poor Rupert,' said Aunt Lynette in a baby's voice. 'Fresh out of public school and still wet behind the ears.'

'Tell me, Rupert. Do I remind you – just a teensy weensy bit – of Mandy Rice-Davies?' said Dawn and pouted her horrible pout and fluttered her sweep's brushes.

'Er . . . I'm not sure . . . Ya, I suppose you do. Just a little.'

187

'And do you know who *you* remind me of? Just a little? Richard Burton. I think it's the eyes.'

'Gosh, thanks,' said Rupert, and couldn't he tell she was making fun of him? Was he, like Jemima Puddle-Duck when the foxy-whiskered gentleman mentioned sage and onions and still she wasn't suspicious, a simpleton, or had Dawn's animal magnetism worked its spell on him, too?

'And I'll tell you something else. You've got Prince Charles's mouth. Anyone told you that before? Blimey, you must be about the most illegible bloke in the whole of Norfolk, what with dishy actor's eyes and a prince's mouth and all that land. Tell me something, Rupert. How does it feel to be both handsome and rich?'

Rupert shrugged and why wasn't Granny stepping in and stopping this? 'Well . . .'

'Do you ever, as you look out of your country mansion at your acres of land and herds of bullocks, think about people less fortunate? People who, say, live four to a room with an outside lav? People who are attacked by alsatians if they can't pay their rent? Have you heard of a Mr Rachman by any chance, Rupert? Have you ever set eyes on a slum – a damp, stinking, shitty, leaking slum, with newspapers instead of glass in the windows, and rafters for roofs?'

Rupert would sigh as he told his parents that Mrs Hillington just sat there letting her common maid insult him. Could they credit it? Could they imagine that happening if Mr Hillington had still been alive? She must, as Sarah had suggested, have gone completely gaga, and she was supposed to be in charge of those two little girls . . .

Rupert squirmed in his seat and said, 'Yah, I know there are people less fortunate than myself, and I'm truly sorry about it, but what can *I* do?'

'You could start by voting Labour at the next election – old boy,' said Dan, and Rupert said yah, but the thing about Labour was they'd probably nationalise everything, including farms. 'Anyway, look all this must be boring Sarah and Hattie rigid. Why don't we return to the safer topic of Sarah and Peter Rabbit? I think her parents were quite right not to read out that bit of the story. I mean, obviously they knew Sarah was a sensitive girl who would be upset by animals being eaten, and used their judgement accordingly.'

'Ah. Hold on a tick,' said Dan. 'Who said anything about animals being eaten? He was just put in a pie.'

'Don't be stupid, Dan. What else would you do with a pie?' I snapped.

'It could be Beatrix Potter's euphemistic way of saying, er, Mr Peter Rabbit Senior had a finger – or should I say paw – in every pie. Or that he was pie-eyed. And he's not the only one – pass the vino, Dawn.'

'You're as mad as a hatter, Dan.'

'Don't you mean drunk as a lord?'

'Do you realise the conversation's come full circle and we're back to discussing the consumption of animal flesh?' said Aunt Lynette.

I thought of a clever way of steering the conversation back my way. 'I think children should find things out for themselves rather than be told. For example, if someone had told me before this afternoon that ponies can behave like devils I wouldn't have really believed them. So anyway, this aeroplane ...'

'Ah! I just want to say one more thing and then I promise I won't utter another word for the rest of the evening,' said Aunt Lynette, raising her arm as if she were in the classroom. Her words were beginning to run together, and she spat when she talked.

'What I meant to say before was that one shouldn't trust these Americans. It's easy to think that because they've got a charming young leader everything's hunky-dory. Because it ain't.'

'President Kennedy's all right – he digs James Bond,' said Dawn. 'Anyway, I thought you had a soft spot for Yanks, Miss Aitch,' she added, winking at me.

Aunt Lynette said they were all right individually, it was just *en masse*, as a country, they weren't to be trusted. Their paranoia about communism was to be seen to be believed.

'They're all right under Kennedy,' said Dan. 'He's in touch with what's going on which is more than can be said for Macmillan. Those two sum up the two countries perfectly: lively, go-ahead, young, dashing, stylish, vibrant versus stodgy, old-fashioned, fuddy-duddy, out of touch. I mean, look at the music business. Apart from the Beatles, who might just swing the balance, we're way behind and always have been ...'

'Hear, hear,' said Dawn.

'Oh, I don't know,' said Rupert.

'That's your trouble,' said Dan under his breath and I prayed that one of the effects of Château Hillington was to make you deaf.

'But Dan, you mustn't be taken in by youth and good looks,' said Aunt Lynette, leaning across the table and dangling her blouse sleeve in the gravy. 'At least Supermac is a wily old dog who knows what he's doing – a true statesman. There's something about JFK. The Bay of Pigs nearly triggered off a very unpleasant incident indeed.'

'You mean he made a right pig's ear of it, Miss Aitch?' said Dawn, and Rupert laughed too loudly and for too long, and please let him go on drinking because then he might wake up in the morning thinking all this was just a bad dream.

It was the first interesting thing Aunt Lynette had said all evening. 'What's the Bay of Pigs?' I asked, imagining a sea of pig soldiers in steely helmets baying like hounds. But needless to say it turned out to be something boring between Cuba, America and the Russians.

'Of course, that's who Brian Pike reminds me of,' said Dawn, snapping her fingers. 'Fidel Castro! He's the spitting image!'

'Yes, but I bet his politics aren't,' said Aunt Lynette, laughing with her mouth open so all her back fillings showed. 'I bet old Fidel has better things to do with his time than killing the odd weasel.'

'You never know, maybe weasel's a euphemism for a CIA agent these days,' said Dan, and the three of them rocked and rolled with laughter, and I couldn't see the joke at all, nor could Rupert or Hattie or Granny. And now they were lighting foul cigarettes at table when Rupert hadn't finished eating and I longed to suggest that us four non-smokers go into the drawing room and play Canasta and let the coarse drunks get on with it, and I would have done but for two reasons: one, we'd miss out on the summer pudding and two, I still hadn't recounted my adventure.

''Ere, Sarah,' said Dawn suddenly. 'A dicky bird told me you're writing a play for when them relations of yours come over. I've always fancied meself as an actress. Can I be the beautiful princess whisked off my feet by an 'ansome prince?' and she gave Dan a revolting, pouty, eyelash-fluttering look that made me feel quite ill.

'Sorry,' I said. 'Hattie's the princess this year.' And I gave her what I hoped was an 'I'd rather have a wildebeest in my play than you' look, but she just laughed and said, 'Blimey, when you pull that face you look like Ena Sharples on a bad day. 'Ere, that reminds me. Would anyone like to hear the funniest thing ever, guaranteed to make you all wet yourselves? Guess why Sarah thinks men's bicycles have crossbars?'

Slowly, calmly, like Dracula emerging from his coffin, I rose to my feet, picked up the carving knife and pointed it at her neck. There was a risk that Rupert would change his story to 'Even Sarah, who seemed normal enough, turned out to be a potential murderer,' but that was a risk I was prepared to take.

'If you utter one more word, Dawn Potts,' I said through gritted teeth, my voice as cool, calm and collected as a surgeon's, 'I will insert this knife into your neck and keep pushing until it comes out the other side. And if you ever tell anyone in private, I will get to know about it and will come and murder you in your bed.'

'Oo-er,' said Dawn looking quite frightened, and Aunt Lynette said, 'Lummy, it's the first time my vino has made someone violent,' and Dan said, 'I think this is Sarah's way of getting attention so she can finish her story.'

I turned and pointed the knife at him. 'That shows how stupid you are, doesn't it, Dan. For I have no intention of wasting my breath on this ... *rabble*. I shall tell my story to deserving people,' and I looked at Rupert, then Granny.

'Oooh, lardy-da,' said Dawn at the same time that Granny said. 'Put that knife down, darling. I think it's high time we cleared away.'

'Blimey, you had me worried there for a minute, Sarah,' said Dawn, relaxing her shoulders as I put down the knife.

'Well, you should still be worried,' I said, retaining my surgeon's voice, 'because I meant every word of it. I take a dim view of people who betray me.'

The moment passed and was forgotten, I would write. *Not by me, though. Oh, no. What power a carving knife can give you! And how amazing that one minute one can be a polite well-behaved schoolgirl and then, just by moving your arm six inches and picking up a knife handle, can turn into an uncivilised murderer! The line between good behaviour and bad, between right and wrong, is as thin as a mouse's whisker.*

The summer-pudding stage of the meal was taken up by the Profumo Affair, and even though Granny and I had spent ages hulling raspberries and red- and blackcurrants, no one apart from Rupert said how nice it was.

You couldn't blame him at all when he said that he really should be going.

'Oh, hang on a sec,' said Dan. 'I was hoping we could have a sing-song round the piano.'

'What, you mean the old Joanna?' said Dawn. 'Yeah, I'm game. Go on, Rupert. Be a devil. Then you can hear how talented Dan is. Okay with you, Mrs Aitch?'

'So long as it doesn't get out of hand,' said Granny. 'And it's time for bed for you two.'

'Oh, Granny, our food won't have digested and we'll have foul dreams.'

'Yes, and we'll never get to sleep if there's a din going on.'

Granny sighed and said very well.

Although Grandpa had been dead for two and a quarter years, the

191

drawing room still smelt of cigars and brandy, still had that dark, thick, rich, 'Do not disturb' air about it. Even now you turned the door knob quietly and tiptoed across the carpet, still expecting to see him in his man-size armchair by the man-size brick fireplace puffing on his cigar like Sir Winston Churchill to help him concentrate on his *Times* crossword.

'This can be the dance floor,' yelled Dawn, hurtling back armchairs and antique tables and family heirlooms as if they were straw bales. 'By rights we should roll up the carpet but I can't be fagged. Turn the main light off, will you, Hat.'

'No, I will not,' said Hattie, her eyes flashing behind her spectacles. 'And put Grandpa's chair back where it was.'

'All right, keep your hair on,' said Dawn looking surprised. 'Which one is it – this one? D'yer like dancing, Rupert?'

'Er, I'm not much cop, actually.'

'Don't worry, you'll soon get into the swing of it. What ya going to play then, Dan?'

Dan shrugged. 'Rupert's the guest. He can choose.'

'Er . . .' Rupert scratched his head. 'How about *The Young Ones* by Cliff Richard?'

Dawn sniggered behind her hand and Dan said, lifting the lid of the grand piano, that he had something a bit raunchier in mind.

'How about *Johnny B. Goode*?' I said hesitantly, and Dan said it was more a song for guitars than pianos.

'How about The King?' said Dawn and I'm sure Rupert was about to say 'I haven't heard of him', when Dan did the thumbs-up sign and said 'Hang on while I find the right chord.'

Hattie and I sat on the sofa to watch, and Aunt Lynette, needing no music danced in a dizzy circle, a bottle of Château Hillington held high in one hand. 'My giddy aunt!' I whispered and we both got a fit of the giggles.

'Right,' said Dan. 'A-one, two, a-one-two-three-four', and he crashed into this extraordinary song about a jailhouse rock, whatever that was.

Poor piano. After a quiet life of gentle Christmas carols and children practising scales, what a rude awakening this was, what a shock to its system. Rupert's system looked pretty shocked, too. And fancy Dan being able to play standing up without sheet music and without looking. The last time I'd heard him play the piano it had been *The Blue Danube*.

'*Everybody, let's rock*,' he yelled in a stirring, snarling voice.

'And that means you two,' said Dawn and went into a sort of trance like Toad with a happy smile on her face, lifting her arms in front of her, clicking her fingers and slowly, deliberately, rocking and rolling her hips, while Aunt Lynette did an energetic imitation of Isadora Duncan.

'And you, Rupert,' said Dawn taking his hand and leading him into the middle of the dance floor where he swung his arms and bounced his large brown feet like an anxious-to-please puppy.

'Isn't it ghastly? So loud and such vile words,' whispered Hattie, and maybe that was another difference between being eight and eleven, because in a funny sort of way the song was making me want to dance – except I never would because I didn't know how and Dawn would snigger behind her hand and Dan would turn red with shame. Besides, what was the betting any moment now Granny would come into the Den of Iniquity looking the way she had when she'd caught us using the telephone. 'You've turned my house into a den of thieves,' she'd say like Jesus which would be quite apt seeing as how the song was about criminals in prison, and she'd march over to Dan and slam shut the piano lid on his fingers.

'*Everybody in the whole cell block,*' screamed Dan, swinging his shoulders. '*Dance to the Jailhouse Rock.*'

'We could do the twist, I suppose,' I said. 'I bet it's easy-peasy, like hula-hooping.'

'No,' said Hattie and looked as though she about to cry.

Then Aunt Lynette staggered over, raising her bottle-free hand as if we were a taxi. 'Darlings, would you do me a huge favour. In the words of some bod or other, will you show me the way to go home? I'm tired and I want to go to bed.'

We guided her tottering form out of the house and across the cobblestones.

'I'm so sorry I wasn't on my best behaviour tonight,' she said, slurring her words. 'I'll have to stick to bought wine in future.'

'Who is worse, Aunt Lynette,' said Hattie, 'the Russians or the Germans? Is the difference that if Russia invaded Britain I'd have to marry a plumber and not be allowed to be rich, and if the Germans took over they'd gas the Jews?'

To our surprise, Aunt Lynette burst into tears. Apart from Miss Rose and Mummy over Hattie's leg, she was the first grown-up I'd seen crying.

'Oh, forgive me, darlings,' she said, taking my handkerchief and blowing her nose. 'The world is such a sad, ghastly place at times.'

'Don't worry, I bet there won't be a war,' said Hattie.

'And even if there is one, we'll win. Our soldiers are very brave, and we'll have the Americans on our side,' I said, opening her front door. 'Er, will you be all right? Can we help you get undressed?'

'Come morning I'll be right as rain, darlings,' she said, managing to balance the bottle on a table before crumpling up on the *chaise-longue*. 'I'm frightfully sorry if I've upset you.'

'Was it the Château Hillington that made her cry, or the thought of there being another war?' said Hattie as we walked back across the courtyard.

'A bit of each, I expect,' I said, knowing both were a disguise for her real cause of misery.

'I hope there won't be a war,' said Hattie. 'And I wish people would stop talking about it.'

'I do, too,' I said because it had just occurred to me that if there was, Mr Richards would rejoin the RAF and we'd get a foul woman teacher.

'The Château H seems to have had the opposite effect on Dawn,' said Hattie as a screech of mad laughter like Bertha Mason's in *Jane Eyre* mingled with Dan roaring, '*Goodness gracious, great balls of fire!*' 'What a perfectly foul evening it's been. Goodness knows what Rupert thought. When Dawn went on about slums and commented on his spot, that was the last straw.'

'Hat,' I added.

'Yes?' she said. 'Oh, crikey, you see, I'm even answering to the foul name she calls me. Why *do* men's bikes have crossbars, by the way?'

'Never you mind.'

'How come you can tell the Foul Dawn but not me and I'm your sister? Honestly. Nobody tells me anything.'

While the din continued downstairs, Granny tucked us up in bed. She looked very tired and very old and very sad, but she didn't say, 'Tonight was one of those unfortunate evenings that are best forgotten about, darlings', like the old Granny would have done.

'Aunt Lynette was crying,' said Hattie. 'I think she's frightened there'll be another war. There won't be one, will there, Granny?'

'Of course there won't, darling,' said Granny. 'I've never heard so much rubbish talked in my whole life.'

'Granny, you will er, keep an eye on Rupert and Dan and Dawn, won't you, please,' I said, suddenly remembering I hadn't had my word with Rupert: I would have to write him a letter instead.

Granny promised she would break up the party straight away.

But she couldn't have done, because the music and singing and laughter got all tangled up in the web of my dreams.

CHAPTER SIXTEEN

I sat on the patchwork quilt behind the black summerhouse and wrote my thank-you letters. I should have written to Rupert, too, but instead opened my notebook and wrote *PLAY, SUMMER 1963*. And then, underneath, *Rough plot*.

It was a still, close, misty-moisty morning, with barely a murmur coming from Lion's Mouth Wood or the wild wooly undergrowth or tangly wood.

A train clickety-clacked by. Even though it was a cheerful passenger train, with people reading the paper or looking out at the scenery, it still acted as a grim reminder of my dream. I wondered if Shakespeare had taken advantage of his dreams when he was stuck for a plot. And if so, were his dreams as troubled and muddled as mine? One thing was for sure: his wouldn't have had rocking roll as background music.

'*Great balls of fire!*' Dan had roared as Dawn wiggled across the Bay of Pigs in an itsy-bitsy-teeny-weeny yellow-polka-dot bikini. 'One yank and they're off,' she laughed. '*Good golly, Miss Molly!*' sang Dan, swaggering casually after her in time to the thump of the piano and there was no stopping him, not in that too-tight, well-hung uniform, no, siree! There was no stopping a train that rumbled by, either, its cattle trucks – seventy people to a truck and one bucket for a lavatory – full of your friends and relations wailing and gnashing their teeth because they were going to the gas chamber.

'STOP IT, STOP IT, STOP IT!' I shouted and managed to wake myself up. But the dream still carried on, for in the distance a train rumbled by in real life.

I had climbed into Hattie's warm, friendly bed and tried to shoo the dream away but it kept creeping back into my mind like a crafty, untrustworthy fox.

Do these nightmares mean I am becoming a disturbed child? I asked in my diary. *Will this summer drive me to tranquerlisers? Or to drink?!!*

It was unlikely I'd ever take to drink, I thought, after seeing the state Dan and Dawn were in at breakfast. In fact I couldn't think of one good reason for drinking alcohol: it made one silly, rude and ill. It was tempting to shout long and loud into their wincing, cringing ears. Instead I said, in an extra-jolly voice, 'Anyone for a game of snap?'

I tried to concentrate on my play, but a laughing bird kept disturbing my thoughts. He only laughed when the wood pigeon wasn't cooing; perhaps the pigeon was cracking bird jokes. 'What did the pigeon say when he saw a pretty lady pigeon? Coo!' *'Heeheeheehee.'*

Staring at Lion's Mouth Wood for any length of time, if you didn't hold back your imagination on a tight rein all hell was likely to break loose. Not only did you have the lion's mouth itself to contend with (out of sight but far from out of mind with its gaping brambly jaws, its growling black cavernous mouth) but, like Mole in the Wild Wood, fungi on stumps resembled caricatures, holes in trees made ugly mouths; in fact the longer you looked at the wood the more you could see little narrow faces, hard-eyed, evil and sharp.

Like Mole I kept looking over my shoulder in case I saw a little evil wedge-shaped face looking out at me from a hole, or some creature rearing its head out of the undergrowth; a half-fox/half-badger, say, or perhaps a snake with a black forked tongue was at this moment silently slithering up behind.

Maybe Dawn was right when she said the countryside couldn't be trusted.

In the distance, a bird or an insect made a noise like a bicycle wheel spinning round. A foppish cock pheasant, as gaudy as a dandy in his bluey-green/gold/red coat of many colours, strutted by with his beak in the air. Then a grey squirrel, whose grandfather must have been red because he had ginger on his face and eyebrows, bounced up to within a yard of where I was sitting.

'Bugger off,' I said, and he did, his tail as long as his body and much bushier than the murdered ones.

To include in my play if poss: I wrote, and then noticed two mayflies stuck together by their bottoms. Were they Siamese twin mayflies? Or perhaps they were mating! There wasn't much to watch, though. Perhaps the woman mayfly was busy thinking of England. Or maybe they were having a rest. Did humans just lie there like that, as still as logs? If so, how very tedious. When I was in the mood I would have to ask Dawn.

In Hattie's bed that morning, I promised she could be the princess and that if Dawn *had* to be in the play I'd make her an ugly old crone who gets killed in the first scene. Or better, a silent tree. Or better still, the wardrobe mistress, and Hattie said she would rather be dressed by the Troll in *Billy Goat Gruff* than by her, thank you very much.

Wicked winter, magic, wicked gamekeeper, I wrote. *Jew heading for gas oven. Nartzi soldier. Jokes. Song on guitar (pref not rocking roll). Beautiful princess (Hattie). Handsome prince (Dan).*

A sleepy wasp landed on the page. Something – was it the devil? – inside me made me snap the notebook shut. There was a quiet scrunch. Immediately, another wasp buzzed angrily up, then another. They must have seen me kill their friend and had come to take their revenge. Say the dead wasp had a thousand friends?

I ran back to the house, expecting a cloud of avenging wasps to follow. But they didn't.

At lunch I asked Granny if it was wicked to kill a wasp. She said not really, they were dirty, unpleasant creatures.

'Yes, but that doesn't mean it's right to kill it, does it? You could say a tramp is dirty and unpleasant, but you wouldn't kill him, would you.'

Granny said it wasn't the same thing at all.

'But surely killing's killing,' I said. 'If I can kill a wasp today it might be a bird tomorrow and a rabbit the next day ...'

'And a fox the next,' said Hattie.

'And a human the next,' said Dawn, remembering the carving-knife incident.

'And then I'd be a murderer and spend the rest of my life in prison.'

'Yeah, look at the Nazis. They got it into their heads ...'

'Thank you, Dawn,' said Granny. 'If I hear one more word about Nazis round this table, or indeed anything of an unsavoury nature, I shall have to ask you to eat your meals in the kitchen. Do I make myself clear?'

'Yeah, Mrs Aitch,' said Dawn, looking down at her tomato-ketchup-smeared fish fingers.

'You see, I killed a wasp in my notebook and then lots of others appeared from nowhere and I'm sure ...'

'I wish I knew what to do about Dan,' interrupted Granny infuriatingly. 'He looks like a vagrant, shows no interest in the farm or his family ... And can anyone tell me whether he's even thought about the cricket match yet?'

'Er – I'm not sure,' I said. 'I think he's *thought* about it.'

'Ner. Course he ain't,' said Dawn, and if only I was the Red Queen I could shout 'Off with her head!' and be done with her once and for all. 'He's got better things to do. He could be the new king

197

of rock 'n' roll. Just think, Mrs Aitch, he could make millions of pounds and get his photo splashed about in the papers.'

'I dare say,' said Granny, and though she didn't say it you could tell she didn't give two hoots whether her grandson became the new king of rock 'n' roll; in her book, farm, family and cricket match came first, and I agreed with her.

'You never know, Mrs Aitch, you might even get to like the stuff he plays. You could be Britain's first swinging granny. 'Ere, that reminds me of that song,' and right there at the lunch table, she had the nerve to sing – if you could call it singing – a foul cockney song called *Fings Ain't What They Used to Be*, that included a line about grandma trying to shock us all by doing knees-up rock 'n' roll.

Granny didn't tell Dawn off for singing at table. Instead she actually smiled and said, 'It's highly unlikely you'll see me doing "knees-up rock 'n' roll", I think, dear.'

'You never know. We managed it with Rupert last night. You should have seen him – twisting with the best of 'em,' said Dawn. 'Once you get past that snotty exterior of his he's quite a sweetie, ain't he.'

'Do you mean he's a peppermint cream?' said Hattie.

'Or a Newberry Fruit?'

'You two,' said Dawn. 'You'll be the death of me.'

'You've got a few pennies on you, haven't you?' said Dawn as she, Clifford and I set off for the village to ring the American Air Force Base.

'Yes,' I said.

'If your aunt sees us in the phone box we'll say I was ringing my mum, okay?'

'I can't imagine you having a mother.'

'Why d'yer say that!'

'Because I can't imagine a mother letting her daughter come to live somewhere like this without sensible shoes and Wellingtons and an anorak. And allowing her to swear and wear all that make-up and jewellery and letting her have her hair like that . . .'

'Yeah, bit of a contrast to your mum, I bet. What's your mum like, anyway?'

We turned into the long hot road under a dull white sky. It was the kind of afternoon that would be a dead loss for kite flying or eating an ice lolly slowly.

I was just wondering what to tell Dawn about my mother, if, indeed, anything, when she screamed, 'Oh, gawd, look at that!'

She had almost stepped on a flattened hedgehog. Its bloody intestines lay smeared across the road.

'Blimey, I'm never going to be able to eat Heinz spaghetti again without thinking of that and heaving.'

'Don't be so foul.'

'Well, it is foul. The countryside, I mean. People think, "Oh, pretty romantic countryside with sweet little lambs and bunny rabbits" but beneath the surface it's downright disgusting – animals dangling from fences like Jesus bleeding Christ, guts spewing all over the place . . .'

'I suppose it does have its darker side,' I said. 'Come away, Clifford.'

'So what's your mum like then? What does she look like, for example?'

I had the choice of saying 'MYOB' or telling her. I decided to tell her because then I wouldn't have to listen to her foghorn voice.

'She's pretty, and slim, and elegant, and has sort of wavy blonde hair.'

'Natural, is it?' asked Dawn, giving me a sideways glance.

'Course it is,' I said. 'You don't think she'd do anything as common as dye her hair, do you?' Sometimes when Mummy came back from June's her hair was more golden than when she went in, but I wasn't going to tell Dawn that. 'She's very elegant, and wears smart clothes and high-heels but not too high, and plays bridge, and is Chairwoman of the Townswomen's Guild and sometimes has coffee mornings for the Conservative Party. She's quite strict about manners and washing your hands before meals and putting your toys away and things like that, like all mothers.'

'Not mine. But what's she *like*? What I'm driving at is, is she as top-drawer as, say, your dad, or did he marry beneath himself?'

I stopped while Clifford snuffled among a clump of deadnettles. Why was it that every time you almost began to like Dawn, just a teeny bit, she'd say something and you'd be back to square one? I was tempted to walk off in great disgust like Alice when the Hatter's rudeness was more than she could bear.

'How should I know? Anyway, I can't see what it's got to do with you.'

'What did your mum's dad do, for example?' said Dawn, poking my arm with her finger.

'He was a civil servant. And don't touch my arm when you talk.'

'That could mean anything, from a dustman to a prime minister. What sort of house does your other gran live in?'

Granny Parker's house in Chelmsford cowered in the shadows

of a privet hedge. The hall smelt of gloomy shoe polish. Dan called Granny Parker Nosy Parker. Although you had to mind your Ps and Qs with her and dreaded spilling something down chair covers, I still loved her very much, though not in the same way that I loved this granny.

'It has two bedrooms and quite a big garden, with a fishpond and a summerhouse.' The fishpond was more like a puddle and the summerhouse was really a garden shed, but Dawn wasn't to know that. 'She used to live in a bigger house, but she moved when Grandpa died because she said there was no point in having lots of empty, draughty rooms.'

'Reading between the lines, I reckon your dad married slightly beneath him. Your blue blood has thinned out a bit. Still, you'll be all right. It doesn't matter so much when it's the *man* who marries beneath him. You still have the name, and it's the man what counts. Take Annie Walker in *Coronation Street*. She married beneath her. Or look at my mum. She came from a respectable line of carpenters, married beneath her and look where we ended up: at the bottom of the slag heap.'

Was she likening my mother's family to *carpenters*?

'If you must know, my mother's brother is a major in the Army and her father threw the javelin in the Olympic Games. He was also president of his golf club, was a Freemason and drove an Austin Westminster even after he retired.'

'So? Civil servants get socking great pensions. Anyway, you can't judge a man by his car these days. I bet there are dukes who drive bubble cars and East End brickies who drive Rollers. By the way, I was just thinking,' and she jabbed at my arm again, 'It's funny your lot coming from Norfolk with a name like *Hill*ington. I mean, it's not as if it's over-endowed with hills, is it?'

'It might have been once.'

'What, and then bulldozers came along and flattened them? Do us a favour.'

'What's a name got to do with anything. I mean, Nancy Spain never lived in Spain, did she? Or Mandy *Rice*-Davies wasn't born in a paddy field. Or you weren't born in a potting shed – or maybe you were. You're potty enough.'

'No but us lot don't claim to go back hundreds of years like your lot do.'

'It just so happens that there's an old-as-the-hills village near King's Lynn called Hillington, so boo sucks to you.'

'All right, keep your hair on, I was only passing the time of day. Does your mum speak proper, by the way?'

'Don't be pathetic.'

'No, I was just wondering. She probably had a few elocution lessons when she met your dad.'

If it wasn't for the phone call which could lead to Aunt Lynette living happily ever after, I would have galloped back to the house and never spoken to Dawn again.

Instead, I said, 'If you must know, she's the best mother in the world. I bet *your* mother never stayed up half the night making your doll a dress and matching bonnet when you were ill, or driving fifty miles through a snow blizzard just to take you to the circus.'

'Too right she didn't, she had better things to do with her time – like scraping together a living to feed and clothe us. Anyway, it was probably a good thing your dad married your mum. If he had married another top-drawer person you'd probably be a loony due to all that interbreeding. Anyway, ignore me. I'm probably just jealous because you're more or less top-drawer and I'm definitely bottom.'

'It's the luck of the *draw*, isn't it, what drawer you're born into,' I said and then, to show I wasn't softening up, added, 'You should be thankful you don't live in India. You'd be called an Untouchable there.'

'Oh, ta very much.'

Neither of us spoke for a while, Dawn's stilettos on the tarmac spiking into the peace of the countryside. Who did she think she was, criticising Mummy like that? Don't rise to the bait. That would be my new policy from now on. Nothing Dawn could say would upset me. Whatever her next question, I would simply reply MYOB. But it wasn't a question but another of her stupid sweeping statements.

'It's funny how top-drawer people don't spend a lot of dough on themselves. Take cosmetics, for example. I bet your mum uses something posh like Helena Rubenstein or Elizabeth Arden, whereas your gran, who's got pots of money, uses cheap old Ponds. Funny, that, ain't it.'

'Actually, my mother uses Yardley,' I said.

'Same difference,' said Dawn.

'Anyway, how do you know Granny's got pots of money?'

'Stands to reason, don't it. She owns that house and the farm. She must be worth thousands.'

'She only would be if she sold them, and she never would.'

Dawn went quiet, and who knew what plot she was hatching in that wren's-egg brain of hers? Then she said: 'I reckon the reason I get on so well with your gran but probably wouldn't with your mum is because bottom-drawer people have far more in common with the top drawer than with the middle-drawer. The middle lot are so busy following rules they've made for themselves they haven't got time to enjoy themselves, whereas us and them don't give a toss. For example, if I were to say to a middle-drawer person 'Oh, so and so's up the spout or has a bun in the oven' or something, they'd look down their nose at me, whereas a top-drawer person would think I was being funny.'

I didn't think she was being funny. Did that mean I was more a middle-drawer person than a top-drawer one?

'That's why your gran and me get along so famously, whereas you and me ... it's a bit more touch and go.'

'How do you know you get along famously? How do you know my Granny isn't just being polite?'

'Because I know, that's all,' said Dawn. 'It's a well-known fact that people can't stand the class beneath them. That's why your gran can't stand your mum, and you can't stand me.'

So she thought I was only middle-drawer did she?

'You see, if your dad married a fellow aristo we'd get on like a house on fire. As it is, I reckon your mum's filled your head with middle-class prejudices. Polluted your mind a bit.'

'How do you know Granny can't stand my mother? Just for your information, she likes her very much,' I said, racking my brains for signs that Granny didn't like her. True, she tended to be a bit frosty with her, but I had assumed that was because Mummy wasn't an actual blood-relative like we were. 'Anyway, if you're at the bottom of the slag heap, who can't you stand? Animals?'

'Nig-nogs, I suppose. And Arabs and gyppos. In theory, anyway. In practice I don't mind nig-nogs, and I've never met an Arab or a gyppo.'

'Anyway, I *can* stand you. I don't like you, but I can stand you. I might even like you if your manners weren't so atrocious.'

'There you are, you see, manners. A classic middle-class word, that. I know my manners are atrocious, but at least I'm honest. I mean, say I was visiting someone and they asked me whether I was warm enough and I was bleeding freezing, I'd say I'm bleeding freezing, and they would go and turn the gas up. Whereas a middle-drawer person would say they were fine, even if their teeth were rattling.'

'Yes, but they'd only say that to spare the other person's feelings. It might upset them to think their house wasn't warm.'

'Yeah, but it would upset me far more if I ended up with flu or something.'

Clifford kept stopping to sniff in the hedge. We were barely past Jack's cottage. At this rate I would be spending the rest of my life walking along a flat road making silly conversation with Dawn. 'Hurry up, Clifford,' I said.

'By the way, you know at dinner last night,' said Dawn. 'I wouldn't have told them about the crossbar thing, honest I wouldn't.'

'Yes you would,' I said. 'If I hadn't stopped you you would.'

'Only because I was sozzled. I wouldn't have done normally. Honest. I may be a lot of things, but I'm not a ... betrayer. I can tell you ain't, neither. If I told you something I know it'd go no further. I knew, as soon as I first clapped eyes on you, that we'd be whatsit – kindred spirits.'

'It's kind*led* spirits, isn't it?' I said, and even though she was so revolting, for some strange reason I felt quite pleased.

'I don't think we should have any secrets from each other,' said Dawn. 'I think we should be whatsits – confidantes. By the way, what's this I hear about your parents' marriage being on the rocks? That's why they've gone on holiday without you lot I suppose, to try and patch things up.'

Way ahead I could see the sawn-off-shotgun church spire, and smoke drifting from someone's bonfire. The smoke was positioned in such a way that it looked as though the church were on fire. Please Snuff Mull or God, whoever's listening, help me to rise above this dreadful woman.

'I've never heard such rot in my whole life.'

Dawn shrugged. 'Makes no difference to me.'

'Who told you?'

'A dickybird.'

'*Who told you?*'

'No one as such. I've just picked up hints along the way. I assumed you'd know, but I suppose if you weren't told about rabbits going into pies ... Just think, you'll get double the presents at Christmas.'

My blood boiled like a fierce witch's cauldron. 'Actually, just for your information, my parents love each other very dearly.'

And they did. Sometimes you found them with their arms round each other in the kitchen, and Daddy often bought Mummy flowers with notes attached with 'All my love' written on. And you'd never put *all* if you didn't mean it, would you.

'They argue sometimes but so do all couples. That's part and parcel of being married.'

'Maybe I shouldn't have said nothing,' said Dawn. 'I didn't think.'

'That's your problem in a nutshell.'

'They've done the right thing getting away. As long as your mum whispers sweet nothings to him across a candle-lit dinner table and does the business now and again ... Did she take any sexy nighties with her, do you know?'

She is only a servant, I must keep telling myself, and if it hadn't been for Granny's kindness she'd still be living at the bottom of the slag heap where she belongs.

' "If everybody minded their own business," the duchess said, in a hoarse growl, "the world would go round a deal faster than it does." '

'What the flaming heck are you on about now?'

'Just quoting from the book you gave me. Perhaps it would do you good to read it. You might learn a thing or two. And I don't want you to say another word about my parents. You don't even know them.'

'All right, all right, keep your hair on. Anyone would think someone had died the way you're carrying on. Divorce is no big deal these days, you know. In fact it's quite a with-it thing to do.'

'It may not be a big deal in the circles in which *you* move ...'

'Look, I'm sorry,' Dawn said. 'I talk a load of codswallop some-times. And now I'm going to tell you a secret about my family. Me dad isn't really me dad. Me real dad's a Yank.'

'So?' I said. As far as Dawn was concerned, I had turned into a shock absorber. If she'd said her father was Prince Philip or King Kong or that she was going to blow up the world or take off her clothes in White Lion Street I'd have said 'So?'

'Me other dad was away at the war and Mum said it was love at first sight. She didn't give in straight away, mind. He was tall and dark with kind brown eyes and ever such broad shoulders and a hairy chest. He was always bringing her nylons and Hershey Bars. He made her feel really special, like a *lady*. He called her Ma'am to begin with, and later Honey. His nickname was Wilbur and he came from Tennessee where Elvis comes from. It was the only time she ever knew real happiness, and cried her eyes out when he went back to America. She says even now, after all these years, she still lives in hope that he'll walk through the front door.'

'Does she love you more than your brothers and sisters because he's your father?'

'Ner, not really. I think she's forgotten, it was so long ago.'

'Does your other father know about him?'

'Blimey, no.'

'But he must suspect because you must look different to the others.'

'Luckily, I take after me mum. He came back soon after Wilbur left, so when I came along nine months later I could have been his.'

'I feel sorry for your father,' I said. 'Being deceived like that.'

'You wouldn't if you met him.'

At last, ahead of us was the phone box.

'If Aunt Lynette marries a Yank, the baby might look like you,' I said. 'How *foul* for Aunt Lynette.'

'Ooh, you rotten little tinker!'

The three of us crowded into the phone box. 'Blimey, why do these things always stink of piss? Now, what shall we look it up under?' she said, flicking through the phone book. 'There isn't a dicky bird under America. What else could it be? Not Yank, surely?'

'Try United States.'

'Yeah, here we are. United States Air Force. Shall I do it or will you?'

'I'd better. They might be put off by your cockney accent.'

'Don't be daft. Yanks can't tell a Geordie from a Brummie. We're all Brits as far as they're concerned. Have you got the money ready?'

She dialled, then handed me the phone.

'I don't know what to say.'

'You'll think of something when they answer.'

'They have.'

'Go on, then, press button A. Blimey anyone would think you hadn't used a public phone before.

The coins went straight through. We tried again, this time successfully. But as soon as I heard the deep male American voice that sounded like Uncle Sandy or President Kennedy or James Cagney my mouth was seized by shyness and I thrust the receiver at Dawn.

'Er – hello? Is that, er, the Yank – er, American Air Base?' she said in the kind of voice one used for speaking to deaf foreigners.

'Ah. Yeah, well, what I was wondering was, you see, I have an aunt – er cousin, in actual fact – who's a fantastic painter, and she's a bit short of work at the moment – not because she's no good, mind, but because er, most of her clients are on holiday,' and she pulled a face at me. 'So what I was wondering was, do you need anything painted at the Air Base sort of thing?'

There was a pause while the man at the other end spoke. She put her hand over the mouthpiece and hissed, 'The prat thinks I mean painter, you know, as in decorator.'

'Shhh, he'll hear.'

'Er, no, er, Sir. I don't mean that sort of painter, ha, ha. Yes, I'm sure you do have your own. No, she's an *artiste*, you know, portrait paintings and scenery ...'

'Landscapes,' I hissed.

'Yeah, landscapes and stuff like that. One of her specialities is dogs, but I don't expect you have many at your air base, do you, Sir, ha, ha! Anyway, I'm sure she's just as good at aeroplanes and that, and at least they won't pee on the carpet, ha, ha!'

'*Dawn!*'

'But what she's best at is *faces* – men's faces, to be precise. So I was just wondering if your colonel – or brigadier, or lieutenant or admirable or whoever it is you have there, would like his portrait done or something. She can make the back end of a bus type of face look handsome, honest ... Yeah, but with respect, Sir, photographs are hardly art, are they?' and she winked at me.

This time there was a long pause, which gave me the breathing space I needed to concentrate on how much my parents loved each other. But try as I might, vague unpleasant memories kept floating to the surface of my mind, like a lavatory that doesn't flush properly.

'Are you suggesting, sir, that my cousin's a *Russian spy*? For your information, she's a member of one of the most respectable families of the English aristocracy. Yeah, course I've heard of Philby and Maclean and Burgess. Yeah, and Vassall. Look, my cousin's just a humble artist – ever such a *pretty* humble artist, looking for work. Perhaps I could leave her address with you, and you could spread the word about in case one of your mates – er, comrades – er, colleagues or whatever they are would like a portrait painted.' She gave Aunt Lynette's name, emphasising the word 'Miss', and address and Granny's phone number. There was another pause and then she said, 'I beg your pardon! No, I don't have any, as it happens. It's my cousin who has. Well, ta very much then. Ta-ta.'

She crashed down the receiver and said, 'What a sauce! He wanted to come and see *my* etchings. Mind you, I had half a mind to say yes. He sounded a dead ringer for Humphrey Bogart.'

'Honestly, Dawn.'

(*What does it take to get Dawn's bra off? One Yank – without even seeing what he looks like first!!!*)

We stepped out into the fresh air, and my breathing apparatus returned to normal.

'How come you got on to spies?'

'He said it would be a breach of security – he was laughing, though. Mind you, for all we know she could be a Commie. From what I've read, that Committee of 100 is as far Left as they come.

That would be a laugh, wouldn't it. A Commie artist painting all their secret weapons, That would be funner than a vegetarian married to a butcher. I wonder if she'll get anyone turning up on her doorstep. A nice, virile forty-year-old officer whose father owns an oil well in Texas. That would do her a treat.'

'And if that doesn't happen, one of their planes will be flying too low and crash into a tree that Aunt Lynette just happens to be painting at the time. She'll drag the tall, dark, handsome pilot away in the nick of time before the plane bursts into flames, and will nurse him better. But the accident has left him with an ugly scar, so he's not attractive to any woman apart from her. She has saved his life, so what else can he do but fall in love with her and marry her? And because the accident didn't harm his wedding tackle, nine months later they'll have a baby and live happily ever after. There you are.'

'Ah. Very romantic. And if that doesn't happen, the Yanks are bound to be doing an air display or something at the Shotestead Show. If we get them all into the beer tent afterwards and shove your aunt in the middle ...'

'Except after a drink or two she'll probably tell them to bugger off back to America.'

'That's true,' said Dawn, and sighed. 'Maybe we're barking up the wrong tree with Yanks. Surely you can think of some country squire whose wife's just pegged it?'

'Well, I can't. Anyway, I don't think she likes country squires.'

'That's the trouble ain't it? She doesn't fit into a category, your aunt, which is probably why she never found a hubby. That's the price you have to pay for standing out in the crowd, for having the courage of your convictions. I suppose she wouldn't want to marry a ginger-haired, virile butcher?'

'He's *yours*,' I said. 'I think he's scrummy. Just how I'd want my husband to be. You're frightfully lucky. Just think, you could be engaged to someone unemployed with a hunchback and a wooden leg who leaves his teeth in a jar at night.'

'Yeah, well,' she said and sighed. Then she nudged me, and if she did it once more, or jabbed at me with her finger, I would smash in her skull with the stone I was kicking. 'Shall I let you into a secret? A really top secret, mind.'

'No thanks,' I said. 'I've heard enough secrets for one day.'

'I've fallen in love,' she said. 'Head over heels smack bang wallop. Like me mum and Wilbur. It's the Real Thing.'

'That's not surprising,' I said like a drowning girl grasping at straws. 'You are engaged, after all.'

'Ah, but it's not Albert I'm in love with.'

The thistle inside my heart stabbed once, twice, three times, and a small trickle of sweat rolled down the small of my back, making up for my mouth, which was turning as dry as a desert.

'And when I say in love, I don't mean a luke-warm, don't care either way sort of love like most relationships between men and women. I mean a burning, aching, all-consuming passion, the kind that Barbara Cartland writes about and sounds soppy until you experience it for yourself. And I'll tell you this for nothing. It's like being high on drugs or something.'

I kicked the stone. If it went past Clifford and as far as the telegraph pole my parents loved each other and Dawn didn't love Dan. It went sharply off at right angles and landed in a bed of nettles.

'Have you noticed my eyes sparkling more than usual?'

'No.' *They look as foul and black and piggy as always.*

When could they be alone together? While we were at church? In the evenings when Hattie and I were in bed and Granny was listening to Mozart? Did Dan really go to his pop-group practices? Did his pop group even exist?

'I feel so alive – like a new person. So full of energy ...' and she did a little dance in the middle of the road. 'You feel like laughing and crying at everything you see. Take that dead bird,' and she pointed to a sparrow at the side of the road. 'I could burst into tears over that if I let myself. That's what love does. Enhances everything.'

'Can I be a beautiful princess whisked off my feet by an 'ansome prince ...?'

'It's funny, everything looks beautiful. Even that old bit of cow parsley looks like white diamonds, know what I mean?'

'No, I don't actually,' I said. Perhaps she thought Dan would inherit the farm when Granny died so she was just pretending to be in love with him in order to get her evil mitts on the money. And Granny already suspected. Hence the detective set.

'No I suppose you wouldn't. But then you're not in love, are you.'

'How do you know?' I said, thinking of Mr Richards. 'Does *he* love *you*?'

'Oh, yeah. He's as smitten as I am. Mind you, they say love's blind.'

Then it couldn't possibly be Dan – could it?

An erect prick has no conscience ...

'How long have you known him?' I asked, my tongue as parched as an unhappy cactus.

'Oh, quite a while now. But it's only recently, er, begun to flower.'

Since she started working here. In that case, please let it be Brian Pike.

'Has he got a black beard, by any chance?'

'Not saying.'

Or perhaps it was the American in the pink car. If only I had been there to hear the conversation instead of cycling off in high dudgeon. Could he have been saying 'See you tonight, honey, same time same place'?

'Well, does he drive a large car?'

'Ah-ha.'

'Well, do I know him?'

'Not telling.'

'Why not? I'd never tell a soul. I absolutely promise, cross my heart and hope to die. I'm the best person in the world to tell secrets to.'

'Yeah, but is your subconscious? You might say his name in your sleep, and Hattie would hear. I heard you yelling "Stop it" through the floorboards. It gave me quite a turn. I thought you were being raped.'

'Yes, but even if I shouted out his name – which I wouldn't because I have more important things to dream about – it wouldn't mean anything. Not without "Dawn loves" in front of it, but I wouldn't because one doesn't talk in sentences in one's sleep.'

'Well, I wouldn't want to take the risk.'

'I'll tell you what,' I said. 'I'll tell you who I'm in love with if you tell me who you are.'

She snorted, like Snap Dragon. 'You're far too young to be in love – really in love, I mean. You're at the hero-worshipping stage, and I bet you ten bob it's a teacher. After him you'll have a crush on an older girl, then it'll be a pop star, and then it'll be boys. but when you fall in love, *really* in love, can happen at any age – at seventeen or seventy.'

Why does she always think she knows best?

'I had no intention of telling you anyway.'

My mouth was dying from lack of moisture. I put my hands in my shorts pockets to look casual and said, 'All right, smarty pants, tell me this much. Is it my brother?'

Dawn burst out laughing, her foulest, most hen-like witchy cackle, that went on for far too long considering it was far from a laughing matter. And anyway, what was she finding so funny? The very idea of being in love with Dan? Or because she was embarrassed I'd hit on the truth and was just filling in time while she worked out what to say?

'What's so funny?' I said crossly and close to tears.

'It's just that . . . Whatever gave you that idea?'

'Well, he's handsome,' I said.

'Oh, I'll grant you he's a looker, but he's just a kid. I go for the slightly more mature type who's been around a bit.'

Moisture began to venture into my mouth.

'Anyway, what makes you think he'd be interested in a common little slut like me? He'll end up with some Blue Stocking or Rupert's sister to carry on the Hillington line.'

'He's going through a funny phase.'

'Yeah, but that's because of his pop group, not because he's in love. When would he find the time, for God's sake?'

'I suppose so.'

'So has that set your mind at rest?'

If I could lie with such ease about Clifford burying his bone, so could Dawn lie to me about Dan being too young.

'No. Not unless you tell me who it is.'

'Well, I won't. I might one day, but not now.'

'Does Albert know?'

'Gawd no. I'm in a bit of a two and eight about it, actually. You see, it's not all plain sailing with this bloke by any means. We can't just go off hand in hand into the sunset like in the movies sort of thing.'

'Why not? Is he already married?'

'Maybe. Something like that.'

'So you don't want to break off your engagement with Albert until you're sure this man will marry you.'

'Kind of. It's what's known as not putting all your eggs in one basket . . . Or you may end up with egg all over your face.' And she laughed at her unfunny joke.

'What's to stop me from saying to you, "If you don't tell me who your lover is I'll tell Albert"?'

'Because I trust you.'

'Why? I don't trust you.'

'Oh, you will, sooner or later.'

'Bet I won't. I feel really sorry for Albert. He could be spending this time finding another girl to marry. It's not fair on him.'

'Who said life was fair?' said Dawn and on that note we walked in silence, and I pondered all these things in my heart but I didn't come to any conclusions.

*   *   *

210

Clifford was growling behind the hedge. Whatever he had found must have been very out of the ordinary because his growl sounded more like a lion's or a tiger's than a dog's.

'What the bleeding hell's up with him?' Dawn said, climbing the hedge to have a look. I followed. 'Oh, my gawd,' she said. 'Clifford, come away. No, Sarah, you're not allowed to look.' And she jumped down, roughly pushed me backwards into the road and gripped my shoulder.

'Not *allowed*? Who says? I'll look if I want. You can't boss me about.'

'Yes, I can. I'm in charge of you and I'm responsible for your well-being, so your gran says. What I say counts.' And she gripped my shoulders harder.

'It does, does it?'

'Yeah, it does.'

'If you really cared about my well-being you wouldn't poison my mind with lies about my parents divorcing and your stupid love affair,' I said through gritted teeth. 'I bet it's just an animal caught in a trap and I've seen hundreds already. You have no right to stop me, you foul, ignorant cow. *Let me see*.'

'Over my dead body,' she sneered.

We stood scowling at one another in the middle of the road, and for a few moments I allowed her the pleasure of digging her filthy pink nails into my shoulders.

The biggest laugh of all was she thought I was scowling because I wanted to see what was behind the hedge. In actual fact, I was scowling because I had decided to kill her.

'You see, ladies and gentlemen of the Jury,' I would say in the packed courtroom, wearing my tartan dress with the white collar and cuffs while Daddy, my lawyer, circulated the cinema car-park photograph with a circle drawn round the deceased so they could see for themselves what type of a woman she was, 'she had been taunting me all afternoon ... Of course I never meant to kill her. I, who only that very morning had killed a wasp and then worried – as my grandmother will testify – that I was a murderer ... All I wanted to do was get her out of my way so that I could see what was behind the hedge ...'

I wriggled my shoulders free of her grip and kicked her shin so hard she reeled backwards but didn't fall. I grabbed her and punched her stomach three times with my knotted rock-hard fist.

''Ere, bloody hell. Steady on. Someone's going to get hurt,' she gasped, making a feeble attempt to grab my wrists but they were

211

far too powerful and strong for her bird-like grasp.

'Yeah. You,' I said through snarling sabre teeth and bit her arm so hard I drew blood.

All my anger turned itself into strength which knew no bounds as I kicked and punched and pinched, and even though she was bigger than me she didn't stand a chance with her namby-pamby weedy lily-white ill-fed body, poisoned on a diet of chips and crisps and tomato ketchup and salad cream and pink sausages and pickles and chocolates and fags and alcohol, she from the bottom of the slag heap, the lowest of the low, scrounger of the state, cowardy-cowardy custard, no-good dirty rascal, versus me superior in every way, my body nourished by first-class protein and fresh vegetables and cod liver oil and malt, healthy and strong and in my prime, me with my proud and noble ancestry, me who was the fastest in the school at climbing to the top of the gym rope, me who could cycle up the steepest hill or run a mile and barely be out of breath, me who was rounders captain two years running and could survive on the back of a bolting pony, me who was as strong as an ox and brave as a lion and would gladly die for my country.

For a moment or two we tussled. She pulled my hair hard and I pulled hers harder and then, mustering together all my hatred, I got her on the tarmac and sat on her stomach, my full weight so that she couldn't breathe, my legs gripping her arms which were pinned to her side. And though she kicked and struggled and twisted she was no match for me.

'Bloody hell,' she managed to gasp, her dying words and most appropriate ones considering that was where she was going to end up.

I put my hands round her throat and pressed. I'd killed once today. Why not twice?

'*I put my hands round her throat only to frighten her, ladies and gentlemen. It never entered my head I could kill her ...*'

Except ... a wasp and a human weren't the same, as Granny had said. With a wasp you just crunched shut the page of a notebook and bingo. With a human it took longer and disgusting things might happen. Would her tongue stick out and turn black? Would her bowels lose control? Would blood run from her nose? Would her eyes pop out? Those eyes, black stuff smudged everywhere but no tears, staring at me, begging for mercy. My grip tightened and she gagged. How long did it take for someone to be throttled? A minute? An hour? Say I changed my mind half-way through and it was too late? What would Mr Richards's reaction be? He had been in the RAF. He must have killed people. He would understand. He had told us to be passionate and what could be more passionate than killing someone? Except, in a war you were allowed to kill. This was peace.

While I tustled with my conscience, she made a sound as though she was trying to gargle. I released my grip, sprang to my feet and climbed up the hedge.

It was a fox cub caught in a snare. It was just alive. It had been gnawing through its leg to set itself free, and had almost succeeded. There was blood everywhere. It raised its head to look at me with blue eyes begging for mercy. Unlike Dawn's, they were kind and trusting.

Leaving Clifford growling and his hackles raised and Dawn groaning and her skirt raised, her head in her hands and both shoes lying higgledy-piggledy in the middle of the road, I ran, like the wind, like Black Beauty, Champion and Aslan combined, all the way to Brian Pike's without stopping once. A useful chemical, adrenalin, Miss Crowe had once said, for when being chased by a bull. Never mind one bull, I had enough pumping inside me to be chased by a whole herd.

Brian Pike was chopping wood.

'A fox has been caught in a snare in Five Acres,' I gasped, bending over to ease my stitch. 'Get your gun,' and even though it was a crisis, even though my equilibrium was all at sixes and sevens, I still managed to think how hilarious it would have been if his name was Annie.

'Oh dear, oh dear. Sorry if it upset you,' he said, snatching up his deerstalker and gun, whistling to the Yellow Dog and running after me down the lane.

'Say sorry to the fox, not me, he's in a hell of a mess,' I said. 'He's been trying to chew his leg off.'

We met Dawn along Cow Parsley Lane. She held her shoes in one hand and Clifford on his lead in the other. She definitely looked the worse for wear. Her hair was all over the place, the bruise on her shin was coming up a treat, the teeth marks showed on her arm and so did the red marks round her neck. She was limping slightly but not crying. She was smoking a cigarette, probably to steady her nerves.

I watched to see whether she pouted or fluttered her eyelashes at Brian Pike, but she was probably feeling too shocked and anyway, people behave in unpredictable ways when they're in love.

The Yellow Dog became very excited as he sniffed Clifford for fox. Perhaps his eyesight was poor and he thought Clifford *was* a fox. Clifford just stood patiently, like an elderly carpet being hoovered.

'My, my,' said Brian Pike. 'I thought it was a fox in trouble, not you. Are you all right, pet?'

'Just get your arse down to that field at the double, you fucking sadist,' she said and was this the way one normally spoke to one's true love? Was 'f...ing' some sort of signal?

Dawn, Clifford and I walked in silence. Without the clacking shoes, it really was silence. I only felt a small twinge of guilt, certainly not enough to warrant saying sorry. I felt more embarrassed than anything and wished the incident could be dead, buried and forgotten about.

Eventually Dawn took a deep breath of cigarette and said, 'Cor blimey, I'm going to be covered in bruises. Let's hope you haven't disfigured me for life, then I'll never win that beauty contest and become rich and famous.'

'What beauty contest?' I said flatly.

'You know. The one they're having this year at the Shotestead Show.'

I looked at her. It was the saddest thing I'd ever heard, sadder than a short man wanting to be a policeman or a deaf woman wanting to be a choir mistress or Snap Dragon being entered for the Horse of the Year Show.

There was another long pause. 'I really thought you was going to kill me.'

'I was,' I said.

'Why didn't you then?'

'I didn't fancy going to prison.'

'Oh, ta very much.'

Fancy her not being livid. If someone had tried to kill me I'd never speak to them again. Perhaps she was seeing me in a new light and would now start treating me with the respect I deserved. Perhaps she had at last got it into her fat head that I wasn't someone to be trifled with.

'I'll have to watch my Ps and Qs with you from now on, yeah?' she said. 'Blimey, I don't fancy going through that little lot again. Where do you get your strength from? You're like a frigging ox,' and she fingered her throat.

'You won't have to go through that again so long as you promise not to have a love affair with my brother,' I said flatly. 'Or ever mention my parents getting a divorce. Or be rude about my mother.'

'Okay, promise,' said Dawn. 'Cross my heart and hope to die. Anyway, I don't know what you're getting your knickers in such a

214

twist for about your brother. I already told you it ain't him. He ain't my type.'

'And as long as you leave my family alone so we can get on with enjoying the summer in peace. And so long as you remember that you are an employee, not a member, of the Hillington family.'

'All right, all right,' she said. 'I suppose it was too much to hope that we should get along. We come from different worlds, you and me. It's funny, I was beginning to think you quite liked me, but after this afternoon I can see you hate my flaming guts.' And she burst into tears, not quiet ladylike ones but great howling sobs and gasping for breath like a sealion. A frenzy of emotions started fighting like blizzards in my head, and I was so taken aback that she cared how I felt about her that I burst into tears, too.

For a while we stood in the road with our arms round each other sobbing our hearts out, and how astonishing human nature is; that one minute you could be killing someone and the next have your arms round them in a loving sort of way.

'I *do* like you,' I said, borrowing her tissue to blow my nose. 'It's just that we're, er, a very private family, and suddenly to have a stranger in our midst takes some getting used to, that's all. I mean, we loved Mrs B, but she didn't try to be one of the family . . .'

'The thing is,' she said snatching back the tissue and blowing her nose so loudly it sounded as though it were in danger of coming away in her hands. 'I know I'm a nosy old cow, but my family are a load of shits compared with yours. I want to feel a part of you lot. You're like the first proper family I've ever had. I'll try though, honest I will. 'Ere, you and I would make a great double act, yeah? You with your muscle power and me with my big mouth. We're a right old pair, aren't we,' and I said yes, I supposed we were.

In the distance we heard the gun go off. 'One more bleeder put out of its misery,' she said, sounding almost envious, and blew her nose again. 'By the way *Compact*'s on tonight, and Dick Van Dyke, if you fancy coming up to watch them.'

'Oh, thanks,' I said. *I don't understand her at all*, I would write later. *How can she be being killed by someone one minute and inviting her murderer to watch television in her room the next? Perhaps in the world she comes from violence is the only language she understands and respects.*

Granny and Hattie wanted to know what on earth we'd been up to and Granny said, 'Good gracious, you haven't been attacked, have you?'

Dawn, to my amazement, and perhaps she'd been telling the truth when she had said she wouldn't betray me, just said we'd had

215

a slight disagreement and no harm done, and she for one was off to have a bath.

'Whatever really happened?' said Hattie when we were alone. 'That bite on her arm. It wasn't *you*, was it?'

'Er, yes,' I said, suddenly feeling terribly ashamed.

'Wow,' said Hattie. 'That's not like you. You're normally so docile.'

'Not any more,' I said. 'This summer has changed me.'

'First Dan and now you. I suppose I'll be next. By the way, I hope you didn't swallow any of her blood, or you'll come up in pus-riddled boils. She must have said something really awful to make you do that.'

'She did quite,' I said. 'I'll tell you when I'm in the mood.'

I went up to the bedroom to write my diary while the incident was still fresh in my mind, but fell fast asleep till supper.

All in all, killing people was very tiring work.

CHAPTER SEVENTEEN

I began to watch Dan and Dawn like a keen-eyed hawk who had just passed a detective's exam with flying colours. I sat in strategic places around the house and garden pretending to read a book but keeping a discreet, sun-glassed eye on the comings and goings. The night might have a thousand eyes but I had a thousand ears as I lay in bed listening for the quietest floorboard creak, the faintest whisper. I counted how often they looked at each other at meal times, whether either went red or smoothed down their hair or lit a cigarette to steady their nerves when the other walked into the room, how often they laughed at each other's jokes, whether they both looked tired at breakfast. I became expert at dropping my table napkin to see whether their knees were touching under the table, and several times I left them alone together and then pretended I'd forgotten something and burst in with my camera like an American sleuth. And not once did I discover anything even remotely suspicious. Even so, I had to be one hundred per cent sure.

'When do you see your lover exactly?' I asked Dawn like a Fleet Street reporter as she scrubbed (or rather dabbed at) the scullery floor. She said not often enough for her liking, and I was keeping mum about it, wasn't I, and I said what did she take me for?

The bite didn't look like a row of teeth any more, more a pink tongue. The bruise on her shin had turned yellow. And the surprising thing was she hadn't moaned at all (nor had Granny, though the old Granny would have done: she would have taken me to one side and told me in no uncertain terms to start behaving in a civilised fashion). As I told Mr Richards, since the 'incident' Dawn seemed to be seeing me in a new light and had started treating me with a shade more respect, even asking my opinion on things. Clearly there were advantages in attempting to murder someone, and it was around this time that my bubbling, boiling hatred for her subsided into a fast and not quite so furious simmer.

'You know your play? I was only kidding about being the princess, but I'd love to be in it. I've never been in one before.'

Never been in a play? Whatever sort of deprived childhood must she have had?

'All right,' I said. However indignant Hattie would be, I could hardly say no with her body covered in bruises of my doing. 'It might have to be a minor part, though. And you have to do – and wear – exactly as I say as I'm the director. For example, you won't be allowed to wear scent in case it puts the other actors off . . . the scent.'

'Okay,' she said. 'By the way, talking of pongs have you noticed how the bathroom pongs after Dan's been in there? He doesn't eat curries on the quiet, does he? It's a right turn-off when you go in there of a morning.'

There were many things I could have said to this remark. I could have said, 'It's a great privilege for someone like you to share a bathroom with people like us. You're lucky you don't have to use an earth closet in the garden and a tin bath in front of the fire, which is all you deserve.' But I didn't, and my whole body, never mind my face, felt like smiling. Because if you are truly, passionately in love with someone, you wouldn't care – notice, even – something as mundane as smells. If Mr Richards smelt like a guinea-pig cage that hadn't been cleaned out for a year, I wouldn't turn a hair.

So all I said was, 'You're a good one to talk. We have to put up with your vile scent day after day, and not just in the bathroom but all over the house.'

'Yeah, but scent's one of society's acceptable smells, sort of thing,' and I said, 'That shows how little society knows. I suppose I should just be thankful you didn't bring the subject of Dan and the bathroom up at lunch.'

'I probably will bring it up at lunch,' she said. 'It's smoked haddock and it always makes me heave!'

Dan was in the courtyard lying down and thinking of Austin of England.

'It's Cassius Clay in drag,' he said, looking at me upside-down. 'What was it all about, anyway?'

'Oh, dead foxes and divorces and class and stuff. In other words Dawn being her usual foul, vile self.'

'Weren't you overdoing it a bit, Sausage? It all sounds a bit vicious to me.'

'It was you who said about nature being red in tooth and claw and I was just behaving naturally. What are you doing down there?'

'Oh, just putting a spanner in the works.'

'How's your pop group coming along, by the way?'

'All right. We had to play in front of three members of the Show Committee yesterday. Rupert was one of them.'

'The old boy network, eh? I'd have thought Rupert had gone right off you.'

'Ah, that's how little you know. He thought I was the bee's knees once he got going with the dancing. That's what rock 'n' roll does, you see – wins friends and influences people. We had to tone down the act a bit but fingers crossed, if they persuade the others to vote for us we'll be playing at the Show dance.'

'Oh, Dan, how wizard.'

'It'll be even more wizard if we get star billing.'

'I bet you will. And being a Hillington must stand you in good stead.'

'Bloody well hope it won't. We'll get there by talent alone. I don't want people to know I'm a blasted Hillington. My stage name is Pete O'Flame.'

'What's wrong with Dan Hillington?'

'Too wet blanket. I wanted something a bit raunchier.'

'Talking of raunchy, I wish you hadn't been so rude to Rupert the other night. He's bound to have told Fiona and she'll go right off you.'

'Who cares? She's hardly my type.'

'I thought she was. She's quite *au naturel,* isn't she. The thing is you've been behaving a bit, er, oddly recently, and I was wondering ... you aren't by any chance in love or anything?'

Dan crawled out from under Austin, his face covered in rust speckles. When he stood up his hair fell in his eyes like a sheepdog's. Maybe he was planning to grow it so long he could sit on it like Rosie Alston, and get in *The Guinness Book of Records* for the man with the longest, wildest hair.

'Why? Does it show?' he said, opening the bonnet and laughing nervously.

'Dawn is,' I said, watching carefully.

'I should hope she is. She is engaged to the bloke, after all,' and he hid his face in the engine.

I wasn't fooled that easily.

'No, not with Albert. With someone else. Oh crikey. I promised I wouldn't tell anyone. But you're not anyone, are you. Promise you won't tell?'

Dan promised.

'She won't tell me who it is, and I know it's stupid but for a nasty moment I thought it might be you.'

'*Me?*' And he reared up his head and crashed it against the bonnet. 'What on earth gave you that idea?'

Did he sound just a shade *too* surprised? I watched to see whether his oily hands were shaking, the way people's hands are meant to when they think of the person they love. They didn't appear to be.

'That's just what she said when I suggested it might be you.'

'Yeah? What else did she say?'

'That you were just a kid and she preferred more mature men,' I said. I didn't mention she thought he was a 'looker'. 'She also said what on earth would you see in a common slut like her.'

'Exactly. I think she's a good laugh, but that's as far as it goes. You don't really think she's my cup of tea, do you?'

'Well, you've gone so odd and political lately. And you're a man in your prime. You're about due for a love affair. And you seem to get on very well with her.'

'That's because I try harder than certain people round here,' he said. 'Anyway, when the hell would I find the time to have a love affair? I'm trying to get a pop group off the ground, remember.'

'I bet the Beatles find time to have love affairs.'

'Yeah, but they're established.'

'Who do you think it could be then?'

'What?'

'Dawn's lover.'

'Haven't the foggiest.'

'I've got a short list of three: Brian Pike, a Yank in a big pink car and Mr English, because married men can't be ruled out. Which do you think?'

'Frankly, I couldn't care less.'

'No, but if you had to put money on it.'

'Look, Sausage, I have better things to think about. Like my own problems in that direction.'

My ears pricked up like the Yellow Dog's. 'What? Who?'

'Oh, someone I met at a school dance,' and it may have been because he was bending over, but he had definitely turned a little pink.

'What's her name?'

'Don't laugh. Hilary Wentworth-Smith.'

What a foul name, I thought but wouldn't dream of saying, the way I wouldn't dream of saying to Dawn that Albert's eyes were the colour of pond water. I would have liked to have asked him whether he'd had his wicked way with her but I couldn't quite find the courage, even though he was my brother. Instead, I said, 'Do you love her very much?'

Dan said he had to confess, he was quite smitten. 'The maddening

220

thing is, she promised she'd write and she hasn't, which probably explains why I'm a bit upsy-downsy at the moment.'

'Oh, Dan, I'm sure she will. Perhaps her letter got lost in the post. Or perhaps she's sent it to Herts. Or perhaps she's waiting for you to write. It's usually the boy – er, man – who makes the first move, isn't it?'

'Usually, but she said she'd write first. Anyway, it's the keener party who's meant to hang back. And in this case, that's definitely me.'

'Are you sure it's you? I bet you're far more handsome than she is pretty.' (How could she be that pretty with a name like Hilary Wentworth-Smith?)

'No, she's quite a stunner, actually. Definitely my type.'

'Does she wear black eye stuff and pink lipstick and things like that?' I asked casually.

'God no. I told you. I go for the *au naturel* type.'

I felt like whooping like a Red Indian on his birthday. Instead I thought of Snuff Mull and said, 'I bet you that within a week you'll get a letter from her. By the way, there isn't anyone in your pop group who would make a suitable husband for Aunt Lynette, I suppose?'

Dan laughed. 'Unless she's into stroppy long-haired types then the answer's no. We are being a little matchmaker today, aren't we.'

I decided to get all the unpleasantness out into the open while the going was good. I took a deep breath and said, 'Talking of matchmaking, have you heard anything about Mummy and Daddy getting a divorce?'

Dan looked genuinely surprised – or as genuine as anything was round here, anyway. 'Where on earth did you get that idea?'

'Dawn, of course. Did you tell her?'

'It's the first I've heard of it. They wouldn't have gone on a Second Honeymoon if that was the case, would they.'

I explained that it could be a last-ditch attempt to settle their differences.

'Come to think of it, they do have a hell of a lot of rows,' he said. 'Oh well, if that's what they want to do, good luck to them. Better happy and apart than miserable and together I guess.'

'It's all right for you, you're grown up,' I said. 'But what about Hattie and me? We could end up taking life seriously like Anne Pond. We're at a very impressionable age, you know. We need to have a stable background or we'll grow up to be delinquents and vandalise telephone boxes and be taken into care by the Council

221

and marry unsuitable men, that is if we don't end up as good-time girls or unmarried mothers living on the top floor of a skyscraper full of dripping washing and screaming babies, and being addicted to tranquillisers or jumping out of the window because we can't cope.'

For some infuriating reason, Dan found this very funny. But one had to make allowances for him. He was, after all, going through a difficult phase, and love, as everyone knows, can do very odd things to a person.

Granny and Hattie were in Grandpa's granite bedroom sorting through an old trunk. Granny said she ought to do it while she was still fit and able. She held up each garment in turn – Grandpa's old ties and shooting socks, Aunt Daphne's and Aunt Lynette's school uniforms and boaters, her own pre-war ball gowns – and Hattie and I gave our verdict on whether they were dressing-up-box worthy. Needless to say Dawn just happened to be hoovering on the landing outside and had to poke her nose in, and Granny gave her a whole heap of things that would have kept ten starving children fed for a year if they had been given to Oxfam.

At the bottom of the trunk, among dull-covered books and music sheets, was a pre-World-War-One photograph album whose spine creaked like a mystery door when you opened it.

'Ooh, mind if I have a quick butcher's, Mrs Aitch? I love old snaps,' Dawn said, and even though she should have been working, even though Granny should have said 'I don't pay you good money to look at other people's private family photo albums,' she plonked herself on the bed in which Grandpa died as if it were an armchair in her own home.

Our ancestors looked out at us as solemn as funerals, as stern as workhouse owners in Dickens' stories. Page after nicotine-coloured page of glum cricket teams and strict picnics. We'd seen them before but Dawn was fascinated. 'Just look at that 'tache. And them hats. Blimey, they must have been so *sweaty* in them days.' And then ''Ere, who's that then, Mrs Aitch? She looks as though she's got a red hot poker up her bum,' or 'Who's he? He looks like Jack the Ripper,' and Granny would have to stop what she was doing and squint at the photograph and say, 'I think that was my husband's Great Aunt Maud, dear,' or 'I wouldn't swear to it but I think that was Lord So-and-so.'

'How come there aren't any of your relations here?' Dawn asked and Granny said it was a Hillington album. Her relations were rather dull in comparison.

Granny's father had been a Yorkshire parson, and suddenly it hit me. I had something in common with the Brontë sisters! Maybe I was even a distant relation! *'Is your writing talent inherited, do you suppose, Sarah?' Mr Richards might ask and I would say, 'Well, not exactly, but my great grandfather was a Yorkshire parson which could explain er, the wild, passionate side of my nature.'*

'Granny, do you know if by any chance your father was related to the Brontës?' I said, and Granny said, 'I doubt it very much, darling. Mr Brontë was Irish, wasn't he?'

'I wonder why all the men haven't got moustaches,' Hattie said and Dawn said it was a free country, even then, and the ones who hadn't got them were probably the most interesting because they were doing their own thing, and Hattie said don't you mean shaving your own thing which I thought terribly funny, and Dawn said, 'Look at him, for example,' pointing to a handsome young man with no moustache. He had his hat tilted jauntily over one eyebrow and he was leaning casually against a wall with his arm crossed and one leg bent, and his trousers were quite tight and you could probably see the line of his wedding tackle if you looked closely.

'I bet he's a Hillington. He's got that ring of confidence . . .'

'How do you know he uses Colgate?' I said and Hattie screamed with laughter.

'I bet that's your old man. Am I right, Mrs Aitch?'

Granny confirmed that it was.

'I approve of your taste,' said Dawn vulgarly. 'He's a real looker, ain't he. And who's all the others then?'

Granny couldn't remember but said they were all Hillingtons in some shape or form. Later we came to some of Granny herself, who looked very beautiful and also very sad.

'It's amazing ain't it,' said Dawn. 'All these blokes and now it's whittled down to Dan. Dying breed, the Hillingtons. Not like my family, who're like bleeding rabbits. Must be all that in-breeding your top-drawer lot get up to. Or maybe they were killed off in the wars. Mind you, I thought it was only our lot who were the cannon fodder. I thought you toffs got off scot-free. Anyway, I think it's a crying shame, great English families dying out like that.'

'We aren't dying out,' I said crossly. 'There's Dan left and he'll marry a girl he meets at Cambridge and they'll have six sons.'

'There's no guarantee,' said Dawn. 'You never know, he could be sterile. There's a lot of it about.'

'Dawn, I believe you have some hoovering to be getting on with,' said Granny in a frosty voice.

'Mind if I just show you something weird I found at the back of my chest of drawers? Seeing all these old photos has reminded me. I'll be ever so quick.'

It was a pre-World-War-One photograph, bent and yellow and dry as an old leaf, of a group of servants standing in front of the kitchen garden wall. In one corner you could just see a branch of the walnut tree. There was a chauffeur in a cap and coat with polished buttons, a man with hair parted in the middle in a checked waistcoat, a man who must have been the butler in a tail coat with a watch chain looped across his tummy. There were two grooms wearing hunting stocks, two maids in long skirts and aprons and a sad-looking woman with a cat on her lap who was probably the cook. In front a young boy sat cross-legged in lace-up boots. There was one very curious thing about the photograph. A figure standing between the two grooms had been cut out.

'Now why do you think that could be, Mrs Aitch? What I thought was, the maid living in my room at the time was jilted by the missing person so she cut him out of her life, so to speak.'

Granny turned and held the photograph to the window so she could see better. 'It looks as though it was around the time of the Great War, so it's quite likely that the young man died in the trenches,' said Granny. 'It's so long ago I can only remember Wilkins, the butler, who suffered dreadfully from hayfever, poor man, and Agnes the cook. As for the others . . . The war wiped out whole villages of men, you know.'

'It must have been worse than the first day of Selfridge's sale, the women fighting over any men that were left.'

'I can assure you that it was far worse for the men in the trenches,' said Granny and if voices were seasons, hers would be the wicked old bugger of a winter at its peak.

Aunt Lynette announced that the time had come the walrus said to begin her portrait of Dan in his prime. She and Hattie set up their easels in the red brick road, and eventually managed to get him to stand still and in the position they wanted; leaning against the MGB, his hands on his hips, his guitar propped up beside him, fields, trees, the open road and billowing clouds stretching before him.

'Oh, *frightfully* Jack Kerouac,' said Aunt Lynette. 'What do we think of a cigarette dangling nonchalantly from his lower lip, Hattie darling?'

'Definitely not,' said Hattie. 'He'd look like Andy Capp. And can't we do something with his hair? It's covering his face like an untidy wedding veil.'

Aunt Lynette said long hair was all the rage, and it would be good to capture the mood of the times. 'Dan, do try to relax. Put your hand on your hip or something. At the moment you look like a schoolboy who's just wet his pants.'

'Thanks,' said Dan. 'By the way I hate to spoil the party but I haven't the time to spend hours staring into space like some moron while you two artists flick paint around. Mind if I use the time to practise on my guitar?'

Aunt Lynette screeched that it would ruin the whole essence of the thing, he was meant to be gazing into the future, not down at some ruddy twanging fool instrument and Dan said sorry, it was either that or nothing, so with much grumbling they had to agree on that.

When no one was looking I took a photograph of Dan while he was still in his 'frightfully Jack Kerouac' pose, and then went for a walk with my camera over my shoulder.

I took a photograph of the row of dead animals, and one of the crucified hedgehog, getting as close as I dared. I took one of the squashed hedgehog on the road, too, the spaghetti now a fuzzy dark-red blur. The caption under these three would read *Hung, drawn or flattened*. I planned to stick all my photos in the middle two pages of my diary under the heading *THE DARK FACE OF THE COUNTRYSIDE*, along with one I'd managed to get of Dawn bending over to admire herself in a puddle (*Who is the ugliest of them all?*), one of a silhouette of Brian Pike with his gun and his Yellow Dog (*One merderer and his dog*), and one of some red monstrosities (*Who is the second ugliest of them all?*) I came across a myxi rabbit in the corner of a field, its eyes all puffed up and gasping for breath, and I took a photograph of that, too, and of a screaming Yank plane going over which would come out as just a blur. I risked taking one of Granny, frail and small in her last straw hat, asleep in a deckchair. If her eyes had been open she would have looked dead. Later I would take one of Mrs B's grave. I would put these two together with the caption *The wicked winter takes its toll*.

I took one of Jack leaning on his gate and afterwards he invited me in for a cup of tea.

I sat in an old brown armchair, resting my head against an antimacassar crocheted by Mrs B. On the tiny window-sill was a fern in a brass bowl, and on the walls were plates suspended by wires, and 'Home Sweet Home' written in pokerwork on a piece of pale wood. There were no invitations on the mantelpiece, just a china carthorse in harness, a carriage clock and an old photograph of Jack and Mrs B with their two shy, neat-haired sons when they

225

were about the same age as me and Hattie, before they were fed to the cannons.

'Here you are, pet,' said Jack, handing me a thick white cup of weak tea which I wouldn't drink too much of in case I had to use the earth closet in the garden.

'Jack,' I said. 'We've got a new teacher who asked us to spend this summer finding out about the past. So I was wondering ... would you mind telling me a bit about the good old days? Not the farming aspect so much as well, living conditions, for example.'

'Be delighted to, ducks,' said Jack looking pleased. 'Now, where shall we begin?'

Later, I sorted out the chaff from the wheat for Mr Richards.

Of all the eye-openers Jack told me about the past, these are the ones that left most impression on me, I wrote later. *1. Because most of the cottages didn't have ovens, all their food was boiled. They ate potatos, apples, sweeds and bread and were always hungry. The biggest treat in the world was cake. 2. People didn't wash then, they swam in the river, but Jack said they didn't look dirty. 3. They never had a newspaper and had nothing to read except the Bible. 4. Laborers dreaded it raining because they would be sent home from work by the farmer and not get paid. 5. People slept six to a room. 6. Most men saw the Great War as an escape route and were glad to get away from the back-braking work on the farms. Little did they know as they set off for the muddy French trenches that most of them would never set eyes on muddy Norfolk fields ever again. 7. Jack hid his faverite horse Prancer in his garden shed when the army officers went round the farm looking for four-legged conscripts. 7. None of the cottages had running water. 8. Village people suffered so many hardships that if they hadn't believed in religion there would have been a revalution.*

That evening, Granny held a Shotestead Show committee meeting in the drawing room.

Mr English was the first to arrive. Normally he came in through the back door in socked feet, having left his Wellingtons outside. Tonight he was wearing brown Hush Puppies, and came in through the front door in a rather above-his-station sort of way, I thought. Perhaps it was because he was this year's president. He had also, I noticed, arrived in his shiny new Land Rover, even though the farmhouse was only five minutes' walk away.

'Hello, you two,' he said. 'Enjoying your hols, are you?'

'Yes thank you,' we said, and I stared hard at him. Could he be Dawn's lover? He was certainly the older, more mature type, though not too old. In fact he was quite handsome in a rugged, red-faced, blustery-farmer sort of way. His blue eyes gave you a knowing, 'I've been around' look, and I seemed to remember from last year's harvest field that he had quite a hairy chest. My only query was, why would Mr English love someone like Dawn when he had a perfectly nice, pretty, smily wife of his own?

Soon the drive was full of cars, ranging from bubble to Bentley, and the drawing room full of people, ranging from Fred Spurrel, Mr Bone and Mr Thirtle to Rupert's parents and Brigadier Benson-Long. They were all men apart from Granny and Lady Margetson, Rupert's mother. Hattie and I handed round cups of tea and chocolate biscuits, and you could tell several wished the tea would turn magically into beer or Scotch, depending on which drawer they belonged to. Grandpa had always offered his guests alcohol. Was Granny economising, or had the Château Hillington evening put her off allowing alcohol to be drunk in her house? You could see she was trying hard to muster herself with her visitors but she seemed to have taken a turn for the worse. She left Hattie and me in sole charge of refreshments, and instead of making polite Show conversation with the others she muttered to us how she was considering getting the telephone disconnected.

'Don't know what's got into this damn country,' announced the Brigadier, thumping his fist on the arm of the chair and becoming enveloped in a cloud of dust. He was well in the clear as far as Dawn's lover was concerned, which was more than could be said for Jeremy the estate agent who was this year's Show secretary; he was suave and handsome and definitely in the running, as would Rupert have been if he'd 'been around' more. He was wearing a nice casual jumper and his spot barely showed. Seeing him reminded me I hadn't yet written him the letter. Perhaps I could speak to him instead: 'Rupert, I'm so frightfully sorry about the other night ...' But he was busy talking to the bow-tied Knick-Knack shop man and what, I'd like to know, was someone like *him* doing on the committee of an old-established agricultural show?

When Hattie and I had served everyone their tea and had answered a few boring school questions, we sneaked out.

'Trust Dawn not to be here the day there's going to be a mountain of washing up,' said Hattie. 'I vote we leave it all to her in the morning.'

'Talking of votes,' I said, 'I wonder if Dan's pop group will get star billing.'

'I don't think it should,' said Hattie. 'He could make a complete fool of himself and bring disgrace to our family. Anyone who's

227

anyone will be there, won't they, and just say he sings – or rather shouts – that awful jail song – or the one about blue swede shoes. Perhaps we had better talk to Snuff Mull about it. Have you been near him since we christened him, by the way?'

'Yes.'

'What did you ask him?'

'Oh, this and that.'

'You're so secretive these days, honestly.'

The rumbling of men's voices down below went on late into the night, and I must have dozed off.

When I awoke in the morning, I already knew the verdict because I'd dreamt that Dan, a hat pulled jauntily over one eye like Grandpa's, shouted 'Guess what – star billing!' and a jay, or was it Dawn? shrieked with glee.

'Bet you ten bob Dan's got star billing,' I said to Hattie.

'Bet you ten million pounds he has,' she said. 'I heard him tell Dawn in the night. I think it's a flaming cheek he should tell her before us, don't you?'

'Yes,' I said. 'Where were they, exactly?'

'On the landing. I think Dan was going into the bathroom and she was on her way up to her room. He said, "Guess what – star billing!"' and she shrieked. You don't think there's anything funny going on between those two, do you?'

'Course not. Dawn's engaged to Albert, remember? And Dan's in love with someone called Hilary Wentworth-Smith,' and I told Hattie about her.

'I bet she wouldn't be in love with him if she could see him with all that long unwashed hair. Mind you, I suppose if you loved someone their hair wouldn't matter. I bet for example there are some women who find Yul Brynner handsome.'

I said *baldly speaking* it wasn't the same thing at all.

CHAPTER EIGHTEEN

THE ICE KINGDOM
Written, directed and produced by Sarah Louise Hillington.
Set designed by Harriet Victoria Hillington (assisted by Sarah
Louise Hillington)
Cast List:
Story Teller/Dorothy the Scatty Witch/Queen
Gloryana/Gertrude the Ghost – Sarah Hillington
Prince Ferdinand – Daniel Edward Hillington
Gwendolin, the beautiful Princess/Primrose Crocas, the Spring
Fairy – Harriet Victoria Hillington
Derek, the Devil Dog – Clifford Hillington
Maude, the Ugly Servant/Warren, the Evil Rabbit – Dawn
Potts

SCENE ONE: The Palace
SCENE TWO: The Ice Mountain
SCENE THREE: The Palace

All in all, I was quite pleased with the way the play had turned out, and I'd managed to: 1) Avoid anything that remotely resembled a love scene between Dan and Dawn. 2) Avoid them being in the changing room at the same time. 3) Give Hattie the chance to put oranges down her front. 4) Give Dan the chance to play his guitar. 5) Give me the chance to wear my new red bathing costume. 6) Put Dawn fairly and squarely in her place once and for all.

The story was that a Wicked Winter spell (I couldn't allow 'bugger of a winter' because the Pinkerton-Snells – or Pinky and Perky Smells as Dan called them – were easily shocked) had been cast over a beautiful kingdom called Hillingtonia. Everything and everyone had been turned to ice apart from the Prince, who grew colder and icier by the minute. Soon the kingdom would lie dead and buried beneath a sheet of ice and snow. In desperation the Prince calls in Dorothy the Scatty Witch to break the spell but she is too cold to remember her magic. She does, though, give him a magic guitar and tells him to go to her cousin, Primrose Crocus, who lives at the top of Ice Mountain. Playing his guitar to ward off

229

fearsome beasts, the Prince eventually gets there. Primrose Crocus advises him to return to the palace, get into his bathing trunks, pretend it's as warm as toast and to play *Summer Holiday* on his guitar. This he does and the princess and queen both burst from their blocks of ice, smiling in sun-glasses and bathing costumes and also singing *Summer Holiday*. The Big Thaw has begun. But Maude, the ugly servant, emerges as a hideous ice witch. It was she who had cast the spell because the prince didn't love her, an ugly servant. Her ice spell had failed so now she would turn them all to stone. But then (and here a watering can would be poured over her), she begins to melt and meets an agonising death. Now the Prince is free to marry Princess Gwendolin, his dearly beloved, and never again will his kingdom suffer at the hands of a Wicked Winter. Then everyone, including the audience, would sing the last verse of *Summer Holiday*.

'The only thing that's bothering me is the bit about melting,' said Dawn at the Play Meeting. 'How *do* you melt, for gawd's sake? It won't involve me getting me barnet wet, will it? And me mascara will run.'

'You just fall to the floor and we'll splash a bit of water on you and then you gradually disappear under a sheet or something,' said Hattie.

'Yes, we promise we won't, er, water your hair,' I said.

'It's going to be a bugger to stage,' said Dan. 'How the hell are we going to depict ice and snow and cold in the middle of summer? It'd be like asking Little Richard to sing a Frank Ifield number.'

'It'll be a good test of our acting skills,' I said icily.

'Yeah, but how are we meant to be blocks of ice one minute and people the next?'

'We step out from cardboard boxes covered in sheets,' I said. 'And for snow we just have pieces of tinsel hanging around the place.'

'By the way,' said Dawn. 'Do I have to be a namby-pamby rabbit? Why can't I be something with more oomph, like a lion or tiger or something?'

Because lions and tigers are proud, noble, intelligent, graceful beasts . . .

'Because we've already got a rabbit outfit in the dressing-up clothes.'

'Blimey, this should be a right old laugh,' said Dawn. 'Watch out, Liz Taylor, here I come!'

She is as exited as a small girl being given her first bicycle. I wrote. *I feel a bit guilty I haven't given her a better part, but tell myself she*

230

should thank her lucky stars she's in it at all. She says it is taking her mind off Stephen Ward, who has taken an overdose and is in hospital. She goes on and on about him, saying it was Society what drove him to it.

By Saturday we'd made all the props and costumes – Dawn and Granny's sewing machine had been so helpful I decided to give her a credit in the programme – and had had a disastrous rehearsal, where everything that could have gone wrong did, including Clifford chewing off one of his devil's horns, and Dan setting fire to his false beard with a cigarette which caused much merriment among certain cast members and Dawn said it should happen in the actual play, that would explain why he hadn't turned to ice like everyone else because his fags stopped him from freezing up and Dan said yeah, it would be a good excuse to chain-smoke and I said when was the last time he had seen a prince chain-smoking and Dan said if Prince Charles could drink Cherry Brandy in public Prince Ferdinand could smoke a fag and Dawn said yeah, it would add a touch of humour to the thing, and I said it wasn't a pantomime but a play and Dan said perhaps that was its problem and come to think of it why did he have to be a prince at all, why couldn't he be, say, a pop star, Dawn a groupie, I could be his manager and Hattie his drummer to make it a bit more hip and really give the Pinky and Perky Smells something to chew on, and I said if he wanted something 'hip' he'd have to go to some foul nightclub in Soho, and Hattie said why didn't we all shut up, she was sweltering in this cardboard box and these oranges made her bathing costume far too tight, it was literally strangling her back, and Dawn said since when could a back be strangled. And that was just one of a hundred and one disagreements or, as Dan called them, healthy creative arguments which reminded him of his band practice.

'It's nowhere near ready for public consumption, is it,' I said to Hattie as we arranged the audience's chairs in the courtyard in front of the stable, filled the watering can, tied a piece of tinsel to Dan's guitar, stuck silver stars on the crowns and all the other hundreds of other things that have to be done on the morning of a play. The dress rehearsal I'd planned had fallen through because Dawn was helping Granny get lunch and Dan had slinked off muttering about a man's gotta do what a man's gotta do.

'At least it's not raining,' Hattie said. 'Wouldn't it be good if the sun came out just as we emerge from our boxes and Dawn starts to melt. It would be like a sort of miracle, wouldn't it.'

'It'll be a sort of miracle if we get that far,' I said.

My play, I wrote, *is as ready for the outside world as a lunch where the potatoes haven't been peeled, the peas are still in their pods, the*

231

chicken is walking around with its feathers on and the hungry guests are sitting waiting at table with their knives and forks raised. I bet Messrs Alfred Hichcock, Ingma Burgman and Aweson Wells combined have never been up such a gum tree.

Talking of gum trees, Austin of England has at last got the better of the number 10 bus driver, who biffed slap-bang-wallop into him. (Granny has given him the benefit of the doubt by saying he probably didn't see him; I suspect otherwise. 'A full bladder knows no con-shance' I said to Dawn which she thought hilarias.) It's not serious in itself because luckily Granny wasn't sitting in him at the time but he will be in dock for at least two weeks. This means we will be marooned here at Gressenham Hall like beached whales with no means of escape.

To get out of helping to prepare lunch, Hattie and I went to the boxroom to look through the moth-riddled dressing-up box for something that would pass as headgear for a spring fairy. We were also listening to *Children's Favourites* on Dawn's radio. Hattie had written to Uncle Mac again; I had seen the postcard on the chest waiting for Mr Ridley to collect, and I'd had a very quick butchers at it.
Dear Uncle Mac,
This is the forth time of writing to ask you to please, please play Champion the Wonder Horse for my sister Sarah, who was 11 last Saturday. Even though you have missed her birthday it doesn't matter, she will still be delited if you play it. It is her favrite song and she knows all the words and so do I.
Yours hopefully,
Harriet Hillington (Miss)
PS When Sarah was younger she thought it was Champion no Wonder Horse!!!
PPS We are spending summer at our grannys in Norfolk without our parents. Things have changed a bit since last year, and my rekwest will cheer us up inormously.

Needless to say, it wasn't picked. Plenty of pop records were, though: *How Do You Do It?* by Gerry and the Pacemakers. *From Me to You* by the Beatles, *Sweets for my Sweet* by the Searchers, *The Night Has a Thousand Eyes*, and a repulsive song called *Come Outside* about a man asking a woman to come outside because 'there's a loverly moon out there' and her rudely telling him to 'leave off' and 'get lost' in a Dawn sort of voice ...

'What an unsuitable record for children to hear,' I grumbled. 'Honestly, it's more like *Teenagers' Favourites* these days,' and Hattie said. 'That man. Do you think if I sent him a *million* postcards he'd play "Champion"?'

232

When we heard the purr of the Pinkerton-Snells' long new white shiny car crunch on the gravel, we peered through the pre-World-War-cobwebbed window to get an aerial view of them.

'Mummy – you look *marvellous*,' we could hear Aunt Daphne say through her loudspeaker voice.

'No, she doesn't, she looks as old as the hills,' Hattie muttered.

'Fancy a woman of her age calling her mother Mummy,' I said. 'I'm going to start calling Mummy Mother to get into practice.'

Uncle William and James both wore checked sports jackets. Aunt Daphne wore a dark green suit and gloves and Susan wore a tweed coat with all the buttons done up even though it was summer, and brown lace-ups and white knee-length socks even though she was nearly thirteen.

'Talk about *square*,' I said.

'They look quite round to me,' said Hattie. 'Uncle William does, anyway. Like a baked potato from this angle. And James looks forty, not fourteen.'

'What's the only difference between Aunt Daphne and Susan?'

'Aunt Daphne's married.'

'No. Aunt Daphne wears a bra. Though come to think of it. Susan might, too, now.'

But it was impossible to tell under the tweed coat.

'It's tempting to stay up here all day, isn't it,' said Hattie.

'Yes,' I said. There were plenty of places to hide. Trunks, boxes, a big old wardrobe ... 'Hattie, I know it's silly, but let's, just, you know ... if we concentrate very hard on being Susan and Lucy in *The Lion, the Witch and the Wardrobe,* if we really *believe* Narnia's going to be there you never know, it might be.'

'Knowing our luck, if we end up anywhere it'll be in Dawn's foul room.'

We stepped into the wardrobe and, like in the book, got in among the coats and rubbed our faces among them. We stepped further in, hoping our feet would begin to crunch on snow, that our hands would touch the prickly branches of trees ...

'Typical,' said Hattie, thumping its wooden back as if it was a door. 'How come things always happen to children in books but never to us?'

'If it didn't happen to children in books they would be as dull as ditchwater,' I said.

'Talking of dull as ditchwater,' said Hattie, 'I suppose we'd better go and say hello to the you-know-whos.'

*   *   *

233

'My dears! How we've both grown! Sarah, you're going to be tall like your father,' boomed Aunt Daphne, looking at Hattie's leg out of the corner of her eye and giving us both a brisk, Pears-soap kiss. 'Are we both behaving ourselves and doing as Granny tells us?'

'They're behaving beautifully. Model grandchildren,' said Granny, putting a frail arm round each of us.

'Jolly good. That's the ticket,' said Uncle William, and Aunt Daphne smiled though you could tell she was thinking Ah, but not as model as my children.

'Which I'm afraid is more than can be said for their elder brother,' continued Granny, and you could see Aunt Daphne's eyes light up, the way the Yellow Dog's had when he heard a mention of animals being killed.

'Oh?' she said, raising her eyebrows, and the two cousins raised their eyebrows, too.

'He's formed a pop group,' I said. 'It's only a phase, though, while he's in no-man's-land between school and university.'

'I say,' said James. His face looked like one of Hattie's rock buns, with two squashed currants for eyes. Then, to prove he knew the name of a pop group added, 'Like Gerry and the Pacemakers, you mean. I say!'

'No, like the Rollin' Stones, actually,' I said quietly.

'Are they going to call themselves Dan and the Pacemakers?' asked James.

'No, the Wild Ones,' I said. 'They wanted something untamed-sounding and angry.'

'Good gracious,' said Aunt Daphne, and couldn't think of anything else to say. She was completely out of her depth on the subject, the way a sweep, say, would be if he had to talk about hunter trials. 'Now, why don't you children go off and play. Your granny and I have simply *oodles* of news to catch up on.'

'Ya, come on, I want to see how the winter wheat's coming on,' said James, who was always showing off his farming knowledge in front of Granny and pretending to know more than Dan, perhaps in the hope that she'd leave the estate to him, though of course she wouldn't because his surname wasn't Hillington. His voice had turned gruff, and there was a foul rash on his chin, probably because he'd started shaving. Susan still reminded you of Mary Lennox in *The Secret Garden,* the most disagreeable-looking child you've ever seen, with a little thin face and a little thin body, thin light hair and a sour expression. Poor Susan. She was as plain as a pikestaff, whatever that was: was it, in fact, a pike on the end of a staff? In which case had Brian Pike been teased at school? Was that what drove him to becoming a murderer when he grew up?

'Your voice sounds different, James,' I said as we set off 'to play'. 'All crackly like a Japanese wireless.'

'That's because it's broken,' he crackled.

'You'd better go to the doctor to get it mended then,' said Hattie and they laughed politely because of her leg.

As always, conversation with the cousins was like walking across a dull, wet, ploughed field in hobnail boots; everything you said they either made heavy weather of or weren't interested in. Still, I didn't mind; the harder work it was the better it would be for my diary. *Even as small children they had chosen to sit and listen to grown-ups talk rather than play with us,* I would write. *Perhaps people don't change as they get older but just become more so.*

We heard over and over again how Susan was going to Benenden next term and so was Princess Anne; they'd have so much in common, both being pony lovers, and simply imagine being in the same class as a princess, and I said. 'You might be in the same class as her but you aren't the same *class*,' and Susan said rather huffily, 'Oh, I wouldn't say that. We're upper-middle which is only one off from Royalty.'

We also heard, again and again, 'I say! The sugar beet's a bit behind,' and 'Phew. Look at all that Fat Hen in the barley,' which eventually prompted Hattie to say, 'That isn't a fat hen. It's a thin partridge.'

We told them about Brian Pike and showed them Death Row, and they didn't turn a hair. 'Just think of the animal as vermin – poachers,' said James, 'because that's all they are.'

'Yes but *they* don't know they are,' I said. 'They're just trying to survive.'

'I say, this gamekeeper chappie doesn't hang about, does he. I'll have to have a word with Pater and see if we can borrow him for a day or two.'

'You mean *poach* him for a day or two,' I said and Hattie laughed and said, 'You make him sound like an egg.'

As we tramped past the sheep, Susan asked us about Dawn. 'I've heard she's fearfully common and cheap looking. Is she?'

'Yah, fearfully,' I said. 'And fantastic fun, too. We're getting very fond of her, aren't we, Hattie? She's teaching us to be more worldly. For example she's told us all about the Profumo scandal and Christine Keeler.'

'Phew,' whistled James. 'She sounds a damn bad influence to me.'

'Who is Christine Keeler, anyway?' asked Susan.

'Don't you know? Where have you *been*?' I said. 'It's in all the newspapers.'

I was secretly pleased that Dawn had chosen today to wear her white-poodle dangly ear-rings, her shortest crimson skirt, her tightest man-made top, her brightest pink lipstick, and hair piled so high it looked like a Yorkshire pudding gone mad. I wished I had taken a photograph of James and Susan's faces: I sort of wished, too, that Dawn would ask James or Uncle William whether she reminded them of Mandy Rice-Davies. She was eating in the kitchen today because Granny said there wasn't enough space round the table, but I suspected the real reason was the Pinky and Perkies would have downed silver if they'd had to eat with her.

Uncle William had to carve because needless to say Dan was late. My dear brother hadn't brushed his hair – in fact if anything he had ruffled it about on purpose – and if his glazed eyes were anything to go by he'd had a pint or two of beer beforehand. His chin was rougher than a stubble field.

He didn't ask how anyone was but just talked on and on about his pop group and this bloody ace song he'd written called *I'm So Hip and You're So Square* – and it was then that he looked at his relations in the eye for the first time.

'What you have to understand about the British music business is that it's always been regarded as America's poor relation. It's easier – and safer – to copy rather than create,' he told Aunt Daphne, who looked the way she would if a BBC weather-forecaster predicted solid rain for a month. 'We never produce anyone brand new, it's always "Britain's answer to", for example Helen Shapiro is "Britain's answer to" Brenda Lee. The golden rule for singers in this country is: love your mother, don't pick your nose in public, be kind to animals and be a good all-round entertainer. But we're gonna change all that – us and the Beatles and a few others.'

'I see,' murmured Aunt Daphne. If her face was anything to go by, the weather-forecaster was now undoing his flies. 'The er, pop group must explain why you've allowed your hair to get so long and unkempt.'

'Yah, it's longer than the Beatles',' said James, whose own hair resembled a sergeant major's with a parting so straight it could have been drawn with a ruler.

'And much untidier, if you don't mine me saying,' said Susan, forking into her pursed mouth two peas, half a carrot and a small triangle of roast pork.

'Not at all – in fact, the untidier the better,' said Dan, cramming

236

a large whole roast potato into his mouth. 'Actually, Susan,' he said, the potato seriously impairing his speech, 'I'm planning to grow it to my shoulders and not wash it for a month. My new image,' and he grinned the potato at her.

Oh, Dan, how could you, half of me felt. The other half felt terribly proud he was so – well, with-it.

Uncle William took off his glasses to sneeze (perhaps he had kept them on once and they had whizzed through the air and hit someone on the nose) before muttering something about National Service, and Aunt Daphne laughed, a false, tinkly teacup laugh, and said, 'Oh Daniel, you remind me of your father when he was your age.'

My ears pricked up. Did Daddy have hair to his shoulders and put a whole roast potato in his mouth in one go?

'Why, Aunt Daphne?' I asked but before she could reply, Granny said, 'We're all quite proud of Dan. His, er, pop group is getting star billing at the Show this year.'

'Oh, how, er, splendid,' said Aunt Daphne doubtfully. 'You'll have to make sure you behave yourself, it'll be frightfully polite company. You know dear Sir Edward is coming this year?'

'Don't fret, my stage name is Pete O'Flame so no one need know I'm your nephew. Your reputation will remain as pure as the driven snow.'

'Just think, the whole county will be watching you practically,' said Susan. 'We don't normally stay for the dance, but I suppose we could take the horses home and come back again, couldn't we, Mummy?'

'Bring them along if you like,' said Dan, slouching in his chair and not looking anyone in the eye. 'They could beat time with their hooves. Yeah, tell them to hoof it down there.'

'They could do the fox *trot*,' I said.

'And *spur* everyone on to dance,' said Hattie.

'Even the *shy* ones,' I said. 'And *nag* them if necessary.'

'You never know, they could start a new dance craze – the Fetlock Twist, or the Horseshoe Shuffle or something,' said Dan.

'To the tune of *The Galloping Major*,' I said.

The Pinky and Perkies smiled politely like vicars, and Susan said after all the events she'd entered Tinkerbell in she was bound simply to want to *flop*, and Dan said he didn't want any flops at the dance, thank you very much, and that he wasn't actually being serious about bringing the horses and Susan said she knew that, she wasn't stupid, and then there was a tense pause that could have turned into an embarrassing one if Dawn hadn't stuck her head round the door.

237

'Blimey, it's like a wet weekend in here,' she said and Dan said they were just discussing whether Susan should bring her horse to the dance and Dawn said, 'That would be a laugh. I've never danced with an 'orse. Mind you, I wouldn't want to be saddled with him all evening.'

Hattie, Dan and I roared, Granny smiled, Susan said 'It's a she, actually,' and Dawn said, 'Give us a shout when you've finished noshing.'

'That girl needs to be taught some manners,' said Aunt Daphne, looking at Granny. 'I've never come across anyone ... She really was a most unsuitable choice in my opinion, Mummy.'

'Yah, one hell of a contrast to Mrs B,' croaked James.

'She suits me very well,' said Granny. 'All the other young girls I saw were so dull and mouselike and wouldn't say boo to a goose.'

'But does she keep the house clean?' said Aunt Daphne, running her eyes along the sideboard.

'Daphne darling, at my age there are more important things in life than a smattering of dust,' said Granny. 'I happen to enjoy her company.'

'But Mummy, if it was company you wanted, there's Gertrude Patterson rattling round in that huge vicarage. She could come and live here. You'd get on like a house on fire.'

'I dare say,' said Granny, 'but would she make me laugh?' and Dan said 'Well said, Granny,' with his mouth full.

The conversation steered itself back to the Show, and Aunt Daphne asked whether we were entering for anything this year, and Dan said yeah, Sarah was entering Snap Dragon for the Beauty Contest and Susan said poor sweet little Snap Dragon, he can't help being ugly, and I felt like saying speak for yourself.

I told them that Hattie and I were going to be donkey stewards as usual, and entering the Fancy Dress, Aunt Lynette had her Ban the Bomb stall, Granny was entering her roses and Dawn was going in for the Beauty Contest.

'What – her?' said Susan, pointing towards the kitchen. 'Crikey, she stands no more chance of winning then Snap Dragon.'

'Actually,' I said, 'She can look quite pretty when she doesn't wear much make-up.'

While I helped Dawn clear away Susan started going on again, purely to show off in front of Dawn, about being in the same class as Princess Anne and how they'd have heaps in common, and Dawn said, 'Blimey, you mean you'll be in the same class as a princess? Can I have your autograph?' and Susan, thinking she was being serious, turned pink with pleasure and said, 'Ya, if you like.'

Aunt Daphne asked me how I was getting on at school, but I couldn't be bothered to tell her much because a) you could tell by her eyes she wasn't really interested and b) the play was taking up all my thoughts now. Of all my worries about it, the main one that kept screaming through my head like a loudhailer on stilts was *What was Dawn's outfit going to consist of in the last scene?* I had told her that as director I had the right to see it in case it wasn't suitable and she said how could I see it because it wasn't finished and I said at least she could give me the gist of it and she said she'd rather it came as a nice surprise. 'I bet you ten bob she'll ruin the whole play with it,' I'd said to Hattie. 'Even though I've told her she must wear a long black witch's dress, what's the betting she'll wear a foul bikini or something.'

'If we're lucky,' Hattie said. 'Maybe she won't wear anything at all. Maybe she'll step out of her box completely *bare.* Can you imagine the Pinky and Perkies' faces?'

'Can you imagine *my* face?'

'Can you imagine Granny's? Or Dan's?' said Hattie. 'He'd go *crimson,* wouldn't he.'

'In his present frame of mind he'd probably just laugh,' I muttered.

Later, I listed all the things that had gone wrong.
1. Stable doors (ie curtains) kept getting stuck.
2. Prince Ferdinand bumped into his throne and said 'Sorry, Guv'.
3. Prince Ferdinand looked round at the furniture covered in sheets and said, 'I say, are we expecting the sweep?' and Maude got the giggles even though she was meant to be frozen.
4. Maude said 'Gord, I've got cramp,' when she was in her box.
5. My witch's hat fell over my eyes as it was meant to and no one laughed, and only Aunt Lynette laughed when my spell went wrong and I conjured up a bed spring instead of Spring.
6. Prince Ferdinand, on his dangerous journey up the Ice Mountain wandered round the courtyard and disappeared out through the gates. When he came back he was doing up his flies and muttering about beer going straight through you.
7. Primrose Crocas forgot her words.
8. Derek the Devil Dog flopped onto his back to have his tummy tickled.
9. Warren the Evil Ice Rabbit took ages to die thus giving Prince Ferdinand ages to play a fowl out-of-tune rocking roll tune on his guitar. Warren danced more than died, and jerked and rythed and twiched on the floor in time to the music like the worst case of

miximitotis in the world. This scene will go down in history as the fowlest double act ever seen on stage. (NB Gertrude died almost straight away, dropping neatly to the ground.)

10. As Princess Gwendolin turned from her block of ice, one of her oranges bounced across the stage, causing Prince Ferdinand to say, 'Ha! Spring is bursting out all over, I see.'

11. Maude imerged from her block of ice in nothing but the itsy-bitsiest of bakeenis made out of kitchen foil!!! *with a matching crown perched on top of her beehive. She stood hogging the limelight, everyone's mouths open in horror. I sprinkled water over her and instead of melting gracefully she said, 'Jesus, it's blinking brass monkeys.' And 'Watch me barnet, for gord's sake.' When she lay on her tummy, more than half of her foul white bottom was showing.*

12. Only Aunt Lynette joined in with Summer Holiday. The Pinky and Perkys were either speechless at the sight of Dawn or to square to know the words and Granny had nodded off.

I managed to force my jaw to smile through *Summer Holiday* with my left eye squinting to block out the glinting, winking foil monstrosity, and as soon as the applause – or what there was of it – died down I ripped off my paper crown, ran through the house and down the drive, my tears blowing like warm rain in a breeze.

Snap Dragon looked round at me through half-closed toad's eyes then continued to rub his bottom shamelessly against the gatepost.

'You and I don't belong in this modern world, you old bugger,' I said, sitting on the gate.

Snap Dragon finished scratching and began to sniff about my person but not in an affectionate way; more a 'where the hell's the sugar lump?' fashion.

At least when I died I would have a funeral where a few people would cry, and I'd be buried in Hillington Corner with a gravestone that would say 'In loving memory of our darling daughter Sarah Louise'. Snap Dragon would simply be slaughtered and end up beside *petits pois* and *pommes frites* on a Frenchman's plate. But – if my parents were divorced they wouldn't want the word *our* on my gravestone. Would that mean I would have two gravestones, both saying In loving memory of my daughter?

It was easier to swim with the tide of despair than concentrate on cheerful things, and I let the tears roll. Snap Dragon gently nibbled my arm with his yellow teeth, and you couldn't tell whether it was his way of saying he understood or bugger off. He stamped his hairy back hoof and swished his tail, and I leaned over and put my arms round his brutish neck and buried my wet face in it. But he jerked up his head and, with a loud, bored 'Shnooosh', wandered off. Bloody hell. What hope was there if even an ugly pony who needed all the friends he could get rejected me?

'Hi, Sausage, thought I'd find you here,' said Dan. He was still wearing his crown, plus a checked shirt over his bathing trunks.

'Bugger off,' I said. 'I want to be alone. And don't say I don't look like Greta Garbo because I know I don't. I only wish I did.'

He put his arm round me and I shrugged it off.

'Look, I'm sorry. I don't know what it is about the Pinky and Perkies but they bring out the devil in me. They obviously did with Dawn, too.'

'She *is* the devil,' I muttered. 'She promised she'd wear something sensible for the last scene. She ruined the play – and you did, too. How *could* you have disappeared like that and come back doing up your flies? And don't bloody well call me Sausage. It's rude.'

'It seemed to go down quite well,' he said sitting beside me on the gate. 'Though you never can tell with the Pinkies. They say something's nice when they really mean it's vile. Ace hypocrites, they are. Aunt Daphne pretending to be shocked by Dawn's er, outfit, but what's the betting she wears lacy black underwear to keep Uncle William happy on the quiet.'

'Exactly. On the quiet,' I said. 'She'd hardly parade around on a stage in it in front of someone else's relations, would she'.

'By the way, I think Susan's got a schoolgirl crush on me.'

'She couldn't possibly have. You're far too rough and rude. Have you looked in the mirror lately?'

'I reckon she's the type who fancies a bit of rough, know what I mean?'

'No I do not. You sound just like Dawn.'

'You know your trouble, Sausage,' he said putting his arm round me again and I didn't bother to shrug it off this time. 'You take life too seriously.'

'No, I don't. I tell lots of jokes. *And don't call me Sausage.*'

'I'm not saying you haven't got a sense of humour. You just take things too much to heart. You aren't frivolous enough. Live and let live, I say.'

'It's easy for you to say that, you're a man so you don't give a bugger what's going on round here. All I want is for things to go back to how they were so I can be a happy child again instead of an unhappy teenager. It's really foul being eleven. It's like living in the suburbs, neither town or country.'

'In the words of Neil Sedaka, growing up is hard to do,' said Dan squeezing me in a brotherly fashion. 'You'll just have to grit

241

your teeth and get through it as best you can. And meanwhile, why don't you try to be a little bit more devil may care-ish? We only have one life, you know.'

'Are you suggesting I start swearing and drinking alcohol and joining pop groups and smoking and wearing bikinis and talking about revolutions? I don't *want* to do those things. I'm not that type.'

'Just keep an open mind about things. Don't prejudge. Do things for kicks every now and again. We don't want you ending up like ...'

'I shall end up like whoever I want to end up like,' I said. 'And I'll tell you one person it won't be; you. Now I wish you'd bugger off and MYOB.'

Dan lit a cigarette – a Woodbine, and if a stranger could see him now he'd be prepared to bet fifty pounds that Dan had never seen inside a public school – and we sat on the gate like a couple of yokels, watching Snap Dragon's back view.

'How come you aren't smoking Players?'

'Far too bourgeois,' he said in his typical silly fashion.

'Dan,' I said. 'Do you remember in *Alice* when she meets the caterpillar and he asks who she is and she doesn't know; she knew when she got up in the morning but had changed several times since then? Well, that's how I feel.'

'Don't worry about it,' said Dan. 'That's a good sign.'

'I've been thinking. Just say you take after Daddy and become a lawyer and Hattie takes after Aunt Lynette and becomes an artist, does that mean I'm going to take after Aunt Daphne? These things might run in families, mightn't they.'

'If you end up like her I'll die of shame. They get more smug and set in their narrow ways by the minute. Come the revolution they'll be the first to go.'

'Shut up about the stupid revolution,' I said. 'The thing is, even though I don't want to end up like them, I don't want to end up angry and talking politics the whole time and working in a factory and going on strike. I don't fit into either category.'

'What makes you think you have to work in a factory to support Labour? Look at Anthony Wedgwood Benn. He's Labour and he would have been Lord Stansgate if he hadn't stuck to his principles. Look at me. I'm Labour and I'm supposed to be going to Cambridge next term.'

'What do you mean, supposed to be?'

'Oh, all right. Am.'

'Yes but I'm nothing like you or Anthony Whatsit.'

242

'I suppose you could always opt for the middle course like the people of Orpington and be a wishy-washy Liberal.'

I thought about this. If Labour made you think of dark rainy cold northern streets and flat caps and revolutions and extreme people like Dan and Aunt Lynette, and Conservative made you think of killing animals and sherry parties and hypocrites like the Pinky and Perkies, and Liberals made you think of kind smily people who let their children climb trees and encouraged them to read both comics and literature, then a Liberal was what I'd like to be.

I felt quite cheered up.

'What do I have to do to be a Liberal?'

'For a start you have to stop being cross with people who mess up plays. A good Liberal is very forgiving.'

'Ha, ha, very crafty. All right then,' I said. 'I wasn't really cross about the *play,* more about life generally. Everything suddenly seemed so sort of hopeless. You don't think the parents *will* get divorced, do you?'

'Ner,' said Dan, flicking ash at a scuttling pheasant. They couldn't face the scandal.'

'I wish everything would go back to normal.'

'You're normal,' said Dan. 'You're the stabilising factor in everyone's life at the moment, which is just how a good Liberal should be.'

'Really?' I said, feeling even more cheered up.

'People might not show it,' continued Dan, 'but they appreciate you enormously. I know I do, and so does Granny and Hattie – and Dawn.'

'How do you know Dawn does?'

'She told me. She said despite the difference in ages, she feels a real affinity towards you.'

'When did she say that?'

'Dunno. Yesterday.'

'*Where* did she say it?'

'Oh, Christ, I dunno. When we were washing up, maybe. Yeah, that's right, because then she went on about the mousetrap and how she dreaded going into the scullery every morning in case she found blood and guts all over the place.'

(Resolution: make sure Dan and Dawn are never alone together, even if it means helping with the washing up after every single meal.)

'Fancy her saying that after I tried to kill her,' I said. 'I think from the world she comes from violence is the only language she respects.'

243

'You'll have to watch that vicious streak.'

'You would have done the same. She was absolutely asking for it. I would never have actually killed her, I just wanted to teach her a lesson. Anyway, it was mainly out of loyalty to you that I did it. The thought of her repulsive ... the thought of you being her lover was too much to bear.'

'Yeah, well now you know I'm not you can start being nice to her,' said Dan. 'God, look at Snap Dragon. He's so bloody ugly.'

'I thought you Labour people were meant to see everyone as equals.'

'That doesn't include weird-looking ponies with Joe Brown haircuts.'

We both laughed and Dan said, jumping off the gate, that we should be getting back; if I didn't show my face it would look as though I'd been sulking, and good Liberals never sulk.

We met Hattie on the way back. 'Greetings, Princess Gwendolin,' said Dan, picking her up and swinging her round.

'I'm not talking to you,' said Hattie. 'And I'm surprised you are, Sarah. You ruined the play, you and Dawn. Didn't they Sarah?'

'You aren't entirely blameless with your oranges popping all over the place like Nell Gwyn. That's what you should have been called: Princess Nell Gwyndolyn, ha, ha!'

'I think we should send Dan and Dawn to Coventry, don't you, Sarah?'

'I'm beginning to see the funny side now,' I said. 'I'm going to be a Liberal, you see.'

'Aunt Lynette said it was the funniest thing she'd ever seen,' Dan said.

'Fancy her being Aunt Daphne's sister. They're as similar as ...'

'Sooty and Sweep,' said Hattie.

'Albert and Brian Pike,' I said.

'Macmillan and Harold Wilson,' said Dan.

We walked holding hands in a row, Dan in the middle, and Hattie said she wished Dawn would hurry up and marry Albert and leave, then Granny could get someone decent. 'She's ruining our holiday. If for some reason she's still here next year, I'm going to refuse to come, aren't you, Sarah?'

'I'm not sure,' I said.

'Oh no, how typical,' said Hattie. 'You've started liking her, I can tell, and any moment now you're going to get all foul and political like everyone else round these parts. God, I wish I wasn't the youngest. I wish Mummy would have another baby and it's a boy. I'd like a little brother, wouldn't you, Sarah?'

If Mummy gets divorced she won't be able to have any more babies.

'Not specially,' I said. 'A little sister's quite enough to contend with, thank you very much.'

Tea was being served on the lawn. Dawn in her silver outfit was nowhere to be seen.

'Ah, there you are,' boomed Aunt Daphne from behind black owl-like sun-glasses. 'We were thinking of sending out a search party.'

'Sorry,' I said. 'I went to check that Snap Dragon was all right.'

'Why – might he not have been?' asked Susan, staring at my red eyes.

'No,' said Dan. 'We were checking he wasn't lying in slices on a Frenchman's plate,' and all four Pinky and Perkies looked at Dan as if he was a man from outer space.

'Thank you for a lovely play, Sarah, darling,' said Granny quietly and wearily.

'Yes, it was, er, great fun,' boomed Aunt Daphne.

'Don't talk rot, Daph, you were appalled,' said Aunt Lynette.

'It didn't go exactly according to plan,' I said. 'But never mind.'

'That Dawn's quite a girl, isn't she,' said Uncle William, chuckling like a walrus.

'A highly unsuitable girl if you ask me,' said Aunt Daphne sharply and Uncle William muttered into his moustaches. 'Oh, quite, quite. That's what I meant.'

Aunt Daphne insisted we got dressed properly for tea and Dan muttered 'Bollocks to that' and went up to his room and played the harmonica with the window open. Its mournful wailing disturbed the dignity and repose of the tea party. I took a photograph of everyone (the caption would simply read: *Note the Pinky and Perky Smells' square clothes*), and then Aunt Daphne said, 'Sarah, would you show me the lily pond? We can count the fish.'

'There aren't any,' I said quickly, because I didn't fancy being on my own with her. 'The bug – er, wicked winter killed them all off.'

'Yes the pond was covered in ice for so long that the fish couldn't breathe because there was no oxygen,' said Hattie. 'So when the ice melted they were all floating on top with one eye staring to heaven.'

'That'll do, thank you, Hattie,' said Aunt Daphne.

'Actually, I wonder if fish *go* to heaven,' said Hattie.

'As opposed to *swim,* you mean?' I said.

'Come along, Sarah,' said Aunt Daphne. 'We'll go and see anyway,' and, holding me firmly by the hand as if she was the Red Queen and I was aged three, strode off across the lawn.

When we were out of sight of the others, she let go of my hand and said, 'I wanted to have a quiet word in your ear, dear,' and her stride turned into a stroll. 'I am extremely worried about you and Hattie. About your well-being, that is. Quite frankly, I've been appalled by what I've seen here today. For a start I hadn't realised how, er, *old* your grandmother had become ...'

'She's getting younger every day,' I said. 'At least she was. She seems to have had a slight relapse. But she's still far better than when we arrived.'

'Be that as it may, she still isn't up to looking after you. Lynette is as mad as a hatter and quite irresponsible but we already knew that. As for your brother, he seems to have turned into a complete *hooligan*. That pop group business ... He's going to have to pull himself together for Cambridge in no uncertain terms. And that *hair*. And talking of hair, when did you and Harriet last wash yours?' and she eyed mine as if it were a smelly dish cloth.

What business is it of yours? 'Er – well, we had baths the other ...'

'And was anyone there to supervise you'd washed your necks properly? No, of course there wasn't. Which brings me on to my main point. Dawn Potts. Never in my life have I met such a rude, rough, cheap, brazen, ill-educated, ill-bred *creature*. Why your grandmother employed her is quite beyond me. She treats the house as if it's her own, behaves no more like a servant than you or I, and is as capable of looking after two little girls as a ... chimpanzee.'

'But I'm not that little, Aunt Daphne,' I said. 'I am eleven.'

'Still far too young to be taking care of yourself. Such an impressionable age and you so sensitive, Sarah. She's such a frightfully bad influence; she could – *will* – have lasting effects on you. You'll pick up her bad language and be saddled with it for the rest of your lives, and you'll never get on. She'll poison your minds, dear, honestly she will,' and Aunt Daphne shuddered.

'She's not that bad,' I said. 'She's quite kind, and good fun.'

'Not that bad? Sarah dear, she's worse than bad. She's *evil*. anyone who presents themselves in such a way – dyed hair, repulsive war paint, short skirts – shows the sort of girl she is. A guttersnipe is the only word to describe her; a thoroughly rotten apple, I'd say, and once a rotten apple always a rotten apple. And were they *bruises* I could see? Do you suppose she's been in some sort of a fight?'

I bent my head over the lily pond and pretended to look for fish. 'It's not her fault she's the way she is. She had a deprived childhood.'

'Be that as it may,' said Aunt Daphne, 'I fail to see why our family should suffer the consequences of other people's misfortunes.'

'Dan says we could learn things from her. That someone from her walk of life could broaden our minds.'

Just as I'd hoped, just as I'd predicted, she said. 'He would, wouldn't he,' and what a complete and utter *scream* Aunt Daphne using Mandy Rice-Davies's catchphrase! I couldn't wait to tell Dan and Dawn.

Then to my astonishment, she began to sniff. Surely she wasn't crying? That would be like the *Queen* crying.

'I don't know what's happening to this country,' she said and she pulled out a crisp white handkerchief from her sleeve and blew her nose. 'What's happened to its traditions, to moral values, to old-fashioned courtesy, to everything that makes Britain special? People have become so ... restless somehow, so desperate for sensation – for chaos even. And so grasping and greedy. Every council house you pass these days has a television aerial and a large car parked outside and as for London – not only did I see several women in Harrods without either a hat or gloves, but Liverpool Street station was simply *littered* with black faces, and while I have nothing at all against negroes, they aren't British, are they? Surely they can't be happy living here, with our unpredictable climate and particular way of life? And are they actually contributing anything?'

I cleared my throat. 'They're doing the jobs we don't want to do. And their music is fantastic. Honestly, if you heard a Chuck Berry song you'd like negroes for ever more. And don't worry about the country, Aunt Daphne. Mr Macmillan is a very wily politician. He'll sort everything out.'

'But Sarah, don't you see, he's on the way out. This wretched Profumo business – the biggest storm in a teacup I have ever come across – has destroyed him. This time next year that ghastly snake in the grass Harold Wilson will be in power, and goodness knows where it'll all end. But can't you see why I'm upset, dear? Because everything that is truly ghastly about this modern world – its brashness and rudeness and greed and don't-care attitude and loose morals – is epitomised by the girl my mother has chosen to be her maid.'

I looked at the gentle lily pond, whose waters would never be troubled by snakes in the grass or council houses with television aerials. 'Er – I know exactly what you mean,' I said kindly and for a moment touched her tweed sleeve in a sisterly fashion. 'I felt exactly like you when we first arrived, but it's amazing how quickly humans adapt. You sort of swim with the tide.'

'But you and Harriet *mustn't* swim with the tide. Once the rot sets in ... You only have to look at the way your brother's gone. What I'm really trying to say, Sarah, dear, is that this is no place for two little girls to be spending the summer. You are being neglected, you're running wild like village children, you're ... And I can't help feeling responsible. Just say something ... happened to you. All in all, I would feel a great deal happier if you and Hattie came to stay with us for the remainder of the summer.'

'Do you sense *danger*?' I asked, but she said she wouldn't be that melodramatic, she simply knew it would be better all round if we went back with them. 'I won't force you to come against your will, dear, but I do strongly advise it. Think of poor little Harriet. For her sake.'

I looked at the lily pond, and pictured what life would be like at Manor Farm. There would be no danger, and I would have no more bad dreams. But if we went, who'd keep an eye on Granny, and Dan and Dawn? Who'd find a husband for Aunt Lynette? I'd never find out who Dawn's lover was and she wouldn't have anyone to confide in. Besides, I still had things to ask her. And, most important, what would I write in my diary?

'Thank you very much for your offer, Aunt Daphne, and it is nice to know you care, but we'll be all right here. I promise to look after Hattie. And perhaps, er, I can ring you if anything goes wrong.'

'That's exactly what you won't be able to do. Your grandmother has got a bee in her bonnet about having the telephone disconnected. I've tried to persuade her not to. She says it's an unnecessary expense. I offered to pay ...'

'Well, I could run like a hare to the public one in the village,' I said. 'Honestly, Aunt Daphne, we'll be all right.'

'Are you absolutely sure, dear?' she said, her head on one side, her forehead raised into questioning wrinkles and reminding me of Daddy. 'If anything happened to you I could never look your father in the face again ...'

'Oh, nothing will,' I said, as confident as a Girl Guide, and it occurred to me then that, all things considered, nothing could. Even if at the very worst Granny went completely gaga, Aunt Lynette mad, Dan off the rails, Dawn didn't marry Albert, and Brian Pike killed a thousand hedgehods and squirrels, nothing could happen to *us,* Snuff Mull would see to that. Like the lily pond, we'd be all right, Jack.

'Remember, we're only a phone call away,' said Aunt Daphne.

'Yes. Thank you.'

'You're quite sure now, dear?'

'Er – yes. I think so.'

If lives were journeys, mine had reached an important crossroads. Little did I know, as I stood staring at the lily pond on that sunless August afternoon, that I had chosen the wrong turning.

PART THREE

CHAPTER NINETEEN

'He's only gone and snuffed it, hasn't he,' said Dawn and from the other side of the runner beans came a tearful sniff.

'I already know. Guess how.'

'You heard it on the news.'

'No. The vicar talked about it in his sermon. See, you should have come to church. Don't you believe in God?'

'Ner. Not any more.'

I remembered Jack's words: '*If people hadn't believed in religion there would have been a revolution . . .*'

Dan, Hattie and I had got breakfast that morning. Granny had vanished and Dawn was having a lie-in. I was chief egg-boiler. Infuriatingly, because I was often saying to Dawn 'You can't even boil an egg', one broke and billowing white parachute clouds filled the pan. Dan, who normally was like a bear with a bandage round his head in the morning, wore Granny's checked apron and sang *Tea for Two* while he warmed the pot. Was this, by any chance, how a man who had had his wicked way the night before behaved? I thought of the times Daddy cheerfully made Sunday breakfast while Mummy had a lie-in. Was Saturday night normally 'hide the sausage' night? Did it always give the man energy and make the woman tired? Tea for *two* – was that a hint?

'You're very chirpy this morning, Dan.'

'Yeah. The band played like a dream last night.'

'Played like a dream.' Was that code for . . . But this was daft; I had established beyond reasonable doubt that Dan wasn't Dawn's lover.

It's surprising how many thoughts one can pack into only one minute; that's all it can have been, because the yolks turned out to be as runny as thin, luke-warm custard. I hoped no one would tell Dawn.

We found Granny wandering among the rose bushes in her dressing gown, her slippers soaked in dew, muttering that she must find the secateurs.

'Don't worry, we'll find them later,' said Dan, steering her arm

253

towards the house but she kept muttering about them to the knitted tea cosy all through breakfast, and though you could see she was trying hard to pull herself together for church, she walked out of the house with the ABC train guide instead of her prayer book.

'Just think, Granny, you could have been saying "Our Father, which art in Paddington".'

'Hallowed be thy 12.49 from King's Cross,' said Hattie.

'Darlings, strictly speaking you really shouldn't make fun of your dotty old Granny,' she said, piecing together the remnants of a laugh.

Dan gave us a lift in the Morris and Granny said how much she was missing Austin. 'I'm afraid it'll mean you two children won't be able to go on as many excursions as usual,' she said, and we said we didn't mind.

Dan came to church (perhaps he'd gone off starting a revolution), which was more than could be said for Mr Allcock, but it didn't really matter. I'd come to the conclusion that I was being a bit melodramatic and Dawn was far too silly to be a cunning murderer.

'Stephen Ward committed suicide, didn't he,' I said snapping off a leathery bean, hoping it would end up on her plate. 'Why did you have a lie-in this morning, just as a matter of interest?'

'Because I was knackered. Anyway, Sunday's a day of rest, innit.'

'All right, keep your hair on. I thought you might be ill or something.'

For a while the only sounds were the coo of wood pigeon and snap of bean.

'If I ask you something do you promise not to laugh?' I said.

'Cross my heart and hope to die.'

'The other day I saw two mayflies mating but they weren't actually doing anything, and what I was wondering was ... I know all about the facts of life and everything, of course, but one thing the Family Doctor book didn't explain was what the man does exactly when everything's er, in position sort of thing. I mean, do they just lie there in a soppy loving sort of way like the mayflies thinking of England until something happens, or what?'

Dawn kept her promise by not laughing. 'You've obviously never slept beside a paper-thin wall with your parents having it off on the other side,' she said. 'The man has to move it about or they'd be lying there till kingdom come. It would be like putting washing in a tub and just leaving it. You have to agitate it around a bit or the dirt wouldn't come out. It's the same with sex and sperm and stuff.'

I thought about this. 'Does the woman move around, too?'

'If she can be fagged.'

'Do you?' I said.

'MYOB,' she said, but I noticed she didn't say, 'Dunno. Never done it.'

This led me into my next question. 'By the way, did you see your lover last night?'

'I stayed in, remember? I watched the box, did a bit of sewing and read some magazines. Am I walking funny or something?'

'Just wondering. Didn't Albert mind?'

'I told him you had your cousins round and that I was in your play.'

'But that was before tea.'

'He wasn't to know that, was he.'

'Poor Albert.'

'Yeah, I know.'

'You can't feel that sorry or you would give up your lover.'

'That would be like you being told you could never ride a horse for the rest of your life.'

'If you'd gone out with him instead of being in my play, you'd have made both Albert and me happy.'

'Here we go,' said Dawn. 'Look, I've said I'm sorry. I thought you was meant to have a sense of humour.'

'I have. "Waiter, waiter, there's a spider in my soup!" "That's no spider, madam, that's one of Dawn's false eyelashes!"'

'That happened to me once. It fluttered down into me beer.'

'What did you do?'

'I pretended to have a coughing fit and rushed into the Ladies with me beer and stuck it back on. He took a barbie overdose – you know, Stephen Ward.'

'You mean he surrounded himself with Barbie dolls?' I said, and Dawn said, 'That vicar of yours sounds a right one; sex scandals two weeks on the trot. What did he have to say about Stephen Ward?'

'He said he must have been a weak character, and suicide was a sin and the easy way out and ...'

'Easy way out! He was driven to it, poor sod. By people like your vicar. And the only crime he committed was that he had an eye for a pretty face.'

That phrase again ...

'I can't see what Mr Rackham had to do with Stephen Ward committing suicide.'

'Not him as such. The likes of him. Respected members of society, all holier than thou, the sort who think their shit doesn't stink.'

I thought about this expression. Although extremely vulgar, it

255

was definitely one of Dawn's better ones.

'I reckon the likes of your vicar are just jealous of Stephen Ward,' she said. 'There aren't many men who can have more or less any girl they want. Yeah, that's it, they were jealous. They thought to themselves "Right, he's had his fun. Time to put the boot in."'

'I wonder if Stephen Ward will go to heaven,' but even as I said it it occurred to me, the way when you're younger it occurs to you that Father Christmas doesn't really exist, that heaven was just another lie adults told children.

'That depends on whether God thinks liking pretty women is a sin.'

'And committing suicide,' I said. 'Mr Rackham said it was a sin and against the law.'

'How can it be against the law once you're dead? The cops are hardly likely to come knocking on your coffin saying "Come out, dead or alive", are they?'

Why was it, I wondered, that Dawn always had to have the last word?

In some areas, Snuff Mull wasn't working at all. Aunt Lynette was no nearer finding a husband, and Brian Pike continued to kill animals (a fresh stoat and a magpie had been added to Death Row that morning). In other areas he was working in waves. I had waves of feeling very fond of Dawn, Dawn had waves of feeling very fond of Albert, and Granny had waves of being back to her old self. And in some areas, he was working one hundred per cent. For on Monday, Mr Ridley delivered not only a letter with a French stamp (or as Dawn vulgarly called it, a French Letter) but a letter for Dan addressed in girl's handwriting.

Hilary Wentworth-Smith had enclosed a photograph of herself and Dan at the end-of-term school dance, which he passed round the breakfast table. Their arms were encircled one another's waist. Dan wore a bow tie and his face looked smooth and shiny and his hair as short and neat as a head boy's. He was smiling a proper, cheeky, handsome smile, not the sneering, lip-curling scowling leer he was working hard on these days. If Hilary Wentworth-Smith could see him now she'd have a fit. Or perhaps now that he had heard from her he'd transform back into his normal self.

She wasn't quite how I'd imagined her, but she looked very nice. She had long hair, parted in the middle, that was probably the colour of a Rich Tea biscuit. She wore a long satin dress, probably ice blue, with a round neck and a high waist so you couldn't really tell what her figure was like. It looked quite frail and not the sort you would associate with bearing six strapping sons. She certainly didn't appear to have much in the way of bosoms, and the top of her head was on the same level as Dan's nose so she was quite tall. She had a slightly pointed weasel-like face, very *au naturel* which of course was what Dan liked, and was smiling but with her mouth closed, which made you wonder in passing whether she had something to hide in the teeth direction; perhaps they were long yellow horse's ones or black stumpy witch's ones. Her eyes were probably pale blue. Overall, she definitely wasn't the female version of Elvis Presley or Mr Richards, but nevertheless looked terribly nice and quite top-drawerish and very, very kind which, after all, was the most important thing.

'She looks very nice – indeed,' I said.

'Coo, she's tall,' said Hattie. 'And look at you, Dan. You look like, er . . .'

'A scout master,' I said.

'Or a hero in a comic who gets a medal for catching a wicked robber red-handed,' said Hattie. 'You've changed out of all recognition.'

'Glad to hear it,' said Dan. 'I'd rather be the wicked red-handed robber any day.'

'Let's have a butcher's then,' said Dawn, and I said I thought she was already engaged to one.

I studied her face for signs of jealousy, but it remained as blank as if she were studying a train timetable or an advertisement for Scott's Porridge Oats. 'Coo, I bet those pearls are real,' she said. 'You've done all right for yourself there, I reckon, Dan.'

Typical, I thought, that her type should judge people by their jewellery. And typical, too, that she should look at the photograph before Granny.

'Hurry up, Dawn, Granny wants to see it,' I said though in fact Granny was staring at her untouched bloater as if it were a painting of a tranquil country scene hanging in an art gallery.

'Yeah, have a butcher's at your possible future granddaughter-in-law, Mrs Aitch,' said Dawn grinning at Dan, and thrust the photo at Granny who, caught unawares, dropped it. I dived under the table to pick it up. Dawn had her shoes off and her and Dan's knees were moderately close, though nowhere near touching. Granny's knees, I couldn't help noticing, weren't neatly together like the old Granny's would have been even when they weren't on show, but wide apart like a boy's.

'Here you are, Granny.'

'Oh, she does look nice,' she said. 'What an attractive young lady.' But she hadn't held the photo at arm's length so it must have just been a misty blur.

Dan let me read her letter. It was on blue Queen's Velvet and written in black ink with a thin-nibbed fountain pen. Her writing sloped slightly, and was very neat and quite grown-up. It didn't start with 'Darling' or 'Sweetheart' or 'My own love' or even 'Honey' or 'Sugar' (though the last two would have been unlikely seeing as how she wasn't American); nor was there SWALK on the back of the envelope. *Dear Dan* it said and went on about her holiday in the Lake District and seeing Beatrix Potter's house. *I expect you'll have started the harvest by now. Do you actually drive the combine? How fearfully brave if you do (they're so monstrously fierce-sounding – and looking). And all that dust can't be good for the lungs.* She ended up by saying, *Simply longing to see you again – perhaps we can manage a few days together before you head south for Cambridge's ivory towers and I head north for Leeds' smoky ones. It seems* yonks *since I saw you last. Keep well, and don't do anything I wouldn't! Lots of love, H,* and three kisses. *PS Thought you'd be interested in seeing the enclosed. Isn't it a scream – and don't we both look* innocent!

All in all, it wasn't the kind of love letter you'd tie in a red ribbon and hide in the attic and years later would be found and auctioned at Sotheby's for thousands of pounds. If I was yearning to see the man I loved, if I was sobbing into my pillow every night because I was missing him so much, I wouldn't use the word *yonks*. Or perhaps she didn't want Dan to know she was in love with him. At least she'd said 'Don't do anything I wouldn't'. And did that reference to looking innocent mean that after the photo was taken Dan had his wicked way with her so they were no longer innocent? But the important thing was she'd written and Dan seemed pleased and Dawn wasn't jealous in the slightest.

I read Mummy's letter – written on funny blue lavatory paper – over and over again, and I didn't find one tiny morsel of a clue that divorce was in the wind. They were now in Brittany by the sea at a place called La Boule. *Daddy goes for a swim every morning before breakfast while I lounge in bed,* she wrote. *You know how fearfully energetic he is on holiday. I keep teasing him about his nose which has turned as pink as a salmon. The food is out of this world and we're making utter pigs of ourselves. At this rate, the first thing I'll have to do when I get home is to join Mrs Peake's dreaded Keep Fit class.* Daddy added a bit about the weather being marvellous – *blue skies every day. Mummy and I lie on the beach roasting like peanuts.* He told us how he'd eaten frogs' legs – *they tasted like rather stringy*

258

chicken, and he hoped harvest would soon be underway and that the cricket match was in hand. We must all be getting very excited about the Show, the first one he'd be missing since it started. Mummy finished by saying it wouldn't be long now before we were all together again, and they were thinking about us every day.

I pictured them lying on the beach reading their detective novels, rubbing suntan lotion on each other's backs, Mummy laughing at Daddy's salmon-pink nose and pulling a face at his frogs' legs. Under those relaxed, happy conditions she was bound to be 'doing the business'. How could they possibly be thinking of getting divorced?

After breakfast I followed Dan to his room. It looked like a jumble sale.

'Judging by the letter it doesn't sound as though divorce is on the cards, does it,' I said.

He sat on his unmade bed tuning his guitar. 'Suppose it doesn't,' he said, twanging away. 'Does that sound in tune?'

'You don't care whether they divorce or not,' I said. 'Just because you've *had* your childhood and don't need a home and family any more. It just so happens that Hattie and I do.'

He touched my arm and said, 'Look, Sausage, even if they do split up – and the chances are they won't – it won't make that much difference to your life. In fact it might even do you good. It might mean you and Hattie won't end up a rebel without a cause like me.'

'What would do us good?' said Hattie walking in. 'Blimey, Sarah, your face is beetroot. Why might we not end up as rebels without a cause? I'm not going to leave this room until you tell me, even if it means standing here for a hundred days.'

'Er, if we had stayed here instead of going to Aunt Daphne's,' I said at the same time that Dan said, 'You might as well know. There's the faintest chance that Mater and Pater will get a divorce.'

'Dan!' How could he! He had betrayed me! Never again would I trust him, the same way that Hattie would never again trust me.

Hattie looked at us both, her bright eyes flashing behind her spectacles. 'Sarah! You lied to me! You promised you never would and now you have. You've ganged up against me. Just because I'm the youngest doesn't mean I shouldn't know what's going on.'

'I only didn't tell you because a) it would upset you and b) it's not even true. It's only a foul rumour, started by the foul Dawn.'

'And the foul you didn't tell me,' said Hattie.

'And the foul Dan did,' I snapped. 'Why *did* you tell her?'

'We did agree to have no secrets from one another,' said Dan looking sheepish.

259

'Exactly,' said Hattie and stuck her tongue out at me. 'Anyway, it's not true, is it? They're always hugging and kissing each other. Or quite often, anyway. You wouldn't kiss someone unless you loved them, would you?'

'Of course you wouldn't,' I said.

Just my luck I was proved a liar again. For later that very morning we had to kiss the two great aunts, not bcause we loved them necessarily but because it was the done thing.

The way you couldn't imagine rabbits living in birds' nests or otters in pig sties, you couldn't imagine the two great aunts living anywhere but in Flint Cottage, which reminded you of Little Grey Rabbit's house. It was tucked up in a blanket of gnarled apple trees and in the golden olden days had been part of the Gressenham Estate. Now it was three miles away from the edge of it and belonged to another village. It was a cluttered, fuddy-duddy, low-ceilinged cottage that sometimes smelt so strongly of damp cat fur and dead flower water you felt like holding your breath until you were in the fresh air.

Once Dan almost brained himself on a wooden beam. He reeled round and round theatrically, clutching his head and muttering that he was seeing stars, and Hattie and I, knowing he was putting it on, rushed into the garden and nearly choked to death, while from within we heard Great Aunt Beth screech, 'He might have permanent brain damage, poor lamb. Fetch the smelling salts at the double, Gertie!' From then on, 'Fetch the smelling salts at the double, Gertie!' became a family catchphrase.

Both great aunts were long and thin like mops, with white untidy hair that was kept out of their eyes with tortoiseshell slides. They wore pre-World-War-One black button shoes and thick Ovaltine-coloured stockings and mothball-smelling print dresses teachers wear in very old school photographs. Great Aunt Beth had a white whiskery beard and Great Aunt Gertie was rather deaf. (*Question what's worse: to have white whiskers or be slightly deaf? To be slightly deaf. You can always shave your whiskers. PS Unless you have to spend the rest of your life with Dawn. Then it would be an advantage to be deaf!!!!*)

Great Aunt Beth did the cooking and was an expert on old farm buildings. Great Aunt Gertie did the gardening and was an expert on *Times* crosswords. The way they talked and walked reminded you a bit of Grandpa, but nothing else did. Grandpa had been much louder and ruder and rounder and more hot-tempered. Great Aunt Beth's claim to fame was that she had never visited a doctor once in her seventy-seven years. Great Aunt Gertie's was that she had got an albatross on the fifteenth hole at the local golf club. They had both driven ambulances in France during the First World War, which gave you something to boast about at school. For as long as I could remember they had been old but never gaga. 'Tough Old Birds' Dan called them. They didn't have a television and rattled around in Carruthers, a black Ford Eight complete with running boards.

'So you two survived the winter, I see,' said Dan jovially, his head skimming a beam by a whisker accidentally on purpose to raise their blood pressure. They said only just, it was reminiscent of the last war as they had lived on tins for weeks, and do watch your head, pet lamb.

We sat at the dining-room table surrounded by sideboards and writing desks and dried flowers in glass cases and willow-pattern plates hanging on the walls and dusty books behind glass-cabinet doors, and tucked into delicious beef pie with hard-boiled eggs in it (the first decent meal we'd had since we arrived in Norfolk, and there was plenty of it, too).

They asked us about school and Cambridge and Great Aunt Beth asked Dan how his grandmother was. (They always directed their questions at Dan because he was the last of the Hillington line, which infuriated me and Hattie.)

Dan said she had been feeling a bit under the weather, but the great aunts didn't seem to show much concern, and not for the first time did I wonder whether they were jealous of Granny having the hall to herself while they had to make do with Flint Cottage.

Hattie told them about Dawn. Dan interjecting every now and again to say 'She's not *that* bad' and they both looked horrified and Great Aunt Beth put her head in her hands and for a nasty moment I thought she was going to cry.

'How's Lawrence, by the way?' I asked to cheer them up. I knew he hadn't died because I'd spotted his water bowl by the Raeburn.

The way, say, Mrs Simpson was Edward VIII's downfall, Lawrence was the great aunts'. Lawrence (named after T. E. rather than D. H.) was an enormous smelly tomcat. He was white with black splodges in unexpected places and was almost as big as a panda. If he was a human, he would almost certainly be an East End bookie or a card sharp or a second-hand car salesman. He was always playing tricks on them, like bringing in dead mice and hiding them in crafty places that took them days to track down because their sense of smell was on the blink. ('Now, tell us, Dan dear. Is it our imaginations or can we smell *mouse*?' and Dan would wrinkle up his nose and say 'Do you mean dead or alive?')

'Who, dear?'

'Lawrence.'

The two great aunts slapped their hands across their mouths and looked at each other in horror. Then, even though it was the middle of lunch, they leapt to their feet and began calling and fussing and flustering and wringing their paws like Tabitha Twitchit.

'Oh, where are you, you naughty naughtikins,' cried Great Aunt Beth, getting down on all fours and peering under the writing desk.

'Come to Mummy, my precious,' wailed Great Aunt Gertie, striding into the hall. 'Really, Beth, you should never have let the poor soul out of the kitchen. You know how strangers unsettle him', and Great Aunt Beth snapped that if cats were meant to spend their life in a kitchen they would have been born with a handle or a spout, which I thought terribly funny and was dying to add, 'Or a silver spoon in their mouth.'

Reluctantly leaving our beef pie to get cold, we joined in the search. Dan eventually found him in an apple tree, and had to climb up to get him. In the car going home he swore that Lawrence had winked at him, man to man, as if to say, 'Fooled the old dears again.'

'You can't blame the poor old devil,' Dan said. 'Can you imagine having those two fussing round you all day. I'm surprised he isn't made to wear a vest and carry an umbrella.'

'I can think of worse sorts of lives for a cat,' I said. 'At least he's well fed – and loved.'

'Smothered, more like,' said Dan. 'Let those two be a lesson to you. You don't want to end up dotty cat-loving spinsters. These things do run in families, you know.'

'We wouldn't, would we, Sarah?' said Hattie. 'We don't like cats. They've got evil eyes.'

'Er, no,' I said though I did quite like them. Not as much as horses or dogs but I still quite liked them. 'Lawrence gives them a purpose in life, the way Clifford gives Granny one. And it's not their fault they're spinsters. There just weren't enough men to go round after the First World War. I wonder why they got so unnecessarily upset about Dawn? We didn't paint *that* bad a picture. Anyway, you should be grateful to Lawrence. It was thanks to him they forgot to remind you about being the last of the Hillington Line.'

'I rather wish they had, actually,' said Dan. 'I had my answer all ready.'

'What was it?'

'Not telling. You'll have to wait till next year. If I'm here next year. If I'm not playing to thousands of rapturous swooning fans at Carnegie Hall – or raving it up at the Whiskey A-Go-Go on Sunset Boulevard in Los Angeles.'

'Did you know, Dan, that your whiskers are twice as long and three times as unbecoming as Aunt Beth's?' I said to change the subject.

The day, as it turned out, was to go down in family history – or in my diary, at any rate – as The Day of the Missing Pets.

As we drove down the drive we encountered Granny wandering like a wild-haired demented ghost in an old grey mac. When she saw us she flapped her arms like a large, wild-haired bird or one of the Railway Children stopping the train minus a red flannel petti-coat. Dan had to jam on the brakes to avoid hitting her.

'You haven't encountered Clifford on your travels, have you, darlings?' she said as if Clifford was a postman on his bicycle or the ice-cream man. 'He's vanished, and I'm so afraid he's been caught in one of Mr Pike's traps. I'm sure I heard yelping in the distance, but perhaps it was just me.'

'Did Granny mean it was *her* yelping in the distance?' I said to Hattie as we set off to search for Clifford.

Soon the afternoon air was filled with whistles and different voices shouting 'Clifford!' Near the black summerhouse we met Dawn. Thank goodness I'd drawn the curtains so she couldn't peer in at Snuff Mull.

'I thought he might have got run over by a train but I can't see no squashed dog.'

'Perhaps we should look in the Aga to check we can't see no *hot* dog.'

'I don't think it's no laughing matter,' said Dawn. 'If he's snuffed it. I reckon your gran'll go off of her trolley.'

'She hasn't got a trolley to go off *of*. Anyway, why should you care? She's not your grandmother,' said Hattie, as we trampled through the wild tangly undergrowth like explorers in Africa, keeping a careful watch out that you weren't about to squelch on dead dog – or come to that dead anything else. It was easy to mistake dead leaves for live stoats, and I was sure I saw a rat's face snarling in the weedy, reedy undergrowth, but when I got closer it was just a knot of brambles.

'No but she's my employer – and I'd like to think my mate, too. I like her – love her, if you must know,' and her voice sounded as though there were tears in her eyes. Then she ruined it by adding. 'Besides, if Clifford's pegged it I'm going to have nothing to kick.'

263

It was Dan who found Clifford. He carried him wrapped in a sack and you knew straight away Clifford had snuffed it because his face was covered, too.

Unlike the two great aunts if Lawrence had been found dead, Granny didn't cry, but just said in her quiet church voice, her hair still wild and her body very small – why, she was shrinking before our very eyes, like Alice – that perhaps we should bury him in the garden, and I said couldn't he go in the Hillington graveyard and Granny said he wasn't quite important enough for that. Dawn said between sobs, that were louder than the Stephen Ward ones but not as loud as the I-don't-like-her ones, that if it was one of Pike's traps that done it she'd personally go and knock his block off and Dan said he'd died peacefully by the looks of things and Granny said quietly, 'Did he, Dan? That makes things a lot easier, doesn't it', and we all knew Dan was lying, why, a small patch of blood had oozed through the sack and you wouldn't bleed from natural causes, but if it made Granny happy . . .

'He was very old, wasn't he,' I said and then went red because Granny was very old, too.

'Just so long as he didn't suffer,' she said, and sighed softly.

When we were out of Granny's earshot we asked if we could see Clifford because otherwise how were we to know it was him? For all we knew it was a fox or a sack of potatoes, so Dan lifted the sack a little to show us his little grey stumpy tail and Dawn started howling and said, 'Oh, gawd, it really brings it home, don't it,' and even I felt quite tearful but refused to give in and cry because that would be a Dawn thing to do.

'Was he caught in a snare?' I asked and Dan said the less said about it the better; he was dead, that was the important thing.

'Was he dead when you found him?' I asked and Dan muttered, 'Just forget it, okay?'

We chose Clifford's favourite sunbathing spot by the wall of the kitchen garden near the walnut tree where the missing-servant photograph was taken. Dan and I did the digging. I said a nice little prayer and even Dawn and the wood pigeon kept quiet through it. We covered him, still wrapped in the sack, with earth, and Hattie planted the cross she'd made from two sticks, and rested a bit of card on it that said *In loving memory of Clifford Hillington, who will be sawly missed by us all, espeshly Granny* and Dan planted a poppy in the grave. Dawn's only contribution apart from howling was to say you're positive he's dead, Dan, and not just asleep, that was her worst nightmare, being buried alive, could you imagine?

*　　　*　　　*

Maybe to keep her mind off dead dogs and wounded cars, Granny went on and on all through tea about Marshall and Snelgrove, her favourite department store, closing their doors for the last time.

'It's been going since 1815. When it was called Chamberlins, it was advertised as one of the Three Cs of Norwich, along with the cathedral and castle,' she said sadly, and poor Granny; in the space of two days she has lost three things most dear to her: her dog, her car and her favourite department store.

After tea Dan went to a rehearsal and Dawn, Hattie and I played croquet. Dawn's ball spent more time in the flower beds than on the lawn and if I'd been her I'd have got extremely bad-tempered but she just laughed, and perhaps that was one of the symptoms of being in love; that it made one good-natured.

Granny sat and watched, or rather gazed, a small lonely shrinking figure in a straw hat, and wouldn't join in even though it was her favourite game; nor would she come with us to the library van the next day, saying she really wasn't in the mood for reading.

'She's always loved reading,' I said as Hattie and I staggered down the drive with the basket of books to be returned while Dawn dinked in front with a tray of tea for Mrs Peabody the librarian and Mr Purse the driver. 'I can't imagine being in the library van without Granny.'

'Or Mrs B.'

'Or Mummy.'

'At least there'll still be fat Mrs Peabody and thin Mr Purse,' I said.

'No, there won't,' Dawn said. 'They've got a new bloke called Keith.'

On the side of the van was a shield depicting a lion with blue claws and a blue tongue. You climbed up three narrow steps to get in. With the sun flooding through its glass roof it was like being inside a quiet, warm, magical, book-lined summerhouse on wheels.

Normally you spent as long as you liked choosing your books because Mrs Peabody, who called you lovey and saved any new books for you, took ages to drink the teapot dry (and without fail she'd always say with a giggle. 'I hope we pass a convenient bush on the way back, Mr Purse,' and Mr Purse would fidget and grin). And while your knees prickled on the doormat carpet as you looked along the bottom shelf, there was lots of jolly background chatter going on about the WI and good books that had just been published and who in the neighbouring villages had got engaged to who and how much a whist drive or a church fête raised; a library van, I often considered, was English village life seen at its best.

265

But that was a thing of the past. Today the conversation consisted of the new bloke called Keith telling Dawn about someone called Jimmy who'd been nicked for speeding, and Dawn telling Keith about a new pop programme on television starting next Friday called *Ready Steady Go*.

Keith was a very different kettle of fish to both Mrs Peabody and Mr Purse. He swigged down his tea in a mouthful, and had the sort of rough and ready, wiry-sideboarded face that wouldn't take kindly to being kept waiting. He was big and burly and wore a gold chain in place of a tie. He handled the books clumsily like old bricks without first looking at the titles and saying, 'Now that's a jolly good read,' the way Mrs Peabody used to. Really, he would have looked far more at home on a building site than in a library van.

''Ere, I suppose you haven't got that book *The Carpetbaggers* by Harold Robbins, have you?' said Dawn and Keith said blast no, they weren't that up to date and if they were he'd be reading it himself; likewise *Fanny Hill*.

We each chose a book for Granny. Dawn chose *Thrush Green* by Miss Read, I chose, after much thought in case it was too frightening and/or the hound reminded her of Clifford, *The Hound of the Baskervilles* and Hattie chose *Powder and Patch* by Georgette Heyer because she said Granny would like the old-fashioned clothes on the cover. For ourselves, I chose my very favourite book, *The Lion, the Witch and the Wardrobe* and my second-favourite book, *The Railway Children* (I liked to pretend I was Bobby, who was kind and good and sensible which was why she was her mother's favourite), and *Jennings Goes to School*. Hattie chose *101 Dalmatians, The Family from One End Street* and a pony book.

Dawn, of course, had to choose one with love in the title – *Love in a Cold Climate* by Nancy Mitford whoever she was, *Claudine at School* by someone called Colette, and (what an incredible coincidence!) *Wuthering Heights* by Emily Brontë.

'That's meant to be really good,' I said. 'According to my teacher, it's very atmospheric and full of passion.'

'Blimey, there's enough passion in my life already, ta very much,' said Dawn and Keith looked up from his book-stamping, winked and said, 'Aren't we the lucky one.' And were my eyes playing tricks or did their fingers touch, very briefly, as he handed her her books?

'How do you know Keith?' I asked Dawn as we trundled up the drive. He would definitely be included on my list of lover suspects.

'From the library van, of course,' she said. 'Oh, and come to think of it I bumped into him at town-hall dances a few times.'

I couldn't think of anything to ask that would reveal whether or

266

not he was her lover, so I said, 'He seemed very nice. Quite handsome in, er, a rugged sort of way.'

'I didn't think so,' said Hattie. 'I thought he looked like a wrestler, and he didn't seem interested in books at all.'

'That's hardly surprising,' said Dawn. 'He was trimming hedges until a few months ago.'

'But now he's turned over a new leaf, has he?' I said and we all laughed, but mine wasn't sincere laughter. What was the world coming to if people could be hedge-trimmers one minute and librarians the next?

On a fresh page in the diary I wrote:

POSSIBLE CANDADATES FOR DAWN'S LOVER
1. *Brian Pike (quite likely).*
2. *The man on the building site who looked like Adam Faith.*
3. *The American in the pink car.*
4. *Mr English (unlikely as he has a pretty wife already).*
5. *Dan (unlikely as he's too young & in love with someone else).*
6. *Rupert (unlikely as he's too young and prone to spots).*
7. *Jeremy the estate agent.*
8. *Keith the librarian.*
9. *Ronnie Bone.*
10. *Someone I don't know.*
11. *No one; her lover is just a figmant of her imagination.*
12. *All of them. One on each night of the week and Albert in between!!!*

CHAPTER TWENTY

Dawn and I cycled through the crossfire of wolf-whistles into Shotestead to run some errands for Granny and in my case run one for Dawn, too.

She wanted me to take a message to Albert, a written one this time.

'Is it good news or bad? Because if it's bad I'm not taking it.'

'You need never know, need you,' she said. 'Buy you an ice after.'

'It's the last time I ever do you a favour.'

Albert was alone in the shop. He had cut his chin shaving and had either started using Brylcreem or his hair was in need of a wash. He'd parted it differently, too, in the middle, which made him look like a spiv. If only, I thought, he could be just a shade more handsome and, well, *with it*.

He was chopping meat as fiercely as if it were made of wood. His brow glistened with sweat. If I had had my camera, the mood of the photograph would have been muscle and gristle and grease and blood. Suddenly a wave of sadness washed over me. Poor, poor Albert, with his funny hair and sweaty brow, slaving over a hot meat counter in order to buy a bungalow with a utility room for his unfaithful fiancée.

Swallowing my tears I walked in.

Albert grinned, stopped chopping, wiped his bloody hands on his bloody apron and said, 'Hello there. Are you all right then?'

'Yes, thank you.'

'Did your old play go all right then?'

'Er, yes, thanks. In parts, anyway. We didn't really have enough rehearsals.'

'Was Dawn all right?'

I said she over-acted a bit and he laughed and said 'That's her all over! Is she all right then?' and I said. 'Yes, fine. By the way we won't be needing any more bones for Clifford because he's dead.' Then I handed him the cheap crinkled brown envelope and said. 'For you. Sorry, Albert, I must dash. See you soon.'

My instincts told me, as I hurried down White Lion Street, that things had gone too smoothly by half, and they were right. For lo and behold, a firm hand was grasping my shoulder like a store detective's.

He was still wearing his white and blood apron. Close up the cut on his chin looked quite deep and for a second I thought of Dawn's long pink nails. Also close up you could see lines below his eyes and on his forehead. Poor Albert. He was obviously going through a harrowing patch and goodness, whatever he wanted must be quite important to leave the shop unattended.

'Look, Sarah, what the devil's she a-playing at?' His voice had turned gruff like a man pretending to be Father Christmas. 'I know you're only a kid, but she confides in you, don't she.'

'Not really,' I said, starting to tremble. 'Well, not about personal things, anyway.'

'She told me she did. You see,' and he looked down at his brown, big, square, round shoes as if the words he was looking for were on the toes or hidden in the laces, 'she's right twisting me up inside at the moment. Has she gone off me or what? What the bugger's going on?'

He looked like man on the brink of either bursting into tears or smashing a plate-glass window with his bare fist, and for the first time, I felt afraid of him. 'She never seems to want to see me no more, and we're meant to be getting wed in the autumn. What's happening?'

My heart felt like a tomtom trying to escape from a small, strong safe as I explained about Clifford and Austin of England and Marshall and Snelgrove and as a result Granny needed quite a lot of looking after temporarily, but I was sure Dawn still loved him, she was just a bit busy at the moment. I also wanted to say that if he bought himself a pair of Chelsea boots, say, and learnt how to dance properly, and somehow made himself more interesting – perhaps he could design men's clothes, and show more of an interest in pop music – if he didn't cut his chin shaving or have his hair in a centre parting and perhaps washed it more often, if he tried to be just a shade more sophisticated and wordly, perhaps she'd love him even more, but I didn't know him well enough to tell him these things.

Albert studied my face and said, 'You are telling the truth, are you, Sarah? Because if you're not ... You see, I get the feeling she's gone and got herself a fancy man. Am I right, kiddo? I won't tell her you told me,' and he gripped my arm with his bloodstained hand as tight as an oar in a storm.

My whole body was shaking like fury and my face felt as though it was about to catch fire, and please let him think I'm blushing because I'm only eleven and shouldn't know about such things as fancy men. Come to think of it, for all I knew she *didn't* have a fancy man. I had no evidence, after all.

'I don't know. She wouldn't tell my anything like that. Honestly, Albert.'

Was it fear that made me add 'honestly'? That made me even more of a liar. And what right did he have to call me *kiddo* and use his superior physical strength to trap me? Why, come to think of it, should I be in danger of having a nervous breakdown over a private matter between a butcher's son and a common maid? I had better things to worry about.

His troubled pond eyes searched my hot, miserable face for clues that I might be lying. 'No gents called at the house, no strange motors parked in the drive?'

At last I had the chance to tell the truth. 'No,' I said firmly. 'And please let go of my arm, you're hurting.'

He released his grip and shook his head. 'Women. Can you make head nor tail of them because I sure as hell can't.'

'No,' I said, anxious to agree with him on something. 'She's quite a complex character, Dawn. There's more to her than meets the eye.' Should I, I wondered, point out all her bad faults in the hope he'd go off her and find a nice ordinary Norfolk girl to marry?

'That there is. I suppose that's her attraction,' he said sadly. 'Blast, it's a rum'un. Here am I, a simple, straightforward, down-to-earth bloke leading a quiet, straightforward sort of a life and then suddenly I find myself driven half-crazy by that bugger of a thing they call love.'

'Oh, Albert.' I said, feeling genuinely sorry for him, 'yes, love does seem to cause more trouble than it's worth.'

Suddenly he seemed to pull himself together. 'Tell you what. You tell her from me,' and he wagged a thick red sausage finger covered in pale hairs, 'That I'm crazy about her and never stop thinking about her, and if I find out she's been playing silly buggers, I'll – slit my throat. You tell her that, will you?'

Two women walked past discussing the price of Victoria plums, and a small boy whined for a raspberry ice lolly. All around people were going about their normal daily busines and there was I, in the middle of White Lion Street, discussing slitting throats!

First Stephen Ward taking a barby overdose and now Albert thret-ening to slit his throat. What is the world coming to! I would write. I wondered, in passing, if anyone would ever feel strongly enough about me to slit their throat.

'Albert, you couldn't! You'd be breaking the law – and going against the church.'

'Bugger the law – and the church. I won't care, once I'm gone. The boys in blue won't be tapping on my coffin and saying, "We're coming to get you, dead or alive"', and we both laughed nervously and I said that's just what Dawn said about Stephen Ward so you obviously share the same sense of humour and Albert said, 'She's always going on about that ponce,' and looked at his shoes again. His trousers, I noticed, were a shade too short, and revealed light blue socks with dark blue diamonds. Nylon, not wool.

'The thing is,' I said, 'there are lots more nice girls you could marry. Dawn needn't be the only, er, contestant for your heart. I mean if, and I'm not saying she has at all because I don't know, she were to have a fancy man, you'd have no trouble finding another girl. You're very er, illegible, you know,' and I blushed again in case he thought *I* wanted to marry him.

'Listen, kiddo,' said Albert, the ponds narrowing into two murky streams, in a sinister, un-Albert-like way. 'One day when you're crazy about someone you'll understand how I feel. And I'll tell you this for nothing. I don't recommend it. It's sheer hell on earth.'

'That's the last message I ever take for you. I'm really furious with you,' I said, pedalling at the double over the hump-back bridge. 'Why did you tell Albert you confided in me?'

'I didn't. He was worried I might be lonely at the hall and I said I had you to talk to. That's all.'

'Well, he thinks you've got a fancy man. Don't worry. I didn't give anything away. I deserve to go in the *Guinness Book of Records* for being the best liar in the world.'

I gave her a watered-down version of the conversation because I didn't want Albert to sound too desperate. I didn't water down the throat-slitting bit, though.

'Oh, gawd, he's using emotional blackmail now, is he?'

'I don't blame him. He's madly in love, and you know what that can do to a person.'

'Too right I do,' said Dawn.

'Is there anything Albert can do to make you love him?' I asked, and Dawn said ner, it was all to do with chemistry. 'The thing is, I know I'll never find a bloke I get on so well with, but ... I suppose if he played a bit harder to get I might be more interested.'

'Why?'

'Human nature. The chase is more exciting than the catch. Take that hunting lark you lot go in for. Where would the excitement be

271

if the fox just sat there in the middle of the field saying "Here I am!"'

It was interesting she should liken Albert to a fox. He had been a fox in one of my dreams.

'I suppose what it boils down to is sex appeal. I mean, however hard you look at Albert you wouldn't call him sexy, would you.'

'He has a very nice physique.'

'So has President de Gaulle,' said Dawn, panting to keep up. 'Why do you think Elvis Presley has sex appeal and Gerry and the Pacemakers don't?'

I wanted to say I don't know and I don't care, but instead I said. 'Because Elvis wiggles his bottom.'

'Because Gerry and the Pacemakers have those eager-to-please boy-next-door faces, the sort of faces that would run a mile just to open a door for you, and who'd probably thank you after kissing them, whereas Elvis is mean, moody and magnificent: he gives the impression he wouldn't give a monkey's about you, it's that look in his eye that says "If you want me, have me. Personally. I don't give a shit". D'yer see what I'm getting at?'

'Yes. That you like rude, ill-behaved men who don't care about you. But say you're really ill with pneumonia or something. Would you like him just to sneer his lip at you and go off to a public house? The sort of man you're talking about is the sort to have a brief love affair with if you must but not marry. You want someone kind to marry, someone who will take care of you when you're ill and old.'

'Actually, you have a point there.'

'Anyway, Albert certainly didn't have a boy-next-door face just now. He was mean, moody and magnificent – and angry – and rude. And his lip curled. I was really frightened of him.'

'I just wish he wasn't so smothering.'

Like the great aunts and Lawrence. 'It's only because he loves you. I think you're foul.'

'Yeah, I know,' she said, and we cycled along in silence for awhile.

'By the way, I don't care two hoots who your lover is any more,' I said in the hope that she might slacken her security arrangements. 'You're still seeing him, I take it?'

'Yeah. Off and on. What's been the happiest moment of your life?'

I thought. Was it when Mr Richards walked into the classroom? If it was, I certainly wasn't going to tell her that. 'I'm not sure.'

'How about when you watch *Champion the Wonder Horse*? You know that nice feeling it gives you. Multiply that by a hundred say. That's how I feel when I'm with my lover. When I'm with him I'm

272

the happiest I've ever been in my whole life.'

'And Albert's the unhappiest he's ever been in his whole life.'

'Yeah, but you have to make hay while the sun shines. Knowing my luck, after this summer the sun might never shine on me again.'

'And then you'll have to make hay while the sun doesn't shine by marrying Albert. Assuming he hasn't slit his throat by then. And talking of hay, if you don't marry him, finding another man as nice as him to marry will be like looking for a needle in a *hay*stack.'

'Yeah,' said Dawn and groaned. 'That's the trouble. I dunno. I really dunno. One way or another, I have an 'orrible feeling it's all going to end in tears.'

Dear Albert,
Here is some advice, but you must promise never to tell Dawn I told you. Start being just a tiny bit rude to her, and ignore her sometimes. Perhaps you could start a hobby – desining men's clothes, for example – so that she isn't the centre of your life. As love is to do with chemistry, perhaps you could change your aftershave. Most of all be mean, moody and magnifacant like Elvis Prezly, if possible. (NB she hasn't said any of these things, it is me reading between the lines.) Incadently, she does love you tramendasly and knows she will never meet another bloke who she gets on as well with, so don't worry! Good luck!
Love, Sarah

Even though I was fond of Albert, I decided he didn't deserve any kisses because he'd frightened me and called me kiddo. I did put STRICKTLY PRIVATE on the envelope, though.

I cycled into the village to post it. Dawn was bound to spot it on the chest in the hall, especially as her library books were still there (we always had to put ours away immediately, so how come she didn't have to?).

When I returned I looked idly through them. *Love in a Cold Climate* seemed to be about silly top-drawer people. Maybe Dawn was hoping to pick up a few tips.

The cover of *Wuthering Heights* was of a man and a woman standing on a mauve, purple and green Yorkshire Moor. Two birds hovered like vultures in a thunderous sky. The woman wore a low red dress with short sleeves which in my opinion was most unsuitable for a bleak, blustery moor. She had light brown windswept hair, red lipstick to match her dress and thin, arched eyebrows. She was very beautiful. She wasn't looking at the man but far, far away. The man wore a white shirt, a brown jacket, brown trousers with

273

leggings and black lace-up shoes. He had one foot resting on a rock, and was drumming his knee with his fist. He had black hair, black eyebrows and a square jaw like the heroes in Dan's old *Eagle* comics. He was very, very handsome and not unlike Mr Richards in some ways. I flipped through the pages to see if I could find any passionate bits and also so that I would be one step ahead of everyone else if Mr Richards discussed the book next term.

It appeared to be full of people being rough and rude to each other in broad Yorkshire accents. Someone called Heathcliff thundered about the place, shouting and calling people toothless hounds and vipers and damning people in hell and yearning to crush out worms' entrails. And there was someone called Miss Cathy, a 'haughty headstrong creature'. And then I found a bit that I supposed in the literary world, though not in Dawn's, could be called passionate. Cathy was wondering whether she should marry someone called Edgar Linton. He was, apparently, handsome and young and cheerful and rich and loved her; but she didn't love him the way she loved Heathcliff. *'I've no more business to marry Edgar Linton than I have to be in heaven...'* she said. *'It would degrade me to marry Heathcliff now; so he shall never know how I love him: and that, not because he's handsome, Nelly, but because he's more myself than I am. Whatever our souls are made of, his and mine are the same: and Linton's is as different as a moonbeam from lightning, or frost from fire.'*

How strange to think that all because of Dawn and her complicated love life I could understand perfectly a passage from a literary classic. Like Miss Cathy, Dawn and Albert's souls were as different as frost from fire, while her and her lover's were the same. Even so, if I had to choose between a rough rude ruffian like Heathcliff and a cheerful handsome gentleman like Edgar Linton. I knew who I'd go for.

I flipped through a few more pages. When Miss Cathy died in childbirth, *Heathcliff cried 'I* cannot *live without my soul!'* He dashed *his head against the knotted trunk; and, lifting up his eyes, howled, not like a man, but like a savage beast being goaded to death with knives and spears.'*

Wow! Now I could see what Mr Richards meant by passion! Clearly, Mr Heathcliff wasn't so bad after all. In fact I wouldn't say no to someone behaving like that when I died.

Claudine at School had a painting of a plump, sullen girl on the cover. The plot was summed up on the back. *Nowhere else have the intimate secrets of a 16-year-old girl been more frankly described than in this novel, originally published in 1900. Observant, impulsive,*

malicious, chastely sensual, Claudine becomes involved in an amazing
succession of emotional experiences, from flirting with the young
masters and being fondled by the visiting ex-inspector to the full-
blown Lesbian affair between Mlle Sergent, the passionate red-haired
headmistress, and Aimée, her tart little assistant . . .

This interested me greatly. Girls at school had talked about girls
having love affairs with each other, but you didn't really believe it –
not until you saw it printed on the back of a library book, anyway,
And then an extraordinary thought punched me between the eyes
like a boxing glove. Perhaps Dawn's fancy man wasn't a man at
all, but a woman! And if so, perhaps her lover was Aunt Lynette!
Perhaps her wanting to get married and have a baby was just one
of Dawn's red herrings to put me off the scent! 'I go for the more
mature type myself . . . Your aunt's like a breath of fresh air . . .'
And Granny saying 'I'm worried about Aunt Lynette. She's on the
brink of . . .' Becoming a lesbian, perhaps? And it explained perfectly
why Dawn couldn't walk off into the sunset with her lover!
The shame! The scandal! The stink if it got into the papers!
LESBIAN AFFAIR BETWEEN ARISTOCRATIC ARTIST AND
COCKNEY MAID.

There was no getting away from it; for the time being, at least, I
would have to add Aunt Lynette's name to the list of candidates.
'Al' she would be called. The matter would have to be handled with
great delicacy in my diary, for even Mr Richards might be a bit
shocked. Perhaps, if it wasn't too 'sucking-up' of me, I could weave
in the bit about Heathcliff and Cathy's souls being one. I was just
picturing Mr Richards's reaction to this literary turn of events,
when Hattie walked by.

'What on earth are you up to, smiling into thin air. Don't say
you've gone loopy, too. That'll only leave me round here who's
normal. Hey, and you're crying, too. How can you smile and cry
at once?'

'The same way that it can be rainy and be sunny at once,' I said.
'Except you won't find a rainbow about my person.'

'Blimey, there are some rum things going on round these parts,'
said Hattie, putting a postcard addressed to Uncle Mac, BBC, on
the chest. 'And no one tells me anything. But I don't care. And no
one, not even you, tell me off for saying blimey any more, so I'm
going to say it the whole time. Blimey, blimey, blimey, bottoms,
buggers, bastards, bloody. How come all rude words start
with b?'

'I'm buggered if I know,' I said, thinking about Aunt Lynette
and Dawn and Mr Heathcliff and Cathy and Albert and Mr Rich-

ards, but they all got jumbled into one person like a modern painting.

Dear Uncle Mac, I read when Hattie had gone outside.

This is my last time of writing to ask you to please, please play Champion the Wonder Horse for my sister Sarah. If you don't play it soon Sarah will have stoped liking it and will like fowl rocking roll instead. You will cheer up our lives inormosly if you do. I wont go into details but they need cheering up at the moment.

Yours trustingly,

Harriet Hillington (Miss)

PS When Sarah was younger she used to call in Champion No Wonder Horse. It used to be a family joke. Its not any more because we might not have a proper family for much longer.

PPS Sometimes Sarah pretends she is champion! She hasn't done it latly. Perhaps this is because she is now 11. I would be him if I could but I cant galop proply with my duf leg.

CHAPTER TWENTY-ONE

It was time for the harvest mice to jump for their lives without first having the chance to pack, and for the little black corn flies to take refuge down your neck and on your pillow and in your food. For the rampaging silver elephant had begun to thunder and plunder through the yellow fields devouring corn, poppies, pink convolvulus, white bindweed, fat hen and anything else unlucky enough to get in the way of its gnashing iron teeth.

The start of the harvest also heralded the start of the heatwave. it was as if the roar of the combine harvester was the electric motor which kept the heat turned on high. If the roar stopped the temperature would drop to normal.

The sky is bluer, the corn more golden, the grass and hedges greener than ever ever before, I wrote. *It's like watching a black and white film that half-way through becomes glorious technicolour.*

Here I sit in the freckled shade of the chestnut tree wrapped in a blanket of heat surrounded by butterfly-flitting countryside that even through my tiger sunglasses is so vivid that for once Dawn doesn't look too out of place.

What a contrast it all is to Wuthering Heights – as different as fire and frost.

Now Austin of England is in dock (and the GPO man has been to disconnect the telephone), our only form of escape into the outside world is a bicycle with no breaks, a pony with no breaks, and a pony by the name of Shanks!!!

'It's like this in California the whole time, lucky bastards,' Dawn said as the three of us lolled under the chestnut tree, idly topping and tailing gooseberries. 'Cor, I wish I could go topless like you two. It's such a drag having tits. You must make the most of it, especially you, Sarah. I reckon this is your last summer you'll be able to get away with it. Come next year, you'll be all trussed up with the best of us. In fact is it my imagination or can I see a bit of a blossoming there already?'

Hattie said 'How dare you make personal remarks about my sister,' and Dawn said, 'I'll tell you this for nothing. If it gets one degree hotter I'm going to strip off.'

I made a mental note to ask Snuff Mull to stop it getting any hotter, for what could be a more hideous sight than Dawn hoovering or picking raspberries with naked bosoms?

The heat affected us all in different ways. Dawn bounced about like Tigger, thriving on it like a flowering cactus; she told me it made her feel sort of free and sexy and I told her it must be the foreign blood in her.

Granny turned woollier by the minute, living in a world for her funny glass eyes only, snapping back into the present at unexpected moments. She took to her bed after lunch and didn't reappear till well past tea; one day she didn't get up at all, and we took meals on a tray to her neat, plain, Mrs Tittlemouse bedroom. Like the grandmother in Little Red Riding Hood when she's locked in the cupboard, she was no longer a major character in the scheme of things, but I never gave up hope that, like Dan and his pop group, it was just a phase and one day we'd wake up and she'd be back to normal and it wouldn't be long before this funny granny would be forgotten about like a person in a dream.

Aunt Lynette flopped about in a deckchair fanning herself with a bamboo fan and saying, 'Phew. It's just not British, and Dan, when he deigned to put in an appearance, snored flat out on his back in just a pair of denim shorts and no suntan lotion in the midday sun; 'Mad dogs and Englishmen ...' I said and he replied 'Woof.' Another time I said, 'You'd feel much cooler with short hair, Dan,' and he said no he wouldn't, it was stopping his neck getting sunburnt.

Hattie had turned rather quiet, but I don't think it was because of the heat. I kept telling her the parents weren't getting a divorce and she kept telling me to belt up about it. She took to sitting in the shade of the chestnut either reading a library book or playing with the model lead farm. She spent hours positioning and repositioning the pigs and sheep and cows and hens and round-mirror duck pond in the little fields. As for the farmer and his family, she became each character in turn, putting on a mother's voice to say breakfast was ready and a father's for suggesting a trip to the sea. Although I was no Sigmund Freud it wasn't hard to work out what was going on in her mind. (I also noticed the man with the gun and the blonde land girl in jodhpurs and a tight green jumper stayed in the box with the three-legged sheep and the cow with one horn.)

As for me, I didn't allow the heat to affect my plans at all. I did less galloping around than usual and, like the sandy-whiskered gentleman with Jemima Puddleduck, sat quietly looking over the top of my comic and observing all through my tiger sun-glasses. Suspicions were coming in as thick and fast as the corn flies; all were faithfully recorded in my diary.

1. Saw Dawn and Brian Pike smoking together in Shady Loke. (Dawn patted Yellow Dog's had, so they must know each other quite well.) Asked Dawn about it and she said she was just passing the time of day.

2. Mr English came to see Granny. While he waited for her to wake up. Dawn made him a cup of tea. She bent unneseserily low to get the milk out of the fridge and he looked right up her skirt – in fact he couldn't take his eyes off her! (I expect he wished I had made myself scarce!!) Dawn said I bet it gets lonely driving the combine and Mr English looked her straight into the eye and said yes it does, it gives you plenty of time to think things over (ie whether he should leave Mrs English and go off into the sunset with Dawn).

3. Rupert and Fiona came round in the hope of seeing Dan (who wasn't here, of course) and we played croquet. Rupert showed Dawn how to hold her mallett proply – he stood close behind her and put his arms round her. Dawn said, ''Ere, Rupert, you ain't getting fresh, are you? I'm not complaining, mind,' and R turned his usual trafficlight red and Fiona looked daggers drawn.

4. Nothing suspicious about Aunt L as yet, though if it is her they have to be extra careful for fear of scandel. She and Dawn laugh and joke as before, and Aunt L took her for a driving lesson on the stubble field in her MGB. NB (as opposed to MGB!) dark glasses are hampering my investigation here, seeing as how eyes are the window of the sole. In fact soles seem to be figuring in my life quite a lot what with W Heights, 'Praise my Sole' in church and, come to think of it, we had lemon sole for lunch todáy!!)

5. Nothing suspicious about Dan, either, but he's hardly ever here. (Dawn has complained about his 'pongy' feet, and on another occasion Dan said to her 'Granny doesn't get her money's worth out of you. You're bone idle!!!')

6. A tempry tracter driver called Johnnie has replaced Dan. He went on my list of suspects like a shot. He is dark and wild looking, has a fag permanently jutting out of his mouth like Andy Capp and has a cockney accent!!! I said to Dawn, 'Where did he spring from?' and Dawn said, 'London, juging by his accent.'

7. Ronnie Bone, Rick Benton and Greg Hannant, the other Wild Ones, are now firmly on the list. Dan invited them round the other day but instead of sitting in the garden or looking round the farm they

sat with Dawn in the hot kitchen smoking themselves to death. The
fug was to be seen to be believed.

8. No more signs of Keith, the hedge-cutting librarian – or should it
be the librarian-cutting hedge! Or the handsome Yank in the pink car.
Or any of my other suspects, but I can't be up 24 hours a day. Dan
has already asked if I'm going shopping with the bags under my eyes!

Dawn and I have started to go blackcurrent picking in order to
earn a bit of money – a bit being the operative word, as you only get
2/6 a basket which takes me nearly all afternoon to fill (though I do
eat quite a lot in order to get my vitamin C intake back to normal).
She uses the blackcurrent bush the way a cathlick uses a confession
box; I am the priest on the other side listening, nodding wisely and
advising. She seems to value my opinions more and more: on marrying
Albert and having children, on giving up her lover, on going to London
and getting a job in a booteek, on setting up her own booteek in
Shotestead, on becoming a model, on love and pain and life generally.

Like eating a blackcurrent, you can never tell beforehand whether
what she is going to say will be sweet or sour and probably for the
rest of my life, whenever I eat a blackcurrent I will be reminded of
James Bond and James Deen, the Carmer Sootra and Lady Chatterly,
Mary Kwant and Max Factor, naked aristocrats in iron masks and
the Duchess of Argyll's divorce case.

Some of what she says is broadening my horizons, and some is
having a bad effect. For example, she is making me clothes conscious.
She says my clothes are square and dull, and that I should perswade
my 'mum' to shop at C&A Modes (that'll be the day, to quote a line
from one of Dan's songs!) Also, thanks to her I have started to worry
about my figure. She says my legs are on the tree-trunk side. I said
'They serve me well and get me from A to B much quicker than your
spindly objects' and Dawn said 'Yeah but mine get the wolf whistles.'
Up till now I hadn't give them a second thought. I met Michael English
wearing my shorts. I managed to distract him from my legs by pointing
to a kestral. I can do without this extra worry and on balance, Dawn
is probably doing me more harm than good, though one thing's for
sure: I'm learning things from her that wouldn't be seen dead on a
school syllabus!! She has decided not to make any decisions about
her future until after the beauty contest. That is going to decide her
destany, she says. She is pinning all her hopes on winning it which,
for ovious reaons, is a huge mistake!

One afternoon Dawn suggested we have a picnic in the harvest field.
This was most out of character. Picnics were no more part of her
world than, say, drinking pints of beer in the Plough were ours.

'Bet she's got an interior motive,' Hattie said as we searched for a rug.

It wasn't a proper picnic, of course, with pork pies and chicken legs and tongue and tomato sandwiches and oxtail soup from a Thermos and pink jelly cream like Mother's picnics, but a bottle of flat, luke-warm Cherryade and a packet of cheese and onion crisps.

We walked through prickly stubble and settled ourselves on the rug in the corner of the harvest field near the bank on to which roots of trees clung like claws. We took off our clothes and sunbathed in bathing costumes. Like a bulging pink carrier bag, Dawn's had to work overtime to stop its contents from popping out.

The 'interior motive' turned out to be having a butcher's at Johnny who, bouncing up and down on his tractor like a jockey, drove bumperty clack past us far too close and far too fast, swerving the trailer in the stubble at the last minute, raising his cap at Dawn and shouting, 'All right, darlin'?' and 'Watcha, doll!' as if we didn't exist.

We lay on the rug in a row and through lazy, half-closed eyes watched the tractor and trailer wend its way towards the shimmering, winking elephant which galumphed along the seam that joined big blue sky and big golden field, leaving in its wake a trail of straw – 'like yellow diarrhoea, sort of thing,' said Dawn – then stopping to spew corn through its silver trunk into Johnny's trailer. (In summers past when Dan drove the tractor, we rode in the trailer; sitting under the shower of grain was the best bit, though you had to keep your eyes and mouth closed and you found corn about your person for days afterwards.) Then the leering Johnny drove back towards us, his heavy load steadying him up, and out through the gate in a cloud of dust to the Red Barn where he'd press a button and the trailer would tip up and the grain would whoosh into the noisy humming drier which was Jack or Reggie's department. Except ... had Dawn really come to have a butcher's at Johnny, who was rather round-shouldered and had a front tooth missing, or was she waving beyond him to the brawny Mr English who was busy 'thinking things over'?

'We're going to the Englishes tomorrow for a birthday party,' I said, screwing up my eyes and seeing orange.

'Yeah, I know.'

'I don't want to go one scrap,' said Hattie. 'They only invite us to be polite.'

'That's why we've got to go – to be polite,' I said, screwing up my eyes tighter and seeing crimson. 'It'll be good for us to mix with children. We're in danger of turning into anti-social old buggers

281

like Snap Dragon. I wonder if Mr English enjoys combining.'

'Expect so,' said Dawn. 'All men enjoy driving big machines. Makes them feel powerful. You can tell a lot about a bloke by what he drives, you know.'

'Actually, I think Mr English is quite handsome in an older-man sort of way, don't you?' I said seeing stars.

'Oh, *no*, not this again,' said Hattie.

'She's growing up,' said Dawn. 'You start noticing these things when you become a young woman, eh, Sarah?'

We strolled back through the amber, dappled afternoon past the Lower Meadows which for one day a year became the Shotestead Showground. The livestock had already been moved elsewhere, the grass cut and turned into silage. Near the gate was a pile of straw bales which would in due course be placed round the rings and act as seats.

Near a stag-headed oak tree two men were digging holes in the ground for the Ladies. They had already dug a long narrow trough for the Gents.

'I'm not going in a hole in the ground for everyone to see, ta very much,' said Dawn far too loudly and I explained, in a quiet voice to set a good example, they would have seats put on them and canvas round them, and she said thank gawd for that and she hoped a Yank wouldn't be flying over at the time. Then she said, in such a loud voice that the men digging looked up and nudged one another and laughed, ''Ere, what happens if a bloke wants to have a crap?'

I'd never been so embarrassed in my life and neither had Hattie who said, 'Honestly, Dawn, you do it on purpose just to embarrass us,' and sulked the rest of the way home.

That evening Dawn went out with Albert and when I asked her how she got on she said it was funny but not only did he reek of Old Spice but he seemed to have gone off her a bit and actually left her sitting on her own in the pub while he had a game of darts. I asked her if that made her keener on him and she wrinkled up her nose and said, 'Dunno. Yeah. Maybe. Ner. Not really.'

Like the Englishes themselves, their house, which was two cottages knocked into one, was neither a top-drawer nor a bottom-drawer sort of house. Mr English's father's farm had been too small to support them all, which was why Mr English was a farm manager. Pigs – and now pheasants – were his sidelines.

Mrs English was smily with freckly arms and pretty cornflake-coloured hair. You couldn't tell which drawer she originated from because she was Scottish.

It was Mary-Anne English's seventh birthday. We gave her our present, *Swallows and Amazons* which I wouldn't have said no to, but she didn't seem that pleased.

The lawn was dotted with little girls in pink, blue and yellow frills like confetti with arms and legs and white socks and black patent shoes. Mary-Anne wore a pink net party dress with a stiff petticoat and a matching bow in her fluffy blonde hair. She only needed a magic wand and she would have looked most at home on top of a Christmas tree. Hattie and I felt as plain as pumpkins in our no-nonsense cotton dress and unpolished shoes that looked like carthorses' feet among ballerinas, and what with Hattie with her leg and me towering above everyone else like an ogress ... *We were like the two ugly sisters among a bevy of nimble Cinderellas* I would write later.

Mrs English blew a whistle and the games began: Musical Bumps, Musical Statues, Musical Parcel, Postman's Knock, What's the Time, Mr Wolf? and Blind Man's Buff. Mrs English judged and, because I was feeling my age, I worked the Dansette record-player with Michael. Like a bamboo, Michael seemed to have grown a foot taller since last year. He went to the grammar school and, although quite handsome with brown pony's eyes and healthy farmer's cheeks, he was at least ten years too young to include on my list of suspects. He caught me looking at him and winked then said, 'What's a nice girl like you doing at a do like this?' and I didn't know what to say, the way you don't with certain sorts of boys.

After the egg sandwiches and fruit jelly and Happy Birthday, Dear Mary-Anne picnic tea on the lawn. Michael asked if I'd like to take a dekko at his dad's new Land Rover, and the egg sandwiches gave a queer lurch in the back of my throat. After checking that Hattie didn't mind being left on her own, I said all right. Of course I wasn't at all interested in a boring old Land Rover, but I was interested to see whether he had an ulterior motive.

'How come Dan's not helping with harvest this year?' he asked as we walked round the side of the house. I told him about his pop group and how he had star billing at the show, and Michael whistled through his teeth like a cowboy. He also asked about Dawn, saying she was a rum choice and tarty-looking wasn't the word for it and I, suddenly feeling as daring as a stallion, said, 'Your father seems to have taken a shine to her,' and he looked at me sharply and said 'What's that supposed to mean?' and I said, 'Nothing. Only pulling your leg.'

He told me he'd started going ferreting for rabbits with Brian Pike; that one day he was going to be the best shot in the country.

I asked him if he liked Brian Pike and he said yes, he was a good bloke. I said he was a sadistic murderer, and he said that was the sort of tommy rot a Townie would come up with, would I really want to live in a place overrun with rats and rabbits, and I said I wasn't a Townie, far from it in fact, so he said all right a girl then.

The Land Rover stood beside Mrs English's Morris Minor in the dark, quiet, cool, mouse-riddled tractor shed.

'Would you care to step inside, Madam?' Michael said, holding open the door and giving a small bow.

'Thank you, James,' I said. I felt quite excited and not nervous or frightened at all. It would be something to tell Dawn afterwards – and possibly Mr Richards. Whatever happened, it would be another adventure under my belt.

Michael sat in the driver's seat and said, 'Where to, Madam?' and I said. 'I think Hunstanton would be rather pleasant, don't you, for a change of air.'

'Right you are, Madam,' he said, pretending to start the engine and change gear, and if we hadn't been staring at a rough cobwebby brick wall we could have been a married couple going for an afternoon drive, and it suddenly occurred to me that if I married Michael when I was older, there was a chance I could spend the rest of my life at Gressenham. He was slightly lower-drawer than I was, but at least Dan couldn't accuse me of being a snob.

Meanwhile, sitting in the seat of a Land Rover in a cart shed in Gressenham, Norfolk, England, Europe, World, I was all prepared for him to ask if he could have his wicked way with me, assuming his wedding tackle was mature enough, or if not ask if he could touch me somewhere. So it came as both a surprise and somewhat of a disappointment when, after talking about school for a while he cleared his throat and said, quite roughly and gruffly, 'I'll tell you what. Let's play a game. Why don't we show each other our bottoms?'

Fancy a boy wanting to see *my* bottom! But *why* did he? Surely boys' bottoms were the same as girls'.

In the distance you could hear the combine driven by Mr English who was thinking things over while his son asked his employer's granddaughter to show him his bottom.

'That's not much of a game,' I said. 'How do you win?'

'Er – well, there's no winner as such.'

I thought about this. 'The thing is, I don't want to sound rude but I've seen boys' bottoms already. Well, my brother's, anyway. It wouldn't be fair me showing you mine and you not showing me anything in return.'

284

Michael cleared his throat. 'Well, I have got something else I could show you,' he said, his mouth suddenly sounding like a dried-up river bed and quite deep, too. 'But you might think it's rude.'

'What's rude about a body?' I said, pretending I didn't know what he meant. And then I hit on a brilliant wheeze. I could use this situation to my advantage, the way Christine Keeler and Mandy Rice-Davies did!

'Tell you what,' I said. 'I'll let you see it if you make sure that from now on Brian Pike *buries* dead animals rather than hangs them up.'

Michael whistled, the way Daddy did over electricity bills. 'You drive a hard bargain,' he said, his mouth returning to normal. 'You can't interfere with how a gamekeeper works. They're a law unto themselves.'

'But your father's his boss.'

'But he's got to keep the vermin down or ...'

'That's what the Nazis said about Jewish people.'

'You what ...? What's that got to do ... You've gone weird, you know that, really weird, like your old aunt.'

'So have you for wanting to see my bottom,' I said, forcing myself to laugh because no one likes to be told they've gone weird.

'Actually, I didn't really want to see it.'

'Why did you ask to see it then?'

'Just testing you. Seeing what sort of girl you are.'

'Well, now you know,' I said. 'Bet you can't catch me,' and I jumped down from the Land Rover and out into the bright blinking farmyard and round the side of the house with him chasing me and shouting 'Weirdo! Weirdo!'

Kick the Can was in progress on the lawn and it struck me that this time next year I might be wearing a bra and sitting with grown-ups and being tested out by boys and I might never play another proper child's game for the rest of my life apart from hide the sausage which sounded the most boring game in the world.

Hattie was sitting under an apple tree, her knees bent so her dress covered her legs, her little white face sad and lonely like Little Lord Fauntleroy's in pink glasses.

'Oh, sorry, Hattie. Has it been beastly?'

'Pretty,' she said. 'Don't worry, I told Mrs English I wanted to watch so she doesn't think I'm sulking. It's not my leg though. It's just – we don't belong here, do we. We're not the right types. We were last year though. It's that foul Dawn. She's ruined us. We'll never fit in anywhere again.'

'We're just growing up, that's all.'

'Speak for yourself. I'm only eight. Anyway, what were you doing? Your cheeks are all red.'

'Do you want to hear something really funny?' I said because I'd decided she was old enough to be told, and she needed cheering up. 'Michael wanted to see my bottom.'

'Your *bare* bottom?' said Hattie, opening her eyes very wide, and putting her hand over her mouth she burst out laughing. It occurred to me that it was the first time I'd heard her laugh for days. It sounded like the song of a very rare, beautiful bird. 'Why should he want to see *your* fat old bottom?'

'It's a very nice bottom.'

'Did you show it to him?'

'Of course not.'

'That's the funniest thing I've ever heard,' she said and laughed again. 'He must want his head examining.'

'Come along, you two,' hissed Mary-Anne, beckoning furiously like a miniature traffic warden in fancy dress. 'We're going to play Farmer's in his Den and everyone has got to join in, Mummy says. Michael's farmer.'

'I bet he picks me for his wife, and I'll pick you for the child,' I said to Hattie as we got up and joined the brightly coloured fairy circle on the lawn. *'The farmer's in his den, the farmer's in his den,'* we all trilled, walking round Michael holding hands, my voice louder and more in tune than all the others put together. *'Ee, ei, ee, ei, the farmer's in his den,'* and even though I was a head and shoulders above everyone else, soon I'd be in the middle with the farmer as his wife. *'The farmer wants a wife, the farmer wants a wife,'* and the farmer stood there, chewing on his nail and scratching his head, looking each of us up and down, pretending it was a hard decision but he *had* to pick me because we were on the same wavelength and we'd just shared a very intimate secret like a real husband and wife. *'Ee, ei, ee, ei, the farmer wants a wife'* (*and it's going to be me*, I sang in my head).

He didn't pick me but a stupid little squirt called Samantha Croft who lived in a modern house with a lamp post outside. She wore a blue swirly dress and bows in her yellow curls and a necklace at her age, and was the type you just knew would grow up to be a silly giggly stupid woman with Dawn-type fluttering eyelashes.

Hattie squeezed my hand in sympathy and the back of my eyes raged and boiled like Baba Yaga's and my bottom lip very nearly went out of control. It was as insulting as, say, a four-stone flat-footed weakling being picked for the school netball team. Except this was more of a moving-in-mysterious-ways grown-up thing, and

286

the question was: *If I'd shown Michael my bottom would he have chosen me to be his wife?*

'*The wife wants a child. The wife wants a child...*' I sang the loudest, the most cheerfully of anyone becaue whatever you do, you mustn't show you're upset. I was Black Champion. Nothing could touch me. So what if a stupid farm manager's son hadn't chosen me in a stupid game? I didn't want to be his stupid wife, anyway. Put on a brave face. That's what Mummy would have said. Except Mummy was hundreds of miles away, lying on a beach roasting like a peanut.

Of course neither Hattie nor I was picked for child, nurse or dog. Mary-Anne was the bone because the the birthday person always was.

'*We all pat the bone. We all pat the bone,*' we sang which just shows what a stupid game it was, and I wanted to pat her so hard that her body became smothered in purple bruises. I had to keep myself on a very tight rein.

We were all given a balloon, then the mothers arrived in cotton frocks, sun-glasses and sensible sandals to pick up their daughters and I could tell Hattie was wishing we had a mother to pick us up.

'You'll be all right, hens, walking home on your own, won't you?' said nice Mrs English in Scottish. Just as she said that, whom should we see round the edge of her cornflake curls but Dawn. Her sky-high beehive soared and tilted like the leaning Tower of Pisa built out of straw, her purple dress with its full skirt showed acres and acres of white leg and thank goodness her black-as-your-hat sun-glasses covered her black-as-your-hat eyes. She was smoking a cigarette and dropping ash all over the lawn. But none of this mattered at all so long as *no one thought she was our mother.*

'Did you have a simply super time, darling?' mothers were saying, and Dawn shouted – and she could have been speaking through a loudhailer – 'Watcha, kids. Thought I'd give you a surprise,' and the mummies and girlies stared round at her as if she were a dog's mess on legs.

'Blithering, blithering heck,' said Hattie softly, and I said if we were going to be the odd ones out we might as well go the whole hog and do it properly.

'They looked a prissy lot,' said Dawn when we weren't out of earshot. 'I felt quite proud of you two. You looked as though you had more personality than the rest of them put together.'

'Well, we weren't proud of you,' said Hattie. 'We could easily have walked back on our own. We aren't babies.'

'She was only being kind, weren't you, Dawn.'

'Yeah, well, I thought you'd see all the other kids with their mums and miss yours. I shan't bother next time.'

'We appreciate it very much,' I said.

'You look nothing like our mother,' said Hattie, dragging her feet.

'I know I don't. I didn't want you to feel left out, that's all. Anyway, I fancied a walk.'

That didn't sound like Dawn. She hated walking. Perhaps she called in at her lover's on the way. Aunt Lynette was at home this afternoon, and she could have passed Brian Pike's cottage. And Mr English was bound to stop for a tea break, as was Johnnie.

'What was it like?' said Dawn. 'They all looked a bit toffee-nosed to me.'

'Everyone looks a bit toffee-nosed to you,' said Hattie. 'Though as a matter of fact they were quite. Tell her about you-know-what, Sarah.'

So I did. I described the new smell of the Land Rover, the dusky darkness of the cart shed, the way Michael's voice went gruff and his mouth turned dry when he made his suggestion.

'What I don't understand is why he wanted to see your bottom,' said Hattie.

'Blokes are crafty old sods,' said Dawn. 'That was just a sneaky way of getting Sarah's knickers down. Blimey, they start young these days.'

'Anyway,' said Hattie, 'what made him think you wanted to see *his* bottom.'

'That's what I said to him, so he said there was something else he could show me . . .'

'Did he mean his *thingy*?'

'Yeah. His wedding tackle,' I said because after all Hattie was eight.

'*Wedding tackle*! It sounds like fishing tackle. If anyone ever talks about anything to do with fishing from now on, I'll *die* laughing.'

'I hope I die laughing,' said Dawn. 'Go on, Sarah.'

So I told them about my suggestion.

'Blimey, you drive a hard bargain,' said Dawn. 'I think you priced yourself out of the market there.'

I pointed out that good-time girls were given fur coats and diamond rings, and Dawn said yeah, but what they had to offer was worth a good deal more than a butcher's at an eleven-year-old bottom.

'You make it sound like a piece of meat,' I said.

'That's what it is, basically. A commodity.'

288

'Would you have shown it to him if he had promised about the animals?' said Hattie.

'I might have done. He only wanted to look.'

'Everyone has their price,' said Dawn, delving in her white plastic handbag for her matches and lighting another cigarette.

'I wouldn't have shown him mine for all the coals in Newcastle,' said Hattie. 'Do you think that because you didn't show him your bottom he didn't choose you to be his wife?'

'That's jumping the flipping gun, ain't it?'

'No. During Farmer's in his Den,' snapped Hattie.

'Oh, I see,' said Dawn. 'Ner, there's no guarantee he would have picked Sarah even if she had revealed all. That's the thing with blokes. Give them the cherry and they spit the stone back in your face.'

'What's cherries and stones ... You do talk rubbish,' said Hattie.

But I knew what Dawn meant. Just because you let a man have his wicked way didn't mean he'd necessarily love you and want to marry you. Especially if they thought you were weird. Perhaps that was why Aunt Lynette had never found a husband; because of her weird political beliefs. How much more straightforward life was if you were a run-of-the-mill person who did as you were told.

'That's life, I'm afraid,' said Dawn. 'Blokes always go for the young pretty, stupid ones. Bloody unfair, but there it is. You can be the nicest person in the world, but if you ain't pretty ... The thing is, I don't reckon you're going to grow up to be much of a looker, if you don't mind me saying, Sarah, so you might as well get used to not always getting what you want now.'

I minded very much indeed but I wasn't going to show her that.

'You're so disgustingly, repulsively rude,' said Hattie. 'Who do you think you are, telling my sister she won't be a looker? And how can you tell, anyway?'

'She ain't got the bone structure,' said Dawn. 'You have, like your bro, but she ain't. You'll be all right, Hat. I was only reading the other day about some kids up north being given contact lenses I think they're called. Bits of glass you put in your eyes and no one knows the difference. But you, Sarah, I reckon you'll grow up to look like a jolly farmer's wife with child-bearing hips.'

A chaffinch twittered above us, its lady-like machine-gun cry warning me to take no notice.

'That's handy because I want to marry a jolly farmer and bear lots of children,' I snapped, fighting off tears and Dawn said keep your hair on, it wasn't meant as a criticism or nothing.

Only that very morning I'd stood at the bathroom mirror pretending my face was a stranger's. But with even the most vivid of imaginations, neither 'beautiful' nor 'pretty' was the first word that sprang to mind. 'Friendly' or 'trusting' or 'open', maybe, but all in all definitely not the sort of face a man would howl or bang his head against a tree or slit his throat over. And now Dawn had confirmed this. The only way round this setback, I decided, was to be a nun or a recluse or a riding mistress when I grew up.

'I thought it was a perfectly foul party,' said Hattie, squeaking her balloon. 'We felt as out of place as, er, witches at a fairy's party, didn't we, Sarah.'

My mouth was too upset to answer.

'Yeah, well, now you know how I feel with you lot sometimes,' said Dawn.

'When you think about it, we're all outsiders in different ways,' said Hattie. 'Us, Granny, Aunt Lynette, Dan. I think it's nice to be an outsider. I've just decided that. Interesting people are outsiders.'

'I dunno,' said Dawn. 'Sometimes I long to be normal. It would make life a lot simpler. For a kick off I'd be happy to settle down and marry Albert if I was normal, instead of being hell bent on winning bloody beauty contests I haven't a cat in hell's chance of winning.'

'You might if you don't wear all that black stuff round your eyes and have so much foul yellow hair all over the place.'

'But that's it, innit,' said Dawn. 'I don't want to conform and look like everyone else. Christ, I would like to win it, though. I've never won nothing in me life.'

'It's like the fancy dress,' said Hattie. 'All the others will be cowboys and Indians and fairy queens, because that's what the judges like to see.'

'What are you going as then?' asked Dawn.

We still hadn't decided. Last year we were the Mad Hatter and the March Hare. The year before we'd been Andy Pandy and Looby Loo. This year we wanted to be something more out of the ordinary.

'I think I should be the Wicked Winter and Hattie a helpless lamb in my evil clutches. At least it would be relevant.'

'I suppose so,' said Dawn. 'Kind of, anyway.'

'I don't want to be a helpless lamb in your evil clutches, thanks very much.'

' 'Ere, I know. Why don't you go as Christine Keeler and Mandy Rice-Davies. That's dead relevant,' said Dawn. 'You could borrow my high heels stuffed with paper, and we could dye that wig red. That would be a real laugh.'

I said it wouldn't be suitable and Dawn said she thought we

290

didn't want something suitable and I said, 'I know, I could be a Nazi with a swastika on my shoulder and you could be a Jewish prisoner. You could wear the Andy Pandy pyjamas.'

'A bit bloody morbid, that,' said Dawn. 'Anyway, you wouldn't want to shave off that lovely hair, would you Hat.'

'No, I would not,' she said. 'Why did they shave it off, anyway?'

'To stop them looking like humans. Then the Nazis didn't feel so guilty about treating them like shit.'

'I bet Yul Brynner isn't treated like ... that word,' said Hattie.

When we got back Dawn tried to give me a twist lesson on the lawn.

'Come on, loosen up. Move your feet as if you're stubbing out fags. Pretend Elvis is belting out *Jailhouse Rock*.'

But all I could hear was the wood pigeon and her foghorn voice saying I wasn't going to be much of a looker.

'I'm not in the mood. Anyway, what's the point in dancing if I'm so ugly no one will want to look at me?'

'You're as daft as a brush. You *ain't* ugly. All I meant was you won't be a *femme fatale*, you know, the type other women hate. When you smile you're beautiful. And when you can dance you'll be beautiful. Come on, swing your arms and hips as if you're towelling yourself dry ... that's it. That's good – bloody good.'

Last year after Mary-Anne's party, Granny came down the drive to meet us and said 'Did you have fun, darlings?' This year she remained in bed (though at least she was sitting up).

'We felt a bit old really, Granny,' I said and Granny said. 'That makes three of us, doesn't it,' and the sound of her laughter gave me as nice a feeling as Hattie's. 'Darlings, would you do something for me? Make sure Dan goes to Fiona's birthday party tonight. I know he said he would, but ... I've failed with the harvest and he hasn't given the cricket match a moment's thought, tiresome boy, but I would very much like him to go to the dance this evening.'

Dan had said all along that he had better things to do with his time than spend the evening in a bloody penguin suit talking to nobs about huntin', shootin' and fishin'. Eventually, after we'd gone on and on about how much it meant to Granny, he had begrudgingly given in. I don't think he'd bothered to reply.

'Certainly, Granny,' we said.

We ran his bath for him and put a fresh blade in his razor that lurked, unused like a rare antique, in his sponge bag. He grumbled like mad, and when I offered to iron his shirt he said, 'Jesus, how bourgeois can you get!'

An hour later he emerged with his hair all greased back (it was long enough for a ponytail!) a gash on his cheek to prove he'd shaved, and wearing Grandpa's too-big dinner suit, yellowing creased shirt, cummerbund round his hips, a crooked-on-purpose bow tie and, worst of all, his newly acquired Chelsea boots!

'Dan! You can't wear those,' I said. 'They don't go.'

'It's either these, sneakers or cricket shoes. Take your pick.'

'I think you look like Humphrey Bogart,' said Dawn picking a piece of fluff off his jacket as if she was his mother.

'Tell us all about the dance,' I said.

'Every gory detail,' said Hattie.

'Yeah, a blow-by-blow account,' said Dawn, and couldn't she keep her nose out of anything?

'If I ever get there,' said Dan. 'The Plough has never seemed more enticing.'

Needless to say, Dan wasn't up for breakfast the next morning.

'Are we sure he's back, even?' said Dawn. 'How do we know he's not a dirty stop out?'

'Because Mummy's car's back, unless it drove itself back.'

After breakfast, Hattie and I took Dan a cup of tea. Boy, was his bedroom a mess.

Dan put the sheet over his head and groaned like a drunk the morning after the night before in a film. 'For God's sake don't draw the curtains. Or talk loudly. Or talk at all. And get me an Alka-Seltzer on the rocks – fizzing, not stirred.' His mouth sounded like two flypapers stuck together.

While Hattie fetched the Alka-Seltzer, I had a quick look round. It was just clothes strewn everywhere, really, and bits of paper with lines of songs with a, d, e or c, f, g written in red underneath. One song was called *Another Cuntry* (Dan's spelling was worse then mine!); I was just having a quick read of it – it seemed to be about the changing times and tipping a lady out of bed, when he opened one eye, like Tommy Brock. It was the colour of a beetroot. In fact he looked terrible, and if only my camera worked indoors it would have made a brilliant photograph. *Drink is not only the curse of the working classes.* I could caption it.

'You look vile,' I said, and just as I said the word 'vile' I noticed that the collar of Grandpa's discarded shirt had lipstick on it.

'So would you if you'd drunk as much champagne as I have. My tongue feels like a dead dog.'

292

'You look like one too,' said Hattie handing him the fizzing glass, 'And you smell like a tramp who's spent the night in a hedge with a bottle of sherry. Bet you didn't clean your teeth last night.'

'You bet your sweet life I didn't. I'd have used my razor and cut off my tongue.'

'And shaved with your toothbrush.'

We sat on either side of the bed and I soothed his fevered brow with a handkerchief soaked in water and coaxed him into telling us about the party.

'As soon as the word got about that I was in a pop group the female guests swarmed round me like bees round a honeypot,' he said, the flypapers beginning to lose their stick.

'Shouldn't it be bears round a honeypot?' said Hattie. 'Bees make honey, they don't eat it.'

'Gee whizz, that's the way to get the girls! Just say you're in a pop group! 'Oh, Dan, how *thrilling*. Do you sing "Yeah, yeah, yeah" like the Beatles?' they squealed. Honestly, I was having to ruddy well fend them off, specially dear Fiona.'

'She must want her head examining,' said Hattie.

'Were any of them as nice as Hilary?' I asked and he said God no, Hilary had a brain and a sense of humour, this lot were about as exciting as listening to Mortimer Wheeler playing Animal Vegetable Mineral, and I asked if any of them had kissed him and he said probably, he really couldn't remember, and I said there was lipstick on Grandpa's collar and he said, rather tetchily I thought, 'Well, they must have done, mustn't they,' and Hattie said why should they kiss your collar; what's wrong with your cheek?

'The biggest laugh is they're all coming to the Show dance. They think it's such a *scream* one of their kind in a pop group. They're expecting to see a tamer version of Cliff Richard. Well, all I can say is they're in for a rude awakening.'

CHAPTER TWENTY-TWO

Another contender for my list of suspects appeared at the front door that afternoon in the shape of the Kleeneze man. He had neat, black, shoe-brush-bristle hair and an all-in-one beard and moustache. He wore a blinding white shirt, a red tie, pinstripe trousers and large suede shoes, dun, my least favourite colour for a pony, that caught your eye even when you were looking at his face. He carried a polished tan suitcase with a shiny gold lock.

'Afternoon,' he said, his smiling teeth matching his shirt. 'Is anyone in?'

I was wondering whether to say 'Yes, I am,' when he said. 'You know, Mrs Hillington or that blonde ... Dawn's the name, if my memory serves me right,' and his cheeks turned a pleasing shade of apricot, and the dun shoes snuffled in the gravel like two shy, excited brown animals.

Dawn and the Kleeneze man! He had a car, quite a big burgundy one with a dog section where he kept the brushes that wouldn't fit into the tan suitcase. At the back window his suit jacket hung neatly on a hanger so he was obviously clothes-conscious like she was, and I was sure that when he wasn't grinning like a salesman he could look mean, moody and magnificent. I wondered in passing whether he had a hairy chest. He had black hairy wrists which was a promising sign. . . .

Or perhaps he'd be suitable for Aunt Lynette! Round his temples were a few distinguished grey hairs so he wouldn't be that much too young for her. The colour of his tie could be a hint as to his political beliefs, and maybe he was selling brushes in order to pay the rent and in real life he was a sculptor or a poet. He did after all have a beard. And wasn't there a sticker on the back window of his car? It was bound to say 'Ban the Bomb'. It was a shame about his shoes, though; I knew Aunt Lynette couldn't abide men in brown suede shoes. Still, it was worth a try. One had to make hay while the sun shone as far as single men and Aunt Lynette were concerned.

'Your granny usually needs something – a scrubbing brush, a soft brush for her furnishing fabrics, a set of dusters, that sort of

294

thing. And I've got a very nice new line in stiff brushes of the highest quality.'

'Oh, I'm sure they're lovely,' I said and explained that Granny was having her afternoon nap and Dawn was out but my aunt might need something. 'She's an artist,' I said. 'A frightfully good one, actually, I'll just go and get her. Won't be a tick.'

Aunt Lynette was in her studio with Hattie, working on their portraits of Dan. They'd given up getting him to pose for them and were doing it from memory. Hattie hadn't drawn in his face so he looked like a ghost in a tramp's wig, and Aunt Lynette's was dominated by a purple sunrise.

'Oh, darling, I really can't be fagged with travelling salesmen on such a *scalding* afternoon,' she said, and why didn't I spot then that she was drinking Vera Lynn and get out while the going was good?

She was wearing a pink, orange and turquoise silk house coat and matching turban. I could already picture the expression on the Kleeneze man's face when he set eyes on her: admiration, perhaps; awe and, most of all, fascination.

'Oh, please, Aunt Lynette. He's driven all this way specially. And he's very handsome.'

'Oh, no, not *again*,' said Hattie.

'Handsome? Is he, by jingo?' said Aunt Lynette, putting down her brush, picking up her drink and swishing it round so the ice tinkled. 'Very well, let's see what this dishmop-touting Casanova has to offer. Lead on, MacSarah.'

Her glass raised in a permanent toast like an actress in a Noel Coward play, she floated round the side of the house and across the gravel in bare, scarlet-toed feet. I hoped the Kleeneze man enjoyed a challenge as far as women were concerned. If his face had turned apricot at the thought of Dawn, surely it would turn raspberry at the sight of Aunt Lynette!

'I've come to give you the brush-off,' she screeched, her shrill laughter slicing through the afternoon like an electric carving knife. 'Oh, I do beg pardon, I expect you've heard that *dozens* of times, you poor man,' and she walked right up to him and rested her scarlet-nailed, paint-splattered hand on his Omo-white shoulder.

The brown animals took a step backwards. Maybe the Kleeneze man felt the same way as Elvis Presley about suede shoes.

'Once or twice, yes,' he said, staring at the brown animals who were trying to make a burrow in the gravel. I willed them to dig deeper so Aunt Lynette wouldn't spot them.

'Now, there's no need to bristle,' she said and her laughter, or maybe it was the Vera Lynn, threw her right off balance, and what a mercy her drink sploshed on gravel rather than shirt or trousers. 'Wouldn't it be simply hilarious, Sarah, if this gentleman's name was Fox – you know, as in brush. It isn't by any remote chance, is it? Oh, shame – and now, do tell me what secrets you have hidden in that fascinating ginger bag.'

With reluctance, the Kleeneze man opened his suitcase. He was probably wishing he'd never turned down Granny's drive but had stopped instead at a cottage in the village where a kind, plump housewife would buy three shoe brushes and a feather duster and offer him a cup of tea into the bargain.

He took out a stiff brush and explained how it was the latest in the line, ideal for those awkward corners that the vacuum cleaner couldn't reach, and Aunt Lynette said. 'Mr Fox – you don't mind me calling you Mr Fox, do you, just for fun? Are you implying that I have *Unclean Awkward Corners*? Because if you are, you would be absolutely correct. I have lived happily with them for many years now, and they'd probably die of shock if a *bendy* brush, let alone a *stiff* one went within spitting distance of them. So I think we'd better let my sleeping corners lie, don't you, Mr Fox?'

'Well, yes, I suppose ...' Mr Fox ran a finger round the inside of his white collar in order to loosen it. His forehead had started to glisten. This could just be, I supposed though it seemed unlikely, the first two signs of a man falling in love.

'Actually, I'll tell you what I *do* need, dear Mr Fox,' continued Aunt Lynette, moving very close to him so that at least if he smelt the Vera on her breath he'd realise this was her drunk self rather than her real self, 'A sable number seven.'

Mr Fox blinked, and ran his fingers upwards through his black hair. This was a mistake because it now resembled more a sweep's than a shoe brush.

'I'm afraid ...'

'Mr ... he doesn't have that sort of brush, Aunt Lynette,' I said. Was it because she found him irresistibly attractive that she was behaving in this cruel way? 'How about a mop – or a feather duster?'

'To brush away the cobwebs? But much of my inspiration is drawn from the humble cobweb,' she said and peered into his case. 'And what's this darling little thing when it's at home? Oh, a shaving brush! Are you proposing to sell me one of *these*, Mr Fox?'

'No, madam, of course not. But your husband ...'

'Come, come, Mr Fox. Here I must come clean ...' and she paused to roar like a waterfall '... and confess that just between you, me and the shaving brush, I am an *unmarried woman!*'

'Er, well, perhaps an uncle or a friend. It's made in Germany of the highest-quality badger hair.'

'*Badger*!' screamed Aunt Lynette, holding her forehead as if there had been a tragedy in the family. 'Did I hear you say *badger*, Mr Fox? *Badger – Mr Fox*!' and she looked at me and shrieked. 'Did you hear that, Sarah, badger – fox … This is turning into a Beatrix Potter farce of the first order! But Mr Fox, to be serious for just a moment. You may not be aware that round here badgers are held in the highest regard. Why, if one walked through my front door tomorrow I would keep it as a pet. And surely you wouldn't use the hairs from your pet's back to remove *your* whiskers, would you Mr Fox?'

'Er …'

'Selling a brush made of badger round here, Mr Fox, would be like selling ponyburgers, or golden-Labrador-hide gloves. Still, let's not have a dust-up *(dust-up*!) over a mere shaving brush. I do, however, find it midly surprising that a man of your persuasion – you are of Jewish faith, I take it? I am going purely by your attractive colouring – stocks products made by the people who at one time made lamp-shades out of your ancestors' skins, who stuffed cushions with their hair … Surely, Mr Fox, it's a classic case of feeding the hand that bites you?'

'The War was quite a while ago …' he muttered, looking at his watch, his eyebrows doing the job for which they were intended: stopping the sweat trickling into his eyes.

'So was Christ's death, Mr Fox, and we still celebrate Easter. We mustn't sweep things under the carpet. Did you hear that, Sarah – *sweep under the carpet*!' and she dived her shaking-with-laughter hand into the case and pulled out a small brush with gold bristles.

'Ha!' she said, holding it high in the air. 'Don't tell me, I'll guess.'

'Aunt Lynette, don't you think we should let er, him get on?'

'Don't be such a killjoy, Sarah, this is such fun. It is a crocodile's toothbrush, perhaps? A mouse's stiff brush to get to those awkward corners the Hoover can't reach. Oh do tell, dear Mr Fox.'

'It's a suede brush, actually, Madam.'

'Ah-ha! That must explain why your darling suede shoes are looking so immaculate – but then one could hardly sell suede brushes while wearing suede shoes covered in fluff. A classic case of not practising what you preach! Which leads one to only one conclusion: that *you*, Mr Fox, don't suffer from Unclean Awkward Corners. Am I right?'

'Er …' Mr Fox said he'd better be going. The brown animals' noses were touching which right then was the saddest sight in the world; even though everything was against him, his brown animals were still friends.

'I'm very sorry if we've wasted your time,' I said. 'I'm sure my grandmother will buy something when you next call.'

'Yes, Ma's always been a sucker,' said Aunt Lynette.

'Such a nice lady,' Mr Fox muttered, implying that we were nasty. Clicking shut his case, he walked towards his car. If he'd actually been a fox, his brush would have been firmly tucked between his legs.

'Adieu, Mr Fox,' shouted Aunt Lynette. 'I trust you don't think we've given you the brush-off, ha, ha, ha.'

Her laughter was drowned by Mr Fox revving up his burgundy car as loudly as an angry American policeman. I made myself inhale the blue exhaust fumes. If I didn't die from this I would chase after him and buy a pink feather duster with my blackcurrant money, just to show that someone round here took his wares seriously. 'I'm terribly sorry about my aunt,' I'd say through his rolled-down window. 'It was the Vera Lynn talking. I think your brushes are lovely.'

I chased him down the drive waving my arms and shouting like Mr McGregor minus rake and white beard, but he didn't stop. Perhaps he was too upset or perhaps he didn't want a girl to see him crying. I waved and shouted until the car vanished round the bend and the only evidence that Mr Fox had been to call were the exhaust fumes hanging in a purple haze among the rhododendrons.

His car sticker hadn't said 'Ban the Bomb'. It had said 'Put a tiger in your tank'.

'Oh, gawd, I wish I'd been here,' said Dawn, wiping black mascara on Granny's thick white table napkin that had H embossed in blue in the corner. 'She's such a scream, your Aunt L.'

'Mr Fox!' said Dan, choking on his baked beans. 'The cheek of the woman. Were you killing yourself, Sarah?'

At that moment I had never disliked two people so much; Dan with his cut cheek and wild hair, Dawn with her black piggy eyes and pink laughing mouth. They were like a couple of cruel barbarians. If I said 'And then Mr Fox dropped down dead', they would have still carrried on laughing.

'No, I was jolly embarrassed.'

'But he was only a brush salesman,' said Dan. 'They deserve all they get.'

'Yeah, they're bloody pushy and never take no for an answer.'

'You're an ace hypocrite, Dan Hillington. And so are you, Dawn, and so's Aunt Lynette. You're all going on about Come the Revolution and treating everyone as equals when what you really mean is 'Treat everyone as equals apart from Kleeneze men'. *Jewish* Kleeneze men as it happens.'

'Uh-oh,' said Dan. 'Sarah's on her high horse.'

'You have to have a laugh sometimes,' said Dawn. 'Better than bloody crying.'

'There's a time to laugh and a time to cry,' I said, seething. 'And talking of crying, that's probably what Mr Fox is doing at this moment, having wasted a day driving across Norfolk to be made a fool of by Aunt Lynette. How would you like it if brushes were your whole life, your whole reason for living, and someone makes fun of them ... It's like making fun of *you*. I mean, how would you like it, Dan, if people laughed at your songs?'

'I'd think they'd got no taste.'

Then Dawn said he can't love his brushes that much because before he sold brushes he sold fertilisers to farmers, and before that he sold life insurance, she knew the bloke quite well, in fact, he lived in Tuttingham and was called Mark Bloom and was a motorbike scrambler in his spare time. He was probably at this very moment propping up the bar in the King's Head making a big joke of the whole thing, and I said why didn't you say you knew him in the first place and she said you didn't ask, did you, and I said how silly of me I should have guessed; after all, you know every other single man round these parts.

'You and I are the only two civilised people round here,' Hattie said as we went for an after-supper stroll round the rosy-pink farm.

I explained that Aunt Lynette was uncivilised at the moment because she was desperate to get married and have a baby.

'*Married? Have a baby?*' screeched Hattie, and a blackbird, equally surprised, screeched 'Tac-tac-tac.' 'She's far too dotty to get married.'

'You don't have to be sane to get married. George the Third was married.'

'She'd wash her husband's socks in paint water and drop ash over his food and put gin in his tea.'

'Yes, but if she wants a baby she'll have to get married. And time's running out. If she doesn't have one by the time she's forty it'll be a mongrel.'

'Crikey,' said Hattie. 'We'll have to think of someone fast, won't we.'

'I've racked my brains but that's why I introduced her to Mr

299

Fox, I thought he was a likely candidate. It just shows how wrong one can be. I'm banking on there being some nice Yanks at the Show.'

'She doesn't like Yanks. And don't call them Yanks.'

'Yanks are meant to have animal magnetism.'

'Honestly, Sarah, you sound just like Dawn. Thanks to her you've gone all silly and boy-mad. I wish you'd go back to how you used to be. You were much nicer.'

We passed the showground and spotted Brian Pike and Michael English walking along the far bank. They were silhouetted against the red sunset like men up to no good in an Enid Blyton book. The Yellow Dog was sniffing in rabbit holes. You could just hear Brian Pike say 'Seek 'em out, seek 'em out.'

We stopped to watch. Eventually the Yellow Dog found a hole he particularly liked the smell of, and, like a conjuror producing a rabbit from a hat, Brian Pike pulled out from a bag a snow-white ferret and put it down the hole.

It wasn't long before a squealing rabbit shot out of another hole and straight into a net. Michael disentangled it and while the Yellow Dog quivered and snarled, he put his hand over its face. Through the cool dusky pink air you heard a soft crunch, like a walnut being cracked in a distant room, and the rabbit was dead.

As we walked away, Hattie said, 'Aren't you glad you didn't show your bottom to that murderer?'

'Mmmm,' I said, and I'd never tell her that seeing Michael standing on the bank with his hands on his hips waiting to kill a rabbit, I'd felt an instinct stir deep inside, the same instinct that maybe cavewomen had when they watched their husbands hunt for wild boar.

'Can you imagine,' said Hattie, 'sitting in your burrow minding your own business and suddenly a ferocious, sharp-toothed tres- passer chases you out of your own home. What a choice! Stay and be eaten alive by a ferret or run straight into Brian Pike's evil clutches!'

'That's life,' I said wondering if Dawn felt like a cavewoman with her lover.

'That's death, don't you mean,' said Hattie.

'That house is a palace compared with where we used to live,' said Dawn the next day as we rode home on the top deck of the number 10 bus. 'What did you think of it?'

Hattie had bet it would be a shed or a barn or a hovel, or like Mr Todd's, even – something between a cave, a prison and a tumbledown pigsty. But it had been built not of straw or sticks but bricks, and had a smart white front door and a little porch with geraniums growing in it. There was a neat lawn bordered by cheerful orange flowers at the front and rhubarb and cabbages and potatoes and peas at the back. There were bits of motor bikes and a punctured football and a rusting pedal car, but it still resembled a garden rather than a jungle or a bomb site. The house's downstairs curtains were drawn, and when Dawn had shouted 'Yoo-hoo' as we walked up the path, no one came to the door. It reminded me of when we arrived at Granny's.

'Very nice,' I said. 'Er – spotlessly clean and quite big really.'

'Yeah, my mum's become ever so house proud – it's the first time she's had something to be proud of. What did you think of them, then? Bit boring, aren't they, compared with your lot.'

"Er, no, I though they were nice,' I said. 'I liked your mother very much. Your sisters and brother aren't at all like you, are they? It stands out a mile you have American blood in you.'

The bus battered against tree branches, making Dawn flinch even though the window was closed.

'That's not all of them, you know. The others stayed in London.'

Hattie had been wrong, too, about the house smelling of cabbage and gas and damp and dirt. It smelt more of pine needles and hair spray and very slightly of Dettol, quite like ours, in fact, and nicer than Granny's. It had vile, swirl-patterned carpets in the hall and red flowery wallpaper, but there were some not bad pictures of London scenes and a mirror that didn't have Woolies gold stuff round it. There was also a picture of Jesus, tormented and dripping in blood, hanging on the cross.

'You aren't *Catholic* are you?' I had whispered and Dawn said, 'Not personally, no. Told you we wouldn't get much of a welcome. I sometimes wonder why I bother. *Mu-um!*'

'In here, love.'

In the gloom of the sitting room, a thin middle-aged woman with black hair in a ponytail and wearing glasses attached to gold chains was sticking pictures of robins on to white cards. She looked up, gave a pale smile and said 'Hello, love' as if Dawn walked in every day of the week. Then her eyes flickered to me and she said, 'Hello, love. Sit down and make yourself at home. You should have warned me you'd be bringing company, Dawn.' She didn't kiss Dawn, or rush off to make tea, though later we had a cup of weak instant coffee and a slice of dry-as-a-bone bought cake.

A young woman who was a fat shadow of Dawn jiggled a waxwork-faced baby on her knee. A thin shadow of Dawn, aged

301

about fifteen and wearing gold ear-rings, sulked at the television with a copy of *Boyfriend* on her knee. A thin boy in a string vest and sideboards managed to wrench his pale Dawn's eyes away from the television screen just for a second to nod at us.

Throughout our visit the television stayed on, the curtains stayed closed and the window shut, I would write. The saddest thing of all was that they didn't seem at all pleased to see Dawn. They didn't ask her about her job or Granny, in fact all they talked about was people on television – who said what to who on Coronation Street sort of conversation. It would be like seeing Mother and Father after all this time and them just talking about Cliff Mitchalmore and Malcom Mugeridge. The only person they seemed quite interested in was Albert. I think they're worried Dawn might break off the engagement. They asked her about her bungalow and what colour bathroom suite it has, etc. Clearly they think Dawn's done all right for herself there.

The father is in the 'nick', like in The Railway Children. Except it's not like that because it's not such a disgrace for Dawn's class as it was for the Railway Children. She won't say what he's done.

Meeting Dawn's family has made me understand much more about what makes her tick. They are all right and I didn't feel at all shy with them like you do with some people's families, and her mother has every right to be a bit fed up because she has had a hard life, but they're what I think is called world-weary – even the 18-year-old – even the baby! Nothing makes them laugh or exites them. They are like zombies. Dawn has more spirit than all of them put together, and because she doesn't get much from them she has turned to our family for love and attention. This must all be due to her American blood. And talking of blood, Dawn's mother is Irish! First you, Mr Richards, then the Brontës and now Dawn. I am beginning to wonder whether, in another life, I wasn't Irish myself, which would explain both my passionate nature and why I feel such an afinaty with them!

I looked out of the bus's window into abandoned birds' nests and dark, secret cottage-bedroom windows.

'How come your family ended up round here?'

'Me Mum was evacuated here during the war with me older brothers and sisters, and she'd been thinking of moving back here ever since. Then when me Dad went inside, she came up here like a shot to make a new life for herself and us sort of thing; mind you, some life, sticking robins on cards at two bob a hundred.'

'Does she regret it.'

'Ner. I think she's found peace up here, and I expect she feels closer to Wilbur. You can't blame her wanting to get out of that place in Notting Hill.'

'Why, what was wrong with it?'

'What was right with it! You know that bloke Rachman I told you about? We didn't know he was our landlord at the time. He's been exposed in the papers and a *Panorama* programme since he died. What he did was, he bought houses on the cheap via one of his many companies and then got rid of sitting tenants by getting his henchmen with alsatians to harass them; apparently he even put rats in babies' prams. Or he'd move noisy blacks in. That's what he did with us and downstairs he moves in these two prossies. So there we was sandwiched between jungle music and the cracking of whips – and me parents having it off next door if me dad wasn't too pissed. No wonder I didn't exactly shine at school. I was too knackered the whole time. Three pounds fifteen shillings those poor prossies were paying each a *day* in rent. We weren't paying that a week. No wonder Rachman wanted us out.'

'Did Mr Rachman's henchmen put rats in your sister's pram to get you out?' I asked. I'd never asked a question of that nature before. It seemed as out of place swishing past a sleeping, brass-bedded cottage as, say, discussing sugar beet in a Soho night-club.

'Ner. We scarpered before it came to that. I remember those alsatians, though . . .'

Now I could see why Dawn fancied living in a new bungalow with double glazing and a utility room.

'What was Mr Rachman like exactly?'

'Short and fat with a squeaky voice, apparently. There's this joke going around: open his grave and you'll find two tenants inside! Some people reckon he's still alive. But the amazing thing is, it's all thanks to the Profumo Affair that he was exposed at all. If it wasn't for that, no one would have heard of him.'

'What's the Profumo Affair got to do with Mr Rachman?'

'He had an affair with both Christine Keeler and Mandy Rice-Davies and his name came up in Stephen Ward's trial. According to the *People* he made love to five different girls a day. I reckon he was partly to blame for the Notting Hill Race Riots. Him and Oswald Mosley's lot – and the Government. The blacks were all so pissed off with living in slums and paying through the nose for the privilege, see – and looking out of their window of a morning and being confronted by 'BLACK BASTARDS GO HOME' type stuff scrawled everywhere. I mean it was the Government who asked

303

them over here in the first place, they should have given them decent housing.'

'Did you see the Race Riots?'

'Yeah, we was in the thick of it. Scared stiff, I was – well, I was only thirteen.'

'If you had had to have taken sides, whose side would you have been on?'

'Oh, the niggers'. I'm no fascist.'

I looked out at a wood and a field of wheat. It was hard to imagine all these things happening in the same country as this green and pleasant land.

I pictured Dawn, a little girl with no black stuff round her eyes, lying in bed listening to jungle music and the crack of whips, rioting going on outside and her father having his wicked way behind a paper-thin wall. After such a disturbed childhood, it was a miracle she had turned out as nice and cheerful as she had.

On the way back from the bus stop, we stopped to watch the showground take shape. (At least that was what I was watching; Dawn was probably ogling the men erecting the tents.)

'Blimey, it's going to be quite a big do, ain't it, not the tinpot affair I'm imagined,' she said and I told her it was one of the most important one-day agricultural shows in the county.

Like a mountain surrounded by molehills, the Show had certainly begun to tower above our other day-to-day happenings. But for my diary's sake, I did my best to turn the molehills into mountains and Dawn, as it turned out, still had some very juicy bombshells indeed up her sleeve.

Even though most of my thoughts are now taken up with preparations for the Show, I still keep my eyes peeled for rum goings on. Yesterday Dawn went off on the bicycle and I followed at a safe distance, convinsed she was going to lead me to her lover. But to my shame she ended up at the disused railway track where she picked wild flowers for Granny's bedroom.

My list of suspects is getting extremely long. Jeremy, the handsome estate agent is now higher up the list (does he really need to come and see Granny quite so often about Show matters?); the laundry man (who wasn't at all annoyed we weren't ready and was happy to have a cup of tea with Dawn while we whizzed round wipping sheets off beds and towels from bathrooms); Mr English has started delivering the milk and eggs himself; Mr Fields the paperman discusses the headlines with her (though surely it can't *be him, he's at least 50); even Mr Ridley the postman's eyes swival as he cycles up the drive in the hope of catching a glimpse of her; it is as if we have a cat on heat which attracts every Tom, Dick and Harry in the nayberhood!! I told her if she doesn't watch it even Ball (aged 80 if a day) will start digging her instead of a flowerbed!!!*

Granny is doing fairly well at mustering herself with outsiders, but with us she slumps back into being old and woolly (for example while Dawn was explaining to Dan that the reason she had gone off the Daily Mirror was because the square pop colomist only ever wrote about jazz, Granny said out of the blue 'A frog he would a-wooing go'!)

Weatherwise it is getting more like an African jungle every hour, and one half-expects to see an almost naked native with a painted face and spear stalking through the rhododendrans. If feels like our bathroom at home when everyone's had a bath on the same night with the electric fire on. How I long to pull the switch, and open the window to let out the sweltering steam. I am getting heartily sick of Dawn asking me to look at her legs every five minutes to see if they've gone brown (of course they haven't, they're as white as Brian Pike's ferret). She has taken to wearing a bikeeni round the house.

If food is anything to go by, apart from milk and eggs no one would guess we were in the heart of the country. For example, for lunch today we had shrivelled-up beefburgers (with probably not an ounce of beef in them), processed peas from a tin which of all disgusting things said Marrowfat, and bread and butter because she's too lazy to peel potatoes, followed by slimy tinned peaches and condensed milk. Meanwhile, wholesome garden produce like plums and lettuces are going to rack and ruin. Hattie and I eat as much as we can so as not to get scervy or berry-berry, plus underripe blackberries we pick from the hedgerows. Dan's earlier pradiction about us living in the wild like dear isn't far off the truth! Even so, our diets are beginning to take their toll, and I can't wait to see our parents' faces when they first set eyes on us: Dan wild and woolly like a moth-eaten mammal, swaring like a trooper and as gornt and boney as a skelington, his hair as long as an unkept lion, his stubble almost a beard, me unwashed and thin (thinner, anyway – my stripey pair of shorts are in grave danger of not staying up) and with a spot on my chin like Rupert's, Hattie pale, withdrawn and constapated. It serves them right. With any luck, Mummy will burst into tears and say, 'Look what we've done to them, Gerald. Oh, what our poor babies must have been through. We should never have abandoned them,' and Daddy will realise he does love us after all and will banish all thoughts of divorse from his mind for ever more.

Meanwhile, Dan has aquired an extremely tight pair of jeens,

305

tighter even than Ronnie Bone's. I caught him wearing them in the bath to shrink them!!! Sooner or later he is bound to develop gangreen. (I tried to have a serious talk with him about his future but he said he refuses to committ himself to anything until the Show is over. He keeps muttering about how he wishes he could get Brian Epstein or Andrew Loog Oldam – I think they are something to do with record companies – to come and watch their act.)

Aunt Lynette had a noisy party to celebrate some Newclear Test Ban Treety being signed that went on till the small hours. Hattie and I weren't invited. Dawn said 'Why don't we have a party to celebrate the Great Train Robbery?' Typical her to be on the Train Robbers' side and needless to say Dan is, too. Dawn sort of hero-worships them (I suppose she needed someone to replace Stephen Ward). Stealing two and a half million pounds of the country's money and coshing the train driver over the head is hardly hero-worthy in my book.

Michael English came to the back door to ask whether the show programmes had arrived and I was afraid Dawn would say 'Seen any good bottoms lately?' or 'Bottoms up!' but she didn't. Perhaps she is more to be trusted than one thinks. Or perhaps she wants to keep in with me because she's worried I'll tell Albert about her lover. Whatever the reason she is being extremely nice to me at the moment. Come to think of it, I'm being extremely nice to her, though only to make up for her family shortcomings. She is helping Hattie and me make our fancy dress costumes, and she is making me a dress for the dance (It's bound to be foul). This afternoon I'm going up to her room to help with some hemming. I am entering the den of aniquity at last!!

CHAPTER TWENTY-THREE

'Come into my parlour said the spider to the fly,' laughed Dawn with a pin in her mouth. I took a deep breath because it was bound to stink of socks and armpits and other things common people's bedrooms smell of, but the little attic window was wide open and apart from her fags and scent, it was quite bearable (in fact it was an improvement on ours which was beginning to smell like the inside of a laundry basket, and fifty times better than Dan's).

It was a small, secret, sunny room with a sloping ceiling. I looked round as sharply as an owl looking for a mouse, but it all looked like a normal teenage girl's room you see in magazines. On the walls were photographs stuck on with Sellotape of Elvis Presley and Cliff Richard and the Beatles with their funny wig-like hair and Stephen Ward (alive) in a pair of silk pyjamas and Brigitte Bardot on a beach and Marilyn Monroe in a tight gold dress. The bed was very narrow, like a camp bed, and certainly not wide enough for two; it had an imitation leopard-skin rug thrown over it and an orange furry red-tongued toy of the shooting-range-prize variety. By the bed on a white vanity case were the library books and some magazines. The top one was called *Honey*. On the marble-topped wash stand stood a blue Dansette record-player and a tidy pile of records. Granny's Polecat, a smelly old paraffin heater, stood in the corner next to the clumpy old-fashioned wooden television. Even the dressing table, which was chock-a-block with bottles and tubes and lipsticks and ear-rings and aerosol sprays and necklaces, was as neatly arranged as a chemist's counter.

Although she seemed to wear something different every day, there were surprisingly few clothes neatly hanging on the rail. It looked like the closing down sale of a dress shop when the only garments left are the ones nobody wants. But the saddest sight of all was her two pairs of high-heeled shoes standing neatly side by side, their long thin crocodile noses stuffed with newspapers, and why did shoes, I wondered, bring out the melancholy side of me? (And fancy someone of her age only having two pairs. Even I, if you included Wellingtons and slippers, had at least eight pairs.)

On the window-sill stood a small plastic owl, a glass dachshund, an ashtray from Southend and a naughty seaside postcard of a timid man and a large bosomy blonde woman who looked just like Dawn.

'What do you think of me little haven then?' said Dawn. 'Sit down and make yourself at home.'

'It's lovely,' I said. 'Very homely. And much, er, tidier than I expected.'

'It's the first time I've ever had me own room. I can tuck myself away up here and be at peace with myself. God, I love it.'

'It *is* very nice,' I said sitting on the edge of the easy chair that used to be in the spare room. It was time to ask a leading question. 'Why have you got pictures of women on your walls.'

Dawn laughed. 'Oh, don't worry, I haven't gone the other way or nothing. They're the two women I most want to look like. What d'yer reckon?' And she put her hand on her hip, shook back her hair and pouted her lips as though she were getting ready to kiss someone. It was almost as sad a sight as her shoes. My eyes must have flickered to the seaside postcard because she said, 'Yeah, I know I've got a common-as-muck face. But inside there's a glamorous sophisticated film star bursting to get out.'

'Judging by all your admirers, men seem to think you're all right as you are.'

She said her so-called admirers weren't beauty-contest judges and I asked her why it was so important for her to win it. After all, if she was going to marry Albert. . . .

'Getting married doesn't mean you shouldn't have ambitions,' she said, treadling fast on Granny's pre-war Singer sewing machine. 'I just want a bit of fame and glory, that's all. *Be* someone, for once in me life. If I win it it would give me confidence to do more things – you know, modelling or dancing or something. Maybe some photographer or film director or someone will spot me mush in the paper. That's what happens to girls in magazine stories, anyhow. That's probably how Christine Keeler started out, winning a beauty contest. My vital statistics are the same as hers: 36.24.36.'

'What if you don't win?'

'I'll probably marry Albert and hope he can cough up enough dough for me to open a boutique.'

'What about your lover?'

Dawn shrugged. 'Dunno.'

'Why don't you dunno?'

'Dunno. 'Ere, you can make yourself useful by hemming up them legs,' and she threw me Hattie's outfit.

We sat sewing in companionable silence, then she said, 'It's a bugger, ain't it, only having one life. If I ruled the world, we'd have three each. In one I'd marry and have loads of kids. In my second I'd work hard at school, go to college or something and become a career woman, a fashion designer or open a chain of boutiques and be stinking rich and have a pretty young lover I'd see once a week; the third is I'd be a good-time girl, flaunt myself around in high society, have a laugh, have fun, have lots of affairs, travel the world on a yacht and end up marrying a wealthy but witty older man who'd take me to the Ritz and the south of France and that.'

'You could combine one and two and employ a nanny to look after your children,' I said. 'And I can't see why you want to be a good-time girl. You'd have to let foul men like Mr Rachman have their wicked way with you.'

'Like hell I would. I'd be ever so fussy.'

I said if I were to have three lives I'd spend one marrying a Norfolk farmer and have four children – two boys and two girls – and when they had grown up I would breed horses. One I would be a nurse and save thousands of people's lives and marry a handsome doctor and we'd spend all our spare time discovering a cure for cancer. And one travelling round the world with my camera and notebook and be the first person to discover parts of darkest Africa; I'd be an eccentric famous explorer and wear long tweed skirts and have a lion or a panther as a pet.

'That last one sounds pretty good,' said Dawn. 'If you decide on that I'll come with you.'

I pictured Dawn in her stilettos dinking through the jungle screaming 'Oh, gawd' whenever she came across a spider or a native, and couldn't help smiling.

'It's not bleeding fair, is it. Men don't have to make these sorts of decisions.'

'Some do,' I said. 'Dan's got to decide between playing in a pop group and going to Cambridge.'

'Ner, you watch, he'll end up reverting to type. Most people do. That's why maybe I should marry Albert while the going's good. I don't want to revert to type and end up at the bottom of the slag-heap – or should I say a slag at the bottom of the heap, ha, ha!'

'What does revert to type, mean?'

'Going back to behaving like how your parents behave.'

'How can you be so sure Dan will? I think he's too far gone.'

'Instinct,' said Dawn, snapping off a piece of cotton with her teeth. 'This is the summer for going wild before Cambridge tames him. And if Cambridge doesn't, that Hilary whatsit-whatsit will.'

309

This is the summer for going wild. Mr Richards would like that phrase.

'This is the summer Hattie and I have gone a bit wild, too,' I said.

'That's no bad thing,' said Dawn. 'Your life was a bit on the tame side.'

'I liked it being a bit on the tame side,' I said hesitantly. 'At least people were polite and things didn't go on behind your back.'

'Sounds bloody boring to me. That's why I have my reservations about marrying Albert. Oh gawd, talking of Albert, do you want to hear the latest? He put a fifty-pound deposit down on that bungalow this morning.'

'Oh, no. Blimey, that means you'll *have* to marry him. He wouldn't want to live there on his own.'

Dawn's shoulders trembled, and a fat tear splashed on to her sewing. 'I can't,' she said, and covered her face in her hands. 'I can't, I can't, I can't.'

I went over and put my hand round her heaving shoulders and held out my hanky and hovered. 'Oh, don't cry. Why can't you, exactly?'

'Can I be blunt with you, Sarah? I've got no one else to tell, see,' and she looked at me through red, black, runny eyes.

'Yes – er, yeah,' I said. 'Sure.'

'Do you know what I mean by passion – ner, course you don't. You're too young.'

'Course I do,' I said hotly.

'I love Albert, you see, I really do love him. We get on like a house on fire. But I don't feel no passion for him.'

And she looked at me and waited for me to say something.

'Can't you pretend you do? There's more to married life than passion, surely. There's friendship, for example, I mean, how many minutes a week would, er, the passionate side of things take up?'

'Dunno. The national average is twice a week I think, but Albert's way over that. I keep telling him to lay off the red meat and he says it's not that, it's his way of showing his love for me. So say it's four times a week, that's, er . . .'

'Sixteen times a month, that's er, 192 times a year. How long does each er, passion take roughly?'

'About fifteen minutes. Twenty if I'm unlucky.'

'That's, er, say 3,840 minutes a year.'

'Yeah, and say I live fifty more years, multiply that by fifty and what do you get? A bloody lifetime if you ain't enjoying it.'

I had to admit it did sound a lot. 'Couldn't you just think of England?'

'I've thought of England till I'm blue in the face. I've also done Wales, Scotland, Ireland, the whole of Europe and the bleeding world by the time I've done. Except I don't think about the places; I think about the women – all lying there in the same boat. I think about Eskimo women in their igloos and African women in their tents and New York women in their skyscrapers and I feel sort of united with them all, know what I mean?'

'Er, I think so. Couldn't you just see it as a household chore like, say, peeling potatoes? Grin and bear it sort of thing?'

'That's what our mums' generation would say. But why should I? It's not wartime or nothing. This is England in the 1960s. Girls have higher expectations these days. The thing is, I would have been happy to grin and bear it until I met my lover. Now I've had a taste of how bloody amazing it can be with the right geezer, how can I spend the rest of my life with one who excites me about as much as King Kong? I'd always feel I was missing out. Like me mum with me dad after Wilbur. It's not Albert's fault, poor bastard. It's not his technique or nothing. It's just the chemistry ain't there. Honestly, him making love is about as thrilling as sticking a Tampax up. Yet me lover only has to look at me, let alone touch me, and it feels like a great surge of electricity ... like me whole body's on fire.'

For a few seconds we sewed in silence while I digested these latest juicy morsels.

'Really, you're in exactly the same dilemma as Cathy over Edgar Linton and Heathcliff,' I said. 'Or it would be like me making do with Snap Dragon when I'd had a ride on Champion.'

'You get the picture.'

'Er – if you did it in the dark couldn't you pretend Albert was your lover?'

'It doesn't work like that. The smell's all wrong.'

'It's all very animal really, isn't it,' I said.

'That's what we are when it boils down to it,' said Dawn.

Some more than others, I thought.

'Let's cheer ourselves up with some music,' she said going over to the record-player. 'Do you like Brian Hyland?'

'Never heard of him.'

'This is my all-time favourite.'

'*Oh, it's gonna be a long, lonely summer ...*' Dawn sang, completely drowning Mr Hyland. '*But darling I promise you this. I'll send you all my love, every day in a letter, sealed with a kiss.* Ain't

311

that beautiful? It's funny, before I was in love I thought it was a soppy load of nonsense. But now I can catch his drift entirely. I suppose you can't because you ain't in love.'

'Yes, I am. Sort of.'

'Go on, then. Concentrate on your loved one,' and Dawn closed her eyes and swayed in time to the music. '*I feel I can reach out and touch you. But darling, you won't be there, I don't wanna say goodbye, to the summer* ...'

I thought about Mr Richards and reaching out and touching him and him not being there but, like during the two-minute silence on Remembrance Sunday when you're meant to concentrate on soldiers dying for their country, my mind kept wandering like a cloud towards Dawn and her troubles.

'It really gets to me,' sobbed Dawn when the song whined to a halt.

'If I were you I'd forget all about it till after the Show,' I said. Let's see. Friday, Saturday ... He could cancel the cheque on Monday, if need be. It's not really the done thing, but in an emergency ...'

'Good thinking,' said Dawn. 'Anything could happen between now and Sunday. God, I must remember to shave me legs. Tell me – honestly. What do you think me chances are of winning this Beauty Contest?'

'Er – it depends on who the judges are.'

'Oh, Christ, that's a point. Say they're po-faced horsy women. I'm done for. Let's just pray they're a bunch of randy farmers. I was thinking, this Show's going to be the crunch for all of us, isn't it, what with me and my Beauty Contest and Dan making his début as a pop singer and your aunt finding herself a Yank. 'Hey, I'd better measure you – for your dress.'

She wouldn't even let me see the material, it was all to be a surprise. I said I wished she wasn't bothering and she said we can't have the pop singer's sister turning up in a tatty old skirt and blouse, and I said I wasn't going to wear a tatty old skirt and blouse, actually.

'Making a dress for someone's a sign of real friendship. This one's going to be the swishest you've ever had. Years later you'll look in your wardrobe and say, "Blimey, that Dawn made me that dress", and it'll remind you of me. Anyway, you've got to have a decent dress if you're going to be my dancing partner.'

'How can I be your dancing partner if I can only do the Gay Gordons and the waltz?'

'Because I'm going to give you a lesson when I've finished this.'

We found an extension lead and rigged up the record-player on the tea table outside. Then, on the lawn dance-floor under the hot yellow revolving light, she taught me to jive to the tune of *Let's Twist Again* by someone called Chubby Checker, *Lucille* by some brothers called Everly, and *Rock around the Clock* by someone called Bill Haley and the Comets.

'Now take my hand, not that one, stupid. I'm the man, remember.'

'You could have fooled me,' I said eyeing her bosoms and we both laughed. We worked out a routine, three jives and then me twizzling, and eventually I got the hang of it, even the bit when you put your hands on the man's shoulders and throw your legs round him, then straight out behind him and then whizz through his legs. Then she taught me another dance which she said was all the rage with Brigitte Bardot and the jet set, which involved swinging your hips, and another one called 'The Locomotion', to a song by Little Eva.

'That's it. Relax. Let the music take you over. Really, it doesn't matter a bugger what you do as long as you move to the beat. That's the beauty of dancing. It kind of frees you.'

I felt far from free, what with Ball glaring at us from across the roses and Granny, too, maybe, out of a window, and the sun so hot and my sandals sticking to the grass, but I did my best.

'You've picked it up really quick. You've got a good sense of rhythm, I'll say that for you,' panted Dawn, waving her arms in the air. 'Boy, do I dig dancing.'

'You'll have to cut down on your fags if you want to keep up with me,' I said, and spurred on by my 'good sense of rhythm', waved my arms in the air too.

Eddie Cochrane, singing about summertime blues, drowned all countryside noises including the wood pigeon.

'I reckon we're going to be the Ginger Rogers and Fred Astaire of the dance floor,' said Dawn.

'Bags be Ginger Rogers.'

'That's what I like about you,' said Dawn. 'Under all your Little Miss Prim bullshit, you're all right, kid. 'Ere, give me your other hand – now *swing*, two, three, four.'

On the eve of the Show, artistic temperaments quivered like nervous ponies' nostrils.

The boat was already rocking nicely when Hattie asked Dan to get his smelly hair cut once and for all and he snapped like a crocodile. To calm troubled waters I told him the joke about the man in a hurry asking for a crocodile sandwich and to make it snappy, and Dan didn't laugh or even smile but just snapped all the more.

Later we caught him at the hall mirror pretending the clothes brush was a microphone and singing in a hilariously deep shivery voice about a heartbreak hotel in a lonely street while jerking his arms and hips and legs around. We had to race into the garden where we rolled on the grass and wept with laughter. And then through our tears we spotted Dawn's head moving through the roses. She was using the strip of lawn between the beds as a catwalk.

'Hi. What do you think? Hand on hip, or what?'

'Just do what the others do,' said Hattie. 'But you must keep your head up.'

'And your shoulders back,' I said and decided the time was right to ask her the question I'd been putting off for days. 'Dawn, you're not going to wear a bikini, are you?'

Dawn looked sideways at me through a strand of yellow hair. 'Yeah, as it happens. Why?'

'You *can't*,' squealed Hattie. 'All the others will be in bathing costumes.'

'So? All the better for attracting the judges' attention.'

'All the better for getting their backs up.' I said. 'It's a *Beauty* Contest, not, er, a *sexy* contest.'

Dawn said if she couldn't be one she might as well be the other.

'Do you remember at the end of *Summer Holiday*?' I said. 'When they got off the bus and ran into the sea?'

'Yeah,' said Dawn. 'Sort of. To be honest, all I can remember is not seeing a full frontal of Cliff Richard in his bathing trunks!'

'The only girl who wore a bathing costume rather than a bikini was the one Cliff Richard was going to marry.'

'So? Are you saying that if I wear a bathing costume I'll marry Cliff Richard?'

'No, that the prettiest girl in the bathing costume ends up marrying the hero. It was all carefully planned by the costumes person, you see, because a bathing costume looks nicer than a bikini.'

'And she wore less make-up and had natural-coloured hair,' said Hattie.

'Oh, I get you,' said Dawn. 'For a kick off it's too late to do nothing about my hair. I've been dyeing it for so long it wouldn't know what had hit it if I suddenly stopped. Same with my face. Without make-up it would look like a naked bum. As for my bikini ... Honestly, you wait. It's so much *sexier* than a boring old one-piece.'

314

'But it's a *Beauty* Contest.'

'Same thing as far as men are concerned. Assuming the judges are men.'

'Assuming they aren't Aunt Daphne or Lady Margetson or Mrs Smedley,' I said. 'Let's pretend we're the judges and we'll ask the questions. Er, how old are you, Miss Potts?'

''Ere, that's rude. You should never ask a lady her age.'

'You can't say that. You've got to answer properly.'

'All right. Eighteen, if it's all the same with you.'

'And what are your hobbies, Miss Potts?'

'Having a laugh.'

'You've got to say things like reading, sewing and tennis.'

'And keep your cockney accent in check,' said Hattie. 'They might be prejudiced against foreigners.'

'Blimey, I don't know why I'm bothering.'

'Do you *have* to wear a bikini, Dawn?'

'Look, you don't get nowhere in this life if you merge into the wallpaper. I mean if Christine Keeler hadn't swum naked in that swimming pool that day no one would have heard of her, yeah?'

'But there won't be any wallpaper at the . . .'

'Now, tell me honestly, which smile do you prefer? This? Or this?'

Temperaments were quivering nicely on the showground, too. The jumps had arrived on the back of a trailer and, following tradition, Dan, Hattie and I, along with an assortment of large, sweating men, helped put them up.

Brigadier Benson-Long, a snapping terrier of a man in plus-fours waving a tape measure, was in charge. 'I need men, not schoolgirls,' he barked when he saw us, and I, boiling hotter than the sun, said 'Excuse me, Brigadier, I'm as strong as any man,' and Dan said 'I'll second that.' This turned out to be a mistake as I then had to prove it by carrying all the heaviest things, but thinking about people in concentration camps toiling in the fields on one bowl of greasy soup a day spurred me on.

'I said a pole not a bar, and where's the bally wing for this one, eh?' yapped the Brigadier.

'Anyone would think we were getting flipping paid for this,' muttered Ronnie Bone, sweat dripping from his newly acquired Beatle-fringed brow, and Dan said 'Hear, hear.' I'm sorry to say they sloped off before we had finished, so Hattie and I stayed to the bitter end as the only Hillington representatives.

The only person who didn't seem ruffled by the Show was Granny.

315

I was reading *The Lion, the Witch and the Wardrobe* to her in bed, while Hattie brushed her hair, conveniently finding a knotty bit if she looked in danger of nodding off. (*What a reversal of roles*, I wrote in my diary. *Last year it was Granny reading to us in bed! The old get weaker and the young get stronger ...*)

I put on the right accents for the characters: Jack's for Mr Beaver and Dawn's for the witch, which made Granny laugh.

I reached the bit where the witch kills Aslan and ties him up and cuts off his mane and Susan and Lucy mourn his death and cry and cry.

'Oh dear, this is very sad,' said Granny.

'Don't worry, Granny, Aslan comes back to life at dawn, I promise,' I said, but it didn't stop Hattie from quietly sobbing, and I began to, too; when Granny died she wouldn't come back to life at dawn. We cuddled up to her the way Susan and Lucy did to Aslan, and it was as if she *was* Aslan, a noble beast robbed of her dignity, and she must have sensed this was what we were thinking because she stroked our hair and said, 'Poor darlings. It must be so distressing to see your old Granny all tired and funny-looking and useless. To think that this time last year we were playing cricket and croquet together.'

'Next year will be back to normal, won't it,' said Hattie. 'The wicked winter will have well and truly worn off by then.'

'Of course it will,' I said but from Granny answer came there none.

Later I went up to Dawn's room to try on the dreaded dress.

'There was a bit of material left over so I've done you some matching drawers,' she said. 'If our dancing gets really wild they'll show. And before you start worrying it cost me nothing because I've used the material from one of your gran's old ball gowns. Right, strip off and close your eyes – as the actress said to the bishop!'

She fussed and fiddled and straightened and smoothed, then steered me to the mirror. 'Right – open your eyes,' she said.

Boy oh boy and pass the smelling salts at the double, Gertie! It was like Cinderella after her Fairy Godmother's visit or the Ugly Duckling on discovering he was a swan. It wasn't like looking at me but at my elder sister. I looked stupendous! It was the brightest blue I had ever seen, as blue as kingfisher in his prime, and rustled pleasingly when I moved. It had thin daring straps so nearly all of my shoulders were showing, a sash tied round my hips and a pleated skirt that swished and twirled beautifully. It made me look quite

316

thin. Aunt Daphne would say it was the sort of dress village children wear, but I loved it, I loved it, I loved it!

'Oh, Dawn! Just looking at it makes you want to dance,' I cried, tears in my eyes, swirling to and fro, swishing round and round. 'Oh, *thank* you. Honestly, it's the nicest dress I've ever seen. And it makes it even more special to think Granny once danced in the material – I'm sort of carrying on a family tradition,' and I was so overcome I hugged her.

'Get off, you old softie,' she said, looking pleased and embarrassed. 'It fits well, don't it. That's the thing with man-made fabrics, they move with you and hang better than natural. Much sexier than the crisp cotton stuff your mum dresses you in.'

'I feel the belle of the ball already,' I said. 'What are you wearing?'

'Wait and see. I'll tell you this for nothing, though. Between us we're going to look a couple of stunners.'

'I feel pretty, oh so pretty,' I sang twirling round and round.

'You don't *look* half bad, actually,' she said and I was tempted to ask her whether she'd changed her mind about me not growing up to be a looker. 'Make sure you wash your barnet though, it's like an oil slick. I'll put in a few rollers for you. A touch of rouge and lipstick wouldn't go amiss, neither.'

She unfolded Granny's old ironing board and switched on the iron and told me to take the dress off before I did something to it and she'd press it.

'Dawn,' I said. 'I've been thinking. About your future. About *our* future, actually. Just say you decided not to marry Albert or carry on your relationship with your lover. What you could do is stay with Granny till she dies, and during that time give up boys – sort of lie low like Brer Rabbit – and concentrate on educating yourself. Perhaps you could do some evening classes – a typing course, English O-level and things like that. Then, when Granny dies you can go to London and be a good-time girl for a while. Then as soon as I'm old enough to leave school – I won't bother with A-levels – we could go to America together. I think America would be more suitable than Africa, don't you?'

Dawn looked up from the ironing board. Her face had lit up like a sunny day. 'Blimey, this is a turn-up for the book, you wanting to go abroad with me.'

'Just think. Land of the Free.'

'Land of Coca Cola and Paul Newman and Peyton Place ...'

'And handsome men in pink Cadillacs who call you honey ...'

'And becoming millionaires overnight ... The adventures we'd

317

have. The *laughs*. The blokes we'd meet. The Grand Canyon. Fifth Avenue.'

'California. New Orleans. The Arizona Desert.'

'New York. Hollywood. I like it, I like it,' cried Dawn and we sang in joyous, little-girl voices, '*I wanna be in America, everything free in America, okay by me in America.*'

Dawn laughed and said what would we do for dough, though?

'Oh, we'd get some from somewhere. I'm bound to come into some sooner or later. Or maybe we could be waitresses in one of those hamburger restaurants they have there or dancers at that Whiskey-A-Go-Go place Dan's mentioned. And what I was thinking was we could turn it into a real adventure, a detective story, even, by hiring a car and driving to Tennessee and tracking down your real father. We might even see Elvis.'

Slowly, a storm cloud gathered across Dawn's face. She bent her head and a large tear plopped on to my dress. (Did salt stain? I wondered in passing. Was it a *mascara-ed* tear?)

'Oh, gawd,' she said, taking my handkerchief. 'Oh, bloody hell.' Then, holding me to her bosom which beat like a squashy drum, she swayed from side to side sobbing her heart out. I comforted her as best I could, and in passing checked over her shoulder that she hadn't left the iron face down on my dress.

She drew away, blew her nose and said in a snuffly voice, 'I've got a confession to make. Two, in actual fact. That thing about my father was a load of bullshit.'

'You mean he isn't really a Yank?'

She nodded, then shook her head. 'Mum did have an affair with him, but I didn't come along as a result.'

'Why did you tell me you did then?' I said in a voice reserved for talking to frightened, naughty ponies.

'So would you if you had a father like mine,' snivelled Dawn. 'I bet you wouldn't begin to know what it's like to be ashamed of your father.'

No, I wouldn't. The only time I could remember feeling ashamed of either of my parents was when Mother was the only one to wear a hat – a silly pink one with tassels – at a school play. And then I thought of something else; one Christmas, when Father got drunk and Beryl Wilkinson's blouse came undone....

I told Dawn this, embellishing the story somewhat, and Dawn cried 'Christ, if that's all you can think of ...' She looked round at me, her eyes sooty blobs, her hair all loose round her face. 'You don't know what it's like for your father to roll up at your first day at a new school drunk and ugly and unshaven and say to your teacher, "What, no bloody tits?" Or beat up your mum just ... Oh, I'm sorry, it ain't fair putting you through all the shit I've been through. Anyway, it's all in the past and he's safely tucked away in nick, hopefully till kingdom come.'

'Oh, Dawn, I *am* sorry.' I'd never met anyone who didn't at least respect their father.

'I suppose I mustn't grumble. Marilyn Monroe spent the first fifteen years of her life in foster homes and was married at sixteen, and she turned out all right. Until she committed suicide that is. That's it, innit, you can always find someone worse off than yourself.'

'Look, we can still go to the Land of the Free,' I said. 'I could take lots of photographs and keep a diary and later write a book about our adventures.'

Dawn looked at me with large eyes full of tears like the Mock Turtle, which turned into constant, heavy, empty sobbing. I too felt this deep, aching feeling inside. Soon the summer would be over and it would be back to school, holidays, school, holidays, and the dullness – the pointlessness – of it all ...

'Do you want to hear the best bit?' she said between sobs. 'Are you ready for this? I've only gone and got myself pregnant, haven't I.'

It took me a second or two to absorb this latest bombshell, though deep inside it was exactly what I had been expecting. 'You mean up the spout?' I said, my eyes darting to her tummy which didn't look any different to normal. 'Oh, *blimey*.'

'So you see,' sniffed Dawn. 'All your exotic plans for the future are a bit how's your father now.'

'Er, yes, it does put a different complexion on things,' I said. 'Talking of fathers is – er – your lover the father or is Albert?' It was the most grown-up question I'd ever asked in my whole life.

'Need you ask?' she said. 'Me lover of course.' Her tears had washed away most of her eye make-up, and for the first time I saw her as she really was; a frightened, ordinary girl.

'Are you *sure* you are?' I asked, feeling more grown-up by the minute. 'It was less than a month ago when we went to the millpond and you had your period.'

'Yeah, well, I was fibbing,' she said. 'I didn't fancy swimming, that's all. I'm eight days late and I'm normally like clockwork.'

'Well, if your lover has the same sort of reddish hair as Albert, Albert need never know he's not the father. And even if the baby has black hair it wouldn't matter. Some friends of my parents, the Lowthers, have jet-black hair and both their sons are mouse.

Anyway, if you don't want the baby,' I continued brightly (and maybe that's what I should be when I grew up – a Marriage Guidance Counsellor!) 'if the worst came to the absolute worst you could have an abortion if you found a good doctor. I'm sure Granny or Aunt Lynette would give you the money.'

'It's illegal, remember, so no good doctor would do it, and I don't fancy becoming sterile. I don't fancy being a murderer much, neither.'

'You wouldn't be. You only would be if you killed something that was alive. A baby isn't alive until it's born and takes its first breath of air. How can something in your tummy be alive? That's like saying an undigested apple pip's alive.'

Dawn said it was murder in her book, she'd feel guilty for the rest of her life, and even though she detested the Catholic church and all it stood for, there were some things drummed into you as a kid that stayed with you and that was one of them.

'I suppose I could have it adopted, but that would mean disappearing into thin air for seven or so months. Oh gawd, I told you it would all end in tears.'

'How do you know? It hasn't ended yet. Have you told your lover about it?'

She said blimey no, he'd probably run a mile. 'You know what I'm going to have to end up doing. Forget all about the lover and all my other fanciful notions and marry Albert and hope the baby takes after me.'

'Yes. And really, I think you'd be very happy. Honestly. It's definitely the lesser of, er, the evils. You'd have a nice home of your own and, er, even though Albert doesn't set *you* on fire, at least you *get on* like a house on fire. And you could still have the boutique and keep the baby in a playpen out the back.'

'You don't make it sound too bad.'

'That's because it *isn't* too bad. Meanwhile, why don't you forget all about it until after the Show. Let's have a wonderful day tomorrow – the best day of our lives – and Sunday can be decision-making day.'

'Yeah. Okay. Blimey, talk bout a problem shared is a problem halved.'

'Er – you being pregnant won't stop you dancing, will it?'

'Course not. Or wearing me bikini in the Beauty Contest. It's far too early for anything to show.'

'Er, Dawn, talking of bikinis . . .'

'It's nearly seven. Can I come up?' shouted Dan from the bottom of the stairs.

320

'Oh, blimey, it's time for *Ready, Steady, Go*,' said Dawn, putting on her sun-glasses. 'Yeah, come on up,' she shouted. 'You'll stay won't you, kid?' The Swinging Blue Jeans are on. And promise you won't say a word to a soul about – my, er condition?'

I was tempted to say something very, very funny but decided not to in case she burst into tears again. I wasn't going to waste it, though, and wrote it later in my diary: *What do you say to Dawn when she asks you not to tell anyone she's pregnant? Mum's the word!!!*

PART FOUR

CHAPTER TWENTY-FOUR

When I awoke the next morning my bedclothes were in chaos, my body damp with sweat. But all was not lost. No siree! For early birds were already starting to sing and the for-he's-a-jolly-good-fellow morning light was winking through the orange and lemon curtains. Get thee behind me, silly old dreams! The night of the thousand eyes and the long knives is over!

I put on my shorts and T-shirt, crept through the house and ran across the dew-soaked lawn towards tangly wood where the rising sun wasn't a shepherd's warning sort of red so much as an oh, what a beautiful day one.

I took a deep breath of fresh-as-a-daisy air. Apart from a bird, maybe, I was the first living thing to breathe it. It was the start of another day. And boy, what a day! Show day! Watershed day! Everything's going my way day! Anyone who's anyone day! When it comes to the crunch day! All will be revealed day! Black Champion rules supreme day! Gee whiz day! Blimey O'Reilly day! The day to end all days!

The air was alive with the sound of birdsong. It was as if the trees, recognising a special occasion when they saw one, had switched on their roots and turned the volume up to 10.

I slowed to a walk when the black summerhouse came into view. I needed time to concentrate on what I was going to discuss with Snuff Mull.

It was a lengthy meeting, and by the time I came blinking out into the brightness the sky was the colour of azure-blue writing paper, one corner scribbled on with Dawn's pinkest lipstick.

'Perfect Show weather,' Grandpa or Daddy would have said if they had been in my shoes. But they weren't so I said it for them.

My next task was to inspect the showground to check everything was in order. It was important, I felt, to keep Hillington traditions going. I ran up the red brick road and along cow parsley lane. My senses were behaving as if I was slap-bang-wallop in love, and my tummy tingled with enough electricity to keep a cooker and a fridge going for six months. I felt as strong as Black Champion winning the Grand National one day and Horse of the Year Show the next, and I cleared a cow-parsley jump with a yard to spare. If anyone crossed my path today, boy, were they in for a big surprise!

As I neared the showground I came across a man banging a sign into the top of the bank. It was the same sign as last year, and the year before, and the year before that. It was written in red marker pen used for writing the numbers on cattle at market and it said MEMBERS' CAR PARK and an arrow. Further along was one which said CAR PARK (cars only). There were still two to be put up; one said HORSE BOXES AND CATTLE LORRIES and another, bigger one said WELCOME TO THE SHOTESTEAD SHOW.

'Lovely morning,' I said to the man, the way you do in the country.

'Mornin' to yer,' said the man looking round and blimey O'Reilly, it was the blond Adam Faith man from the building site who had whistled at Dawn! Was this Snuff Mull at work already? I'd requested that he should reveal Dawn's lover to me during the course of the day, or at least give me a sign, and then, the first person I meet, one of my prime suspects, is putting up a *sign*! If this *was* Snuff Mull's doing, what a wit!

I couldn't let this opportunity go by. My next remark was going to be 'Perfect Show weather' but never mind that; there were now more important things on the agenda!

'Er – you know Dawn Potts, don't you?'

'Yeah,' he said. He hadn't gone red, but his type wouldn't unless they'd been drinking beer and it was far too early for that. He was wearing tight pale blue jeans, a white T-shirt and winklepickers; the arm that was doing the banging was smooth and brown and muscular. He was really quite handsome in a common, long-haired, if-you-like-that-sort-of-thing way. He jiggled the sign to test its firmness and began banging again. Were those the hands, I wondered, that inflamed Dawn's body?

'Why?' he asked. (He pronounced it 'woy').

'She – er, lives in my granny's house,' I said. One couldn't help noticing in passing the outline of his wedding tackle through his jeans.

He looked at me through dazzling sailor-trouser-blue eyes. 'Oh yeah. I recognise you now. You're the one on that bicycle. How is she?'

'Getting a bit nervous about the Beauty Contest,' I said. 'Do you think she stands a chance?'

'Well now, that all depends on the judge, don't it? If he likes a blonde, busty, forward type of bird then yeah, I guess so.'

'Yes but do *you* like a blonde, busty, forward type of bird?' I was dying to ask.

'She's going to wear a bikini,' I said, watching his face very carefully. I would have liked to have had another brief glimpse at his jeans, too, but say he caught me looking … 'I think that's a mistake, don't you?'

'Well now,' he said, testing the sign wasn't wobbling and springing down from the bank. 'Even if the judge don't like it, the fellers certainly will, yeah?' and he winked at me and grinned. I went red and grinned and began to walk on.

'See you later, kiddo,' he said and I said, 'Yeah. Okay.'

The showground was already swarming with people busy as ants and buzzing with the sound of posts being banged into the ground and crates being crash-bang-walloped in the beer tent and men shouting 'Back a bit, George. Go on, you're all right. *Whooo.*'

I strode round as Daddy normally did, my hands behind my back like Prince Philip, pretending I was looking for someone. People were setting up their stalls, the brigadier was giving the jumps a final check, and food and drink was arriving by the vanload for the Members' Tent. A man was saying 'Testing, one, two, three … okey-dokey, Jim?' into the loudspeaker.

Near the cattle ring was a row of straw-lined pens. Already, a few friendly Friesians, dainty Jerseys, big, cream-coloured Charolais and one short-legged, wide-chested surprised Hereford had arrived. As if before a town-hall dance they were, as Dawn would say, 'getting tarted up in the Ladies' (which would explain the look of surprise on the Hereford's white face because clearly he was a male). Their coats were being oiled and polished as lovingly as if they were the paintwork of precious Jaguars or Rolls Royces. Their grooming kits were kept in brown trunks whose lids displayed their rosettes, and the cowmen ranged from handsome to ugly, from sideboards, beard, moustache and glasses to none of these things. In fact the only thing they had in common was their love of cows. It made you wonder whether they paid their wives as much attention. Perhaps sometimes they mistook their cows for their wives or vice versa.

'Mornin' to yer,' they said and I said 'Morning' back, and waved like Princess Anne.

Everything seemed to be in order. I ran down the road and into the farmyard. Outside the cowshed, Jack was sandpapering the horns of Mildred Minor the Second and whistling *Waltzing Matilda*, and Michael was washing Laura Louise's udders with soapy water. Laura Louise didn't seem to mind at all even though it was a boy doing it, though of course cows weren't shy like girls. Mildred was a brown and white Ayrshire and Laura Louise was a black and white Friesian. Both had their tails plaited, doubled up and wrapped in crêpe bandages.

'Hello, my booty,' said Jack, and Michael looked up and grinned and said 'Hi.'

'Hi,' I said. 'Perfect Show weather, isn't it.'

'Let's hope harvest won't keep too many of 'em away,' said Michael. He was wearing dungarees and Wellington boots and had his shirt sleeves rolled up. His arms weren't hairy but for a boy of his age were quite broad and strong. He was taking great care to get Laura Louise's udders clean. He was being very gentle with them as if they were rare exotic fruits. I wondered what it felt like. Did it tickle slightly, for example? One thing was for sure; I'd never find out from Laura Louise.

I rubbed her white curly forehead and told them the showground was already a hive of industry and Jack said, 'People get there earlier each year.' He wasn't wearing his cap and had washed his hair specially for the Show. It had turned as fluffy as a dandelion clock. That reminded me; I would have to wash mine when I got back.

I remarked how smart the cows looked and Jack muttered that this one had good bone all right, it was just a shame her teats were more suited to the days of hand milking. I said it was funny but I bet at this very moment Dawn was preening herself for the Beauty Contest, and Jack said there you are you see, no difference really between us and animals.

'Good luck then. See you later,' I said and Michael said 'Cheerio. By the way, I'm expecting a dance off you later,' and my heart soared as I thought of my oh-so-pretty dress and said 'Righty-ho.'

I looked back before I turned the corner to see if he was looking at my bottom, but he appeared to be looking at Laura Louise's instead.

I burst into the kitchen like a gazelle on the first day of spring. The kettle was belting out steam and its lid wobbled and danced like a thing possessed.

'About time too,' said Hattie, looking up from slicing bread. 'I thought I was going to have to make breakfast and wash up and do all the other boring work that needs doing round these parts on my own. And in case anyone had forgotten, I am only eight.'

'Where is everyone?' I said moving the kettle across, though the lid went on dancing for quite a while.

'Granny is feeling below par and wants breakfast in bed, Dan's

328

preserving his strength for his début and Dawn's dyeing her hair.'

'I thought it was already dyed.'

'Well, she's killing it off once and for all,' said Hattie. 'It's made the bathroom stink like a stable that hasn't been mucked out for ten years. By the way I've got some bad news.'

'What?'

'Who would be the worst person in the world to be a donkey steward with us?'

'Oh, she *can't*. We can manage on our own. She doesn't know one end of a donkey from another.'

We told Granny this – she looked a thousand – when we took up her breakfast. 'She'll get everything wrong, Granny, and she'll be rude to the judge. We can manage quite well on our own. Honestly, she'll be more of a hindrance than a help.'

'Couldn't she announce the classes over the loudspeaker, darling? She can't go wrong there, surely, if you tell her exactly what to say.'

'She's bound to say gawd or blimey and everyone will hear and it'll lower the tone of the Show.'

Granny said it was a risk we'd have to take and we should be grateful she was offering her services at all.

'*Dis*services, she means,' I said to Hattie as we ate breakfast at the kitchen table. It was a golden opportunity to eat as much as we liked without anyone telling us we were being greedy or that we'd go off pop. But due to pre-Show nerves we could only manage half a bowl of cornflakes each. 'By the way, why would Dawn make a good donkey steward? Because she'll make a complete ass of herself.'

Hattie thought this very funny. 'What's the one and only difference between Dawn and a donkey?' she said. 'Dawn walks on two legs.'

'Why did the judge ban Dawn from the donkey ring? Because she talked the hind legs off a donkey!'

We washed our hair in the evil-smelling bathroom – the water ran as black as soot! – towelled it dry and changed into cotton dresses. Hattie's was red and green stripes and mine was pale blue with white panels of blue rose-buds and a small matching bow at the neck. Looking in the mirror I could see what Dawn meant about looking frumpy, and I just hoped anyone important who saw me would be staying for the dance. 'My, look at that Sarah Hillington,' they would say. 'Talk about an ugly duckling turned into a swan.' We put on knee-length white socks and sandals, and for a moment I wished more than anything else in the world I had a pair of black pointed slip-ons.

'Do you realise,' I said, 'that Dawn will be given a steward's badge and you know what that means.'

'Oh no! Not the Members' Tent! That's the last straw hat of all. That's like a dustman, say, going to Buckingham Palace.'

'Don't worry, we'll give her the slip,' I said, though most of me thought it would be quite a laugh, Dawn causing havoc in the Members,' which was strictly top-drawer only – just so long as everyone realised she was a servant and not our cousin or something.

We cleaned our teeth and tied on our members' badges and Hattie polished her glasses and I said aye, aye, I'd forgotten what her eyes looked like. We put our Fancy Dress things in two large carrier bags. Aunt Daphne was allowing us to use her horsebox as a changing room, and that included Dawn. 'As long as there's no bleeding horse ogling me,' Dawn had said. 'Or horse shit. Oh, and there will be a mirror, won't there?' and I said of course, how else would the horses be able to put on their mascara and lipstick, and she said all right, no need to be sarky.

We said, 'See you later, alligator' to Dan and he mumbled, 'In a while, crocodile'. Then he opened an eye and said, 'Wow. What smart sisters I have. Don't talk to any strange men now.'

Dawn was doing some last-minute whirring on the sewing machine. 'See you in the donkey ring, kids, and we can make complete asses of ourselves together,' she yelled down the twisty stairs.

Granny was still in bed, still looking a thousand, and shouldn't she be getting ready? 'You look nice, darlings,' she said (last year she wouldn't have said nice; 'a credit to the family', perhaps, but never 'nice'). She said that after considering the matter carefully she had decided to give the Show a miss this year. 'One needs to feel so strong for all those people ... I'd only be a burden. It would be much better all round if I pottered around here. Would you send my apologies to all concerned?'

'But you *must* come, Granny,' I said. 'The Show without you would be like ...'

'... bacon without eggs,' said Hattie.

'Or a postage stamp without the Queen,' I said. 'It just won't be the same without you, honestly.'

What a hypocrite I was. Because secretly I was quite pleased; now there would be not one single person to keep an eye on us and we'd be able to go as wild as we liked. Except there were disadvantages, too. Like there'd be no one to give us money for an ice cream.

'Anyway, who will present the cups? You've been doing it ever sine the Show started.'

'All the more reason to let someone else take over,' said Granny. 'Mrs English will do the job perfectly.'

'Couldn't you just muster yourself to watch us in the Fancy Dress – and Dawn in the Beauty Contest? And you'll miss your roses winning first prize,' but Granny said she'd love us to describe everything to her afterwards; we could be her eyes and her ears. She gave me two pounds for lunch and treats, plus an extra ten shillings for Dawn's lunch.

'Oh, thank you, Granny,' I said and wanted to add, 'Does Dawn *have* to have lunch with us?' but decided not to bother. Granny would only say everyone was equal in the eyes of the Lord, though surely even the Lord would agree that Dawn would stick out like a sore thumb in the Members' Tent?

'Hillingtons are very thin on the ground this year,' said Hattie as we trundled down the drive. 'Do you realise we've got no one to keep an eye on us?'

'We've got each other. I think this is going to be the best Show ever. I can feel it in my bones.'

'Well, your bones are a different kettle of fish to mine,' said Hattie. 'My bones say it's going to be the worst Show ever. By miles. By the way, you owe me ten bob.'

'What for?'

'You know. My "ailment". I haven't been yet.'

'Blast! That was the only thing I forgot to ask Snuff Mull about. That just goes to show,' I said, giving her Dawn's lunch money.

All cars great and small, cattle floats and horseboxes were queueing bumper to mudguard in both directions outside the showground. Mr Glister the policeman was concentrating on beckoning with one arm and halting with the other, so he didn't risk complicating his life further by waving to us. There was no sign of a budgerigar ladder or aniseed balls about his person. His wobbly cheeks were already traffic-light red; the mind boggled as to what shade they would be by teatime.

We walked through the Public Car Park past large old clean cars and small new clean cars and motor cycles with sidecars, and through the Members' past large new muddy cars and shooting brakes and Land Rovers.

Uncle William and James, both in suits and Uncle William in a bowler, were the Members' Car Park stewards. Uncle William looked like the Fat Controller in *Thomas the Tank Engine*. He

331

waved and said 'Lovely morning', and James said. 'They've got the most abominable chappie on the loudspeaker. Talk about lowering the tone. Come back Bill Ewing, all is forgiven.'

'Okey-dokey, folks, we've got fun, fun, fun lined up for you all through the day right into the wee, wee hours,' said the loudspeaker man. *'Sheep-dog trials, clowns for the kiddies, military bands, jumping events, a gymkhana, goats, sheep, cows, dogs, beauty queens ... You name it, we've got it for you here today. So just enjoy yourselves, folks, and remember that every penny made goes to local charities.'*

'I don't think he sounds too bad,' I said.

'I don't think he should have said wee wee hours,' said Hattie. 'Since when have hours needed to go to the lavatory?' and I told her that she had lavatories on the brain.

'There's no business like Show business,' we sang as we walked past the horseboxes that had spilling out of them horses, ponies, foals, horse rugs, dogs, saddles, bridles, picnic hampers, hay nets, body brushes, curry combs, whips, shooting sticks, boots, bandages and buckets.

Snatches of conversation rang out like telephone bells.

'Penelope darling, what *have* you done with Starlight's thingamyjig.'

'Is my number the right way up, Mummy?'

'Stand *still,* you wretched creature.'

'Oh, you *beast.* He's trodden on my toe, Daddy.'

Sometimes it was hard to tell whether they were talking about horses or other people; or indeed whether it wasn't the horses themselves talking.

There was also much neighbourly gossip. 'I say, Audrey, I've gone and left the bally bandages behind. You couldn't lend ... You'll simply never guess what happened to Amanda at the Marlingham Show ...' It only needed a few garden fences and it would have been like watching a top-drawer version of *Coronation Street.* There were already plenty of Ena Sharples hair-nets in evidence.

'I'm glad we aren't horsy people, aren't you?' said Hattie. 'I think it's much nicer to be a *general* person.'

'I suppose so,' half of me said; the other half very much wished I was wearing jodhpurs and had a number tied to my back and was grooming the glossy coat of Black Champion.

'Hello, you two. You found us all right then,' boomed a voice from up above. It was Aunt Daphne on Boxer. Both were done up to the nines. Aunt Daphne wore a black jacket, cream jodhpurs and long black boots, lipstick and powder but no mascara. From under her bowler poked neat, hair-netted curls. Boxer's mane had been plaited into small knots as if he'd just had a very tight perm. If he'd been a human rather than a horse his schoolfriends would have teased him for looking like a girl. Between them, there wasn't a hair out of place.

'Hello, Aunt Daphne. You look smart and so does Boxer,' I said.

'So he should,' she said as crisp as a frosty morning. 'There's been a good three hours' work spent on the old chap.'

We put the dressing-up clothes in a quiet corner of the leaf-green horsebox and helped Susan groom Tinkerbell. Her horsy smell and the way she nuzzled her soft as marshmallows nose in my hand made me ache to have my own pony.

'You can ride her in some of the gymkhana events if you like. I'm too old for most of them now,' Susan said, and since when had she been a mind reader? 'You can borrow my jods.'

'Oh, thanks. Very much,' I added though I wouldn't take her up on her offer. Dreaming about riding in shows was one thing, actually doing it was another. Besides, today I had too many other things on my plate.

'For Pete's sake don't let Mummy hear you say thanks,' said Susan. 'She'd have a fit, wouldn't she, Tinkerbell my precious darling.'

'*Standing on the corner, watching all the girls . . .*' sang Hattie.

'And boys,' I added, though I hadn't seen one boy yet who was worth looking at twice.

We were waiting for the donkey judge outside the secretary's tent. People milled around, horsy types mainly in headscarves and very large- or very small-bottomed jodhpurs, watching the hunter classes in the grand ring with their hands on their hips or holding the leads of big dogs. Over their heads you could see Aunt Daphne looking grim and Boxer's chestnut ears pricked forward.

Judge: Lady Thoroughgood. Stewards: Sarah and Harriet Hillington it said in the programme.

'Do you think she's thoroughly good or a thoroughbred?' said Hattie.

'Both by the looks of things. I bet you ten bob this is her.'

And it was. She had a long thin face and a long thin nose. She wore a headscarf covered in dark yellow horses' heads, a beige twinset, a pair of dun, sharply creased trousers and expensive shoes whose day would be ruined if they stepped in a horse's mess. My stomach gave a small lurch. I hadn't been on my best behaviour for so long I'd got out of practice. Did it come back automatically, like riding a bicycle? Normally it was Mummy who did all the talking to the judge.

'Sarah and Harriet Hillington I presume?' she boomed, smiling as briefly as a passing express train. 'Shall we get cracking? We've got a fearful amount to get through.'

As we strode towards the donkey ring, I said, 'Er, I should warn you. Lady Thoroughgood. There might be another steward coming and she's a bit – er . . .'

'*Three* stewards!' exclaimed Lady Thoroughgood. 'I *am* honoured. Nothing should go wrong then, should it.'

'Well, I wouldn't say that, exactly.'

We marched importantly into the middle of the ring. 'And the first class is . . .' said Lady Thoroughgood, consulting her programme.

'Colts, geldings and fillies born in 1962,' said Hattie.

'I'll go and round them up,' I said sounding like, but not looking or feeling like, John Wayne.

Several people lurked by the ring with their donkeys and, having checked the number on their backs and ticked them off on my programme, I politely asked them to go into the ring and start walking round. Then I went into the caravan, cleared my throat, waited for the grand-ring loudspeaker man to stop talking and said through the microphone: 'Will all competitors for class 31, colts, geldings and fillies – er, donkeys, that is – please hurry along to ring number four as judging is about to commence.'

Then I joined Hattie in the centre of the ring. Eight people and their donkeys, in all shapes, shades and sizes, walked round, watched by the eagle eye of Lady Thoroughgood who stood with her arms folded.

'With any luck, you-know-who has forgotten,' said Hattie in a low voice.

'Would you tell them to trot on, please, Miss Hillington?' said Lady Thoroughgood, so I walked over to a small man in a suit and bowler and said. 'The judge said would you trot on, please.' The man touched the rim of his bowler with his crop, clicked his tongue on the roof of his mouth and they all trotted on.

Lady Thoroughgood stroked her chin as if she had a beard, watching each donkey like a hawk. She was just getting ready to tell me her order of preference for calling them into the middle, and everything was going as smooth as clockwork, when suddenly, '*Yooo-hooo*' filled the air like a 20-foot poisoned arrow. And there, bending under the rope and dodging between the donkeys, causing one to stop in mid-trot and the one behind to crash into him and soon there was a complete donkey jam, was Dawn.

For a moment, everything – the donkeys, the donkeys' owners, the spectators, the judge, the crowds and horses and dogs – seemed to stand still and merge into the wallpaper. Only Dawn, dinking across the ring in tiny high-heeled steps, was alive, looking more magnificent, more defiant, more modern, more wicked, more stupendous than I'd ever before seen her.

She wore a blinding red suit that fitted like a kid glove and was so short you could see at least four inches of thigh. Round her neck fluttered a red and white spotted scarf. She wore lacy white gloves and from her wrist swung a white bag on a gold chain. Her necklaces and bangles and ear-rings clanked and twinkled and jangled like mad, her eyes were the blackest and fiercest ever, her lips as pale as a corpse.

But like when we first saw Granny, the biggest shock of all was her hair: the dirty straw had turned pure white and towered into the sky like an elongated snowball. It was as if any remaining evidence of the wicked winter had gathered together and ended, plop, on top of her head. She was the Snow Queen ... the *Show* Queen, for no one, not even the clown, would attract so much attention.

Everyone stared, including the donkeys. Perhaps they felt peeved because it was, after all, their show ring. All year they looked forward to being the centre of attention and now their thunder had been stolen from them by some red and white human monstrosity.

'I'm ever so sorry I'm late,' she shrieked. 'My blooming barnet wouldn't go right. I ended up using half a can of hair spray, and then blow me if I didn't go and get a ladder in me stocking ... Anyway, you don't want to hear my tales of woe, I'm sure. You must be the judge. Dawn Potts at your service.'

Lady Thoroughgood looked as though the thunder had been stolen from her, too. But she was too much of a thoroughbred to allow it to remain that way for long.

'If you want to be of service, Miss er, Potts, you can start by making no sudden movements so as not to upset the donkeys, and secondly by not interrupting my train of thought. You've put me right back to square one.'

I dug my nails into my palms and prayed Dawn wouldn't say, 'Pardon me for breathing' or 'Keep your hair on', and it worked because instead she said. 'Oh, I'm ever so sorry, Mrs, er ...'

'Lady Thoroughgood. Now get them to walk again will you, Miss Hillington. And please *keep still,* Miss Potts, your costume is most alarming for the donkeys.'

While Lady Thoroughgood went back to square one with her

judging, Dawn came over to us and said, 'What d'yer think of the barnet then? Snow White. That's me new name. Blimey, judging by your faces I've just smothered me head in dog shit. You do like it, don't you?'

'It looks as though you've had a dreadful fright,' said Hattie – and *look* like one, I knew she wanted to add.

'It's certainly, er, different,' I said. 'Look, we must concentrate on ...'

'That's what I thought. At least I'll stand out in the crowd. I thought I'd have it up for the donkeys – to make me look official like – then take some of it down for the Beauty Contest, then let it all down for the dance. Geddit? Let my hair down for the dance!' and she laughed so loudly that Lady Thoroughgood looked round frowning and said, 'Shhh, *if* you'd be so kind.'

'Sorry, Mrs er, Lady Thoroughbred,' shouted Dawn dinking over to her. ('Good,' I hissed. 'Thorough*good*'.) Which one do yer fancy then? I'd go for that nice little black one with the long ears if I were in your shoes.'

'Blimey O'bloody Reilly,' whispered Hattie.

'Would you indeed,' said Lady Thoroughgood, and looked beyond her to Hattie. 'Incidentally, Miss Hillington, are you aware you've scattered rosettes all over the ring?'

Talk about going from bad to worse. Talk about wanting to die on the spot.

'Who does she think she is – Lady bleeding Muck?' muttered Dawn as we bent to pick up the rosettes, two scarlet faces and one snow-white one. 'She's only a bloody donkey judge and I bet she's forgotten we don't get paid for this lark.'

'Trust you to think about money,' said Hattie and I said, 'Dawn, please try and behave. Even if you don't take donkey judging seriously, everyone else round here does. And you called her Thoroughbred on purpose, didn't you,' and Dawn said, 'Yeah. All right. I'll try. But that type brings out the devil in me.'

It was going to be one of those days; and today of all days. It was almost as if she was *taking* something. Perhaps she had helped herself to some Château Hillington before she came out. Or was it merely her showing off in front of the handsome Jeremy who stood nearby waiting to talk to the judge?

'We'd better call them in,' said Lady Thoroughgood and what a tragedy of the first order that Dawn was standing closest to her. 'I think we'll have that nice little gelding, followed by the filly, and then I think that black colt. Now if you'll excuse me for a moment,' and Jeremy began to discuss with her the prize for the Reserve Champion.

Dawn looked at me, *Help* scribbled across her painted face in capitals.

'Which one does she flaming well mean?' she hissed.

In the heat of the moment my brain downed tools (and say it remained that way for ever more?). Was a gelding male or female? On balance I decided it was male, but how could you tell if it was a gelding or a colt? Wasn't it something to do with wedding tackle being removed, but if so you could hardly go peering about between their legs, that would be most impolite.

'Look for the wedding tackle,' I whispered. Then – 'No, look for the one *without* wedding tackle.'

'Yeah, but does it have balls or don't it, that is the question,' said Dawn and she might just as well have been speaking through the loudspeaker.

There was a ripple of laughter among the spectators, and if only; if only I could be one of them, tittering at a scarlet woman with a white beehive, without a care in the world.

'What are you talking about!' hissed Hattie, her face purple. 'She means that one.'

'How do you know?'

'Because that's the one she pointed at first.'

'Yeah, that's what I thought Hat,' hissed Dawn. 'Leave it to me,' and she teetered towards a small donkey as hairy as a gorilla, led by a fat puffing woman in a candy-striped dress.

'Excuse me, miss,' cried the little man in the bowler hat, raising his crop like a schoolboy raising his hand in class. 'I may be mistaken but I think the judge was referring to my donkey ...'

'Bollocks,' barked Dawn, and the little man cringed like a seaside postcard. 'What I mean to say is, yours has bollocks and he shouldn't have. 'Ere, you,' and she pointed a white-gloved finger at the fat puffing woman. 'The judge wants you to go into the middle.'

The woman's face, as red and shiny as a freshly washed apple, looked as surprised and pleased as if she had just been told it was her birthday. The donkey looked surprised, too. This was maybe the first time she'd ever come first in anything in her life; she wore the same expression as the ugliest girl in the school when she's chosen to play the Virgin Mary.

'Right you are,' puffed the woman. 'Come on, Cleopatra old girl.' But Cleopatra, suddenly overcome by shyness, neatly braced her hooves.

''Ere, shall I shove from behind?' bellowed Dawn. 'As long as she don't kick me or do a whatsit down me leg.'

Just as Dawn said that, two things happened. The man in the bowler hat's donkey, clearly jealous he hadn't been asked to go into the middle first, stretched forward his neck and, baring his teeth, started braying, a loud, sobbing, heart-rending bray. And Lady Thoroughgood ran over crying 'No, no, no, Miss Potts – I'm frightfully sorry, there's been a slip-up – Miss Potts, I said loud and clear the gelding.'

'Yeah, I know you did, Lady Whatsit,' and it didn't matter what Dawn did now. She had blotted her copybook so thoroughly there was no copybook left, it was just one great big blob.

Like motor-racing spectators who can foresee a head-on collision, a tremor of excitement rippled through the crowd

Of course Dawn couldn't just leave it at that. No, siree! Not on Devil-may-care Day. 'How do you expect me to know the sex of the flaming animals?' she shrieked. 'I can hardly go round lifting up their tails to see which ones have bollocks, can I? What do you take me for? A frigging pervert? You know what you can do with your . . . *gelding*,' and winking at us she turned and strutted off, her handbag swinging in time to her bottom.

The braying donkey turned its head and watched her wiggle her way to the edge of the ring. Perhaps 'Hee-haw' was a donkey's version of a wolf-whistle.

'Know just how you feel, mate,' she shouted. There was a smattering of laughter among the spectators and Jeremy smiled behind his hand and a couple of men clapped, and if only I could laugh or smile or clap, if only I could cross that final hurdle and not give a bugger. But I just couldn't. Because the judge was bound to tell her colleagues how unprofessional the Shotestead Show was and how the stewards were the lowest of the low, the competitors were bound to pass the word around that it was run by a bunch of rude, swearing amateurs and to avoid it like the plague . . .

'Oh dear, oh dear, oh dear,' muttered Lady Thoroughgood, shaking her horse-scarf head. "Let's try again. We'll have the gelding . . .' and she must have noticed the look of desperation in my eyes because she said, "Perhaps we should make it easier. We'll have the man in the bowler hat, followed by the woman in the tweed jacket . . .'

When the judging was finally over for all classes and the rosettes and prize money correctly dispensed with, Hattie went to the secretary's tent to hand in the results and then to watch the Junior Jumping Class, and I took Lady Thoroughgood to the Members' Enclosure.

I opened my mouth to apologise about Dawn when she said, 'My dear, I simply must know. Where *did* that girl come from?'

'Er, well, she was born in London . . .'

'I guessed that. No, I mean what is her connection with the Show? She seems so frightfully out of place, and as for being a donkey steward . . .'

I explained who she was, and apologised for her unsuitability.

'Oh, my dear, no need to apologise. I'll be dining out on Miss Potts for weeks,' and she laughed (a loud bray of a laugh, as it happened).

Dine out. What did that mean? That when she dined out she would talk about Dawn?

'Oh, don't look so embarrassed, my dear. The world would be a very much duller place without people like Miss Potts. Is this where I go? Thank you so much for your help. See you next year, perhaps.'

She left me standing there speechless. Someone like *her* had found someone like Dawn *funny*? There was only one conclusion to be drawn: that Lady Thoroughgood was top-drawer and I was only middle.

She was right about one thing: that the world would be a duller place without Dawn. I set off to look for her.

CHAPTER TWENTY-FIVE

The Showground was filling up nicely with ruddy tractor drivers and their families, old farmers in tweed suits and their Clark's-sandalled, hen-basketed wives, fresh-faced young gentlemen farmers in jaunty trilbys cocking a snook at the world and his wife beside cock-a-hoop, Alice-banded, flouncy-skirted sisters talking loudly to broadcast their breeding, groups of 'Blast we only see you once a year' second cousins chatting about harvest and sugar beet and funerals while their dogs growled or wagged and their children clustered round a stilted clown with legs a mile long, bossy little girls showing off on prancing ponies, wistful girls without ponies wearing jodhpurs so no one need know, slim-as-whippet women with faces haughty as hawks riding too-big-for-their-boot hunters, large, tweedy, striding Prince Philip men carrying shooting sticks, red-handed old rustics, pale-handed young Townies, poultry farmers, pigmen, millers milling about, barrel-shaped brewers, cowmen, milkmen, slaughterhouse men and ploughmen, gardeners and gamekeepers, rat and mole catchers and thatchers and saddlers barely recognisable in their fresh-out-of-mothballs Sunday best proudly displaying their freshly permed limping-shoed wives; small sparrow-coloured aunts, retired marching military men in Panama hats, men fresh from the harvest field shaved and bathed and going against the grain in shirts and ties; sharp-eyed potato women baking in jackets, fruit-picking women stewing in bright new coats, goat women nannying bearded, Billy-Goat-Gruff husbands, blustery bull-by-the-horns bachelors, calm, keen-as-mustard spinsters, good old boys, bors, bores, buggers, rum' uns, members of the Women's Institute, the rugby club, the rotary club, the Round Table, the Mothers Union, the Young Farmers. And there was just one thing all these people had in common: not one of them would have the foggiest idea who Chuck Berry was.

I found Dawn not in the beer tent surrounded by admirers, but by the cattle ring. She stood out in the crowd like a red admiral among a swarm of brown ants.

Because of Mildred's out-of-date teats, she and Jack were still walking sadly round the edge of the ring. Jack, with his polished

340

ginger shoes, white coat and dandelion-clock hair, looked like a gone-to-seed doctor.

'Oh, hi,' said Dawn. 'Still speaking to me after the donkey cock-up?'

'I've become immune to your cock-ups.' I couldn't see any lover candidates among the cowmen, but beauty was in the eye of the beholder. 'How come you're watching the cows? I thought the beer tent would be more your style.'

'Just because I'm a Townie don't mean I'm not interested in country matters. 'Ere, this class is for Young Cow in Calf. D'yer reckon I'd stand a chance?'

'Keep your voice down,' I said, staring at Mildred with interest. So she was pregnant too, was she? Had a bull had his wicked way with her, or had she been artificially inseminated? And if it was the latter . . .

'Dawn,' I whispered, 'I'm going to ask you something very secret, and if you shout anything out I'll never speak to you again.'

'Fire ahead,' she said in her normal voice.

'You know artificial insemination. How do they get the, you know, thingy out of the bulls exactly?'

To give Dawn her due, she didn't shriek. 'Blimey, I've never thought about it,' she whispered as loud as a normal person's voice. 'Maybe they give them cow pornography to read. *Playboy,* maybe, or rather *Playbull,* ha, ha!'

'Or perhaps they have cows – Jersey cows because they're the prettiest – doing a strip tease.'

'Ner, that wouldn't work. Cows don't wear clothes, yeah? Maybe they put a machine on their wedding tackle,' and her voice was getting too boisterous by half. 'Like a milking machine that's really a wanking machine.'

A man in a blue blazer looked sharply round before suggesting to his button-lip wife that they should go and watch the Arab class.

'I'll tell you one thing and that ain't two,' said Dawn. 'This steward has a much easier time than we did – he doesn't have to piss about looking at what sex they are because they've all got dirty great udders.'

'They look quite clean to me,' I said, waving to Jack. 'Would you like me to give you a conducted tour of the showground?'

'Yeah, why not,' said Dawn.

How strange that one could change one's tune at the drop of a hat. Suddenly, I (and perhaps the judge had something to do with it; after all, if she could 'dine out' on Dawn, so could I) felt almost proud to be seen with her. Compared with everyone else in their plain clothes and sensible shoes, she looked somethin' else, as Eddie Cochran would say. *You don't get nowhere in this life if you merge into the wallpaper,* she had said, and she was right. Boy, were we the centre of attention wherever we went – including the goat tent!

'Poo, what a pong,' she said as we walked in. Then, ''Ere, look at that one's eyes. Just like the devil. Ugh, it gives me the creeps,' right in front of its twinset and brogues owner. And then, ''Ere, look at that kid,' and I said 'Do you mean "Look at that kid" or "Look at that, kid"?' and Dawn said, 'Ooooh, you are a scream!' and disturbed the dignity and repose of the entire tent.

We watched the Heavy Horse class and Dawn shrieked, 'Ain't they *gor*geous.'

'Which?' I said, expecting her to go for the kindly, feather-footed Shires.

'Them ginger ones. Honest, they're the most beautiful animals I've ever seen.'

She was referring to the Suffolk Punches! I was about to remark on the fact that they were a bit like Albert, weren't they, when she said, 'They're so big and ungainly and lovable. Look at the way they stand with their short legs apart and their feet too big. And look at that one trotting! Its wobbly fat bum ... It reminds me of someone's back view, I can't remember whose.'

'Granny had one called Smiler but he snuffed it during the bugger of a winter,' and Dawn said it was probably a good thing, she would have spent all day stroking it and done even less work than she did already and honest, if she won the Pools she'd have one in her back garden like a shot.

We bought raffle tickets and had a go on the tombola and looked round the Army Recruitment stand and Dawn cracked a few jokes with the soldiers. I kept bumping into people I hadn't seen for a year and introduced them to Dawn, making it clear she was 'Granny's helper' and Dawn said each time, 'Pleased to meet yer.'

'Blimey, you know a lot of people,' she said, clearly impressed.

Albert was in charge of bowling for a pig. 'Roll up, roll up, ladies,' he said when he saw us, grinning and rubbing his hands. 'All proceeds to local charities.' He was wearing a straw boater and a striped butcher's apron and, like the Suffolk Punches, feet too big in round square shoes. The boater made his ears stick out.

'Blast,' he said, kissing Dawn's cheek and proudly looking her up and down. 'Who looks a right little stunner then?'

Dawn tipped his boater over his eyes and said 'You don't look so bad yourself,' but my female instincts could tell she didn't really mean that.

342

'That hair of yours – hasn't it changed colour?' Albert said and Dawn said to me, 'Blimey! Men! They're as observant as bats.' Albert muttered something about not seeing what was wrong with the natural colour and Dawn said, 'Don't be such a square. All girls dye their hair these days. Anyway, gents are meant to prefer blondes, aren't they?'

'That's not blonde, that's white,' said Albert and if only, if only he could be a shade more, well, *hip*.

'Right, let's have a butcher's at what we're winning,' and I said yes, we don't want a pig in a poke, do we, and Dawn roared.

The small, pale pig stood in its pen staring at the notice that said Kiddies Korner in joined-up curly writing with no apostrophe. (Last year it had said CHILDREN'S CORNER in no-nonsense capitals; another sign of the times.)

'I wonder if he knows what's coming to him,' said Dawn. 'Poor little bleeder. Come on, Sarah, let's win him then we can set him free.'

'He'd last five minutes in the wild, that one would,' said Albert.

'All right, I'll keep him as a pet then,' said Dawn.

'He'd still only last five minutes with me around,' said Albert grinning. 'He'd end up as pork chops in my shop window.'

'Coo, you can't half go off a person, eh, Sarah?' she said. 'Trust me to end up engaged to a bloke whose job makes me want to vomit.'

'Blast, it could be worse,' said Albert cheerfully. 'I could work in a slaughterhouse.'

'Over my dead body,' said Dawn and her laughter caused the pig in its pen and a baby in a bonnet to stare through small, surprised eyes at Dawn and Albert playfully smacking each other. I stared too, through small, sad eyes; little did poor Albert know that because his chemistry was wrong his fiancée had a baby growing inside her womb that wasn't his.

'Right, what do we have to do then? Get the balls in them holes? Blimey, they'll never fit – as the actresses said to the bishop, ha, ha, ha!'

The pig didn't look round this time but the baby did, and so did its mother and her friend. The mother rearranged the baby's sun bonnet, or perhaps she was covering up its ears.

Crack went the balls against the wood.

'Oh, well, can't win 'em all,' said Dawn. 'See, Mr Pig, we tried to save your bacon, ha, ha!'

'See you later, kiddos.'

'Ta-ta, love.'

343

As we walked off I glanced back at Albert. He was staring at Dawn's back view. His expression, of love and longing and pain, was so intense it almost took my breath away. I'd never seen such a look on a face before, not even in a film.

'Blimey, you and I would get stuck half-way down that thing,' said Dawn, nodding at the helter shelter. 'That's what comes of having big bums!'

We stopped at the bottle stall run by Mr Rackham and his wife. It had boring prizes like HP sauce and 1001 carpet cleaner and Cyprus sherry and Evette bubble bath. But Dawn still had five fruitless goes, saying she was a sucker for this sort of thing.

'Oh dear,' beamed Mr Rackham. 'Better luck next time,' and Dawn said. 'What d'yer mean, "next time"? I'm not made of money, mate. Anyway, I reckon it's all a massive con.' Mr Rackham's chubby jaw dropped open and he started to protest but Dawn wiggled off in high dudgeon.

'Take no notice, Mr Rackham. It's just that your name reminds her of her ex-landlord, Mr Rachman,' I said and ran off after her.

As always, Mr Bone was in charge of the hoopla. He was wearing his smartest mustard-yellow Show Day waistcoat. He had got a fraction fatter since last year and, like Tom Kitten, if he wasn't careful he would shed buttons right and left. At present they were hanging on by their threads. I didn't envy those buttons; but they had a long, tiring day ahead of them.

We looked at the prizes. Most were from Mr Bone's shop and still had their price-tag on: packs of nails and paint brushes, a torch, a razor, a golf ball, plus sweet cigarettes, real cigarettes, glass ashtrays and a plastic doll.

'Nah, nothing much worth having there,' said Dawn loud enough for Mr Bone to hear. ''Ere, though, look at that ladies' watch. I wouldn't half say no to that. Let's go for it. How much, mate?'

'For you, my booty, one go for sixpence or six for two bob,' and he winked at me.

We had six goes each, but didn't do very well. 'I reckon it's all a massive con,' she said and unlike Mr Rackham he didn't bristle – laughed, in fact, and heave-ho groaned the buttons – and said, 'You're just a rotten old shot,' and demonstrated how the hoop would go over the wooden stand. Just.

'All right then. Three more each and that's your lot.'

Wooden hoops clackety-clacked all over the place except the watch.

'Bugger this for a game of soldiers,' said Dawn. 'Let's go and watch Brian Pike and his performing dog. At least that won't cost us nothing.'

'Okay,' I said. 'I'll meet you there. I've just got to go to the Ladies.'

When she'd gone I gave Mr Bone four shillings, the last of my blackcurrant money. 'Twelve, please,' I said in a slightly showing-off voice, like a woman in Harrods requesting a mink coat.

'Blast me,' said Mr Bone. 'Someone's pushing the boat out.'

I got hotter and hotter as I hurled the hoops at the watch. Even if I had to spend my lunch money and faint from hunger in the middle of the Fancy Dress I was going to win that watch for Dawn. Like William Tell shooting at the apple on his son's head, it had suddenly become the most important thing in my life.

One went over the watch but not the stand. The very last one went half over, but that wasn't good enough.

I was about to ask for another two bob's worth when Mr Bone rattled the trestle table and the hoop clattered home. 'No one saw that, did they?' he said winking at me, and handed me the ladies' watch in its black case. 'Your family do enough for this Show as it is, and if that there watch means that much to you . . .'

'That's cheating,' I wanted to say, but I didn't. Instead I said 'Oh, thank you, Mr Bone.' I also wanted to explain how Dawn had made me a beautiful dress for the dance and I'd been beastly to her all summer and this was my way of making up for things, but I didn't.

'Hope she's worth it,' said Mr Bone, his chuckle causing the buttons much discomfort. 'By the way, any idea what sort of din them musical members of our families will be making tonight?'

I said I wasn't sure but I bet we were going to be really proud of them. I knew they were going to play one nice song called *Johnny B. Goode* and Mr Bone said, 'Never mind about Johnny being good, let's hope *they* will be, hee, hee, hee.' He said he was right looking forward to seeing his boy up there on stage playing in front of the whole county, and he just wished he'd do as his mother told him and get that hair of his cut and I said, 'Same here with Dan. Still, long hair for boys is fashionable,' and Mr Bone said bugger fashion and winked.

I weaved in and out of the crowds like a supple fish through weeds towards the dog ring.

People sat on straw bales watching eight men and their dogs on their best behaviour. It was hard to tell whether all the men were gamekeepers. Certainly you wouldn't have guessed Brian Pike was one. He was wearing a beige safari suit (if he was wearing a pith helmet he'd have looked like Dr Livingstone) and cunning, pointed, see-you-later-alligator shoes. In one hand he held what looked like a clothes brush. The Yellow Dog stood as still as a statue beside him, staring ahead like a well-trained soldier.

I joined Dawn on a straw bale. 'Hello,' I said, my voice barely able to contain its excitement. 'You haven't got the time, have you?'

'Don't rub it in. Oh, well, you can't win 'em all. Only trouble is, I never seem to win any of 'em.'

'Oh, no?' I said, producing the watch from behind my back. 'For you,' I said.

For a second she looked at it in astonished silence. Then she said, '*No!* Blimey. Really? Don't you want it?'

'No, it's for you,' I said and to my embarrassment tears filled my eyes.

With greedy, red-taloned fingers she tore it from its box, held it to her ear to check it ticked and put the thin gold strap round her non-bracelets wrist. Then she stretched out her arm to admire it from afar and said, 'Oh, it's a real beauty. Twenty-carat an' all. I'll treasure this for ever more. Honest, Sarah, it's the nicest present I've ever had. Who's a right little gem – geddit?' and I laughed through my tears and she said ''Ere, you're not crying are you, you soppy sod? Blimey, you'll set me off.' Then, in front of all and sundry, she threw her arms round me and hugged me.

Why, I wondered, does there always have to be an unpleasant consequence to anything nice that happens? For round the side of her shoulder I saw the Yellow Dog break ranks and come bounding towards us.

'Ooh, er, now look what we've gone and done,' said Dawn. 'No, I ain't got no chocolate for you. Go back to your master, you bugger.'

The Yellow Dog stood at the edge of the ring, grinning under the rope at Dawn and wagging his tail. Perhaps he was jealous Dawn wasn't hugging him. Or perhaps he was being jealous on behalf of Brian Pike because up till now he was the only person the Yellow Dog had ever seen Dawn hug!

Whatever the reason, he was in grave danger of getting court-marshalled by his master, who strode over in his city-slicker shoes, his face as thunderous as a corporal's.

'Heel, you bugger,' he growled, looking at us with eyes that would have liked to have skinned us alive.

'Time to make ourselves scarce,' she muttered, standing up and putting on her sun-glasses as if to act as a disguise. I put mine on, too. 'How come I attract trouble wherever I go? It ain't fair.'

346

'Who said life was fair?'

'Blimey,' said Dawn. 'No need to get deep.'

By the Starting Handle Club we came across the Wild Ones in pointed sun-glasses. They were slouching and smoking, and would have looked more at home outside a Labour Exchange in a litter-strewn city centre than at an agricultural show. Dan hadn't shaved, of course, let alone put on a tie. I just hoped the dark glasses and greased-back hair would stop people from recognising him. I also hoped he would steer well clear of the Members' Enclosure.

All three whistled at Dawn, and Dan added coarsely without a shadow of a blush (though of course blushing was now a thing of his past) that she looked a bit of all right. Which is more than can be said for you, I wanted to say but didn't in case I was accused of being square.

'You don't look so bad either, Sausage,' Dan said to me but only so I wouldn't be jealous, and I said for the millionth time, don't call me Sausage.

'Look at what "Sausage" has given me,' said Dawn, showing Dan the watch.

Dan gave a surprised smile. I explained I won it sort of thing on the hoopla and he put his arm round my shoulder and squeezed it. 'Thanks,' he whispered. It obviously meant a great deal to him that his prissy sister had accepted Dawn. We smiled quite intimately at one another for a moment then he put his shoulders back and said loudly, 'Let's split, man.' So we all ambled off and boy, how grown up to be walking along in sun-glasses in a gang – the Sun-glasses Gang! – instead of with Mummy or Granny or Hattie. I slouched my shoulders and casually shuffled my feet so as not to look too out of place and wished my sandals would magically turn into black pointed slip-ons.

'Dig that swinging beat,' said Rick Benton as the military band started up again in the main ring.

'See what I mean?' Dan said through his Woodbine, nodding at a double-glazing stand. 'I ask you. What's in it for us?'

'There are some things – surely,' I said doubtfully as we passed a fertiliser stand.

'There are if you're a square,' said Ronnie Bone.

'Or a farmer or into horses or flower arranging or growing marrows or keeping goats,' said Rick Benton.

'Or want to join the Army or work in pissing Barclays Bank,' said Greg.

'There must be other hip people about apart from us,' said Dan.

347

'Though I'm damned if I can see any.'

'That's what I was thinking,' I said because I'd decided on a new policy: if you can't beat 'em, join 'em. 'Guess what all these people have in common? None of them knows who Chuck Berry is.'

'Too right,' said Dan and Dawn said, 'Wait till tonight. When the Wild Ones start playing they'll all come out of the woodwork.'

We passed a tractor stand and a caravan selling saddles and Dawn and I told them about the donkey judge and even though it went against the mean, moody grain they all laughed.

Among the assortment of millinery milling round the Women's Institute stall, I spotted two Panamas belonging to the great aunts.

'Dan,' I said. 'Do you see who I see?'

'Oh, shit,' said Dan. 'Let's hope they don't recognise me.'

'There's no fear of that,' I said. They did me, though, and waved. I took off my sun-glasses, straightened my back, switched on my polite face and strode over.

'Hello, Sarah dear, we were just saying where have they all got to, weren't we, Beth,' said Great Aunt Gertie. 'We were expecting to see Dan in the Young Farmers' Ploughing Contest.'

'And the tug of war,' said Great Aunt Beth. 'He's not harvesting, surely? In fact, are my eyes deceiving me or is that him. No, surely it *can't* be. Not with that *hair*.'

'Er, well . . .'

'Gracious, it is, you know, Beth. He's going the same way as his grandfather. And who are those people he's with?' cried Great Aunt Gertie.

'They're sort of fellow musicians.'

'And who's the creature with that vulgar hair-do? Is it . . .?'

'Yes, it's Dawn – Mrs B's replacement. She's much nicer than she looks.'

The two great aunts looked at each other in horror which gradually melted into a strange sadness that made me feel sad, too. Then they pulled themselves – or their shoulders, anyway – together and Great Aunt Beth said, 'Did I hear you say something about musicians, Sarah?'

'Er, yes. Dan's going to play in a group at the dance tonight. He plays the guitar – and the piano – and the harmonica – and sings.'

'Dan in a group! A jazz group, do you mean? Well, I never did! I wonder where he gets his musical talent from.'

'Our mother could play the piano beautifully,' said Great Aunt Beth. 'And of course we were both in the school choir. What time will he be performing?'

'Er, very late because he's star billing,' I said craftily, knowing they went to bed early. 'It'll be deafeningly noisy because all the instruments are electric. If you don't stay for it, I'll tell you all about it. Isn't it perfect Show weather? Anyway, I expect we'll see you later in the Members – er, for tea that is,' and, feeling guilty I wasn't spending more time with them, left them twittering about Dan's musical talent.

Dawn and the Wild Ones lurked like stray dogs at the back of a crowd outside the flower tent. Sir Edward Potter-Smith stood on a straw bale. His wife, in a paisley hat, stood at his side holding the leads of the hairy rodents. Sir Edward wore a brown bow tie and a bold tweed suit; his white hair had been cut in a short fringe. He could have been mistaken for a ticktack man on a race course or, if he wasn't so portly, an American golfer.

'You can tell there's an election in the wind,' muttered Dan. 'Thanks for dealing with the great aunts,' and he squeezed my shoulder again. He had become very affectionate all of a sudden. And he had stopped calling me Sausage.

'This should be good for a laugh,' said Dawn. 'That geezer looks a right git, and dig that swinging haircut.'

I was about to say he was an old friend of the family when Sir Edward bellowed: 'Because the Shotestead Show is a non-political event, ladies and gentlemen, the last thing I want to do is turn this into a Party Political Speech but I would just like to say a few words ...'

'Yeah, bet you do, mate,' muttered Dawn.

Sir Edward droned on about farming mainly, his well-nourished chins wobbling at the double, and Dawn said, "Ere, Sarah, remember what we were saying about bulls and *Playbull* and that?' and she burst out laughing and several people looked round to see what the joke was. Then Dan opened his Woodbine packet and took out not a cigarette but some blue sweets wrapped in tissue paper. He handed them round to the others, including Dawn.

What about me?' I said and he said what did I want a cough sweet for, they were for smokers only, and I said I'd never seen cough sweets that colour and why keep them in a cigarette packet, and he put his arm round me yet again and said you learn something new every day.

So that was it! They were taking drugs! Thanks to an episode of *Dixon of Dock Green,* I knew all about purple hearts. Perhaps that's what they were, dyed blue as a disguise. Purple hearts. What a repulsive picture that conjured up.

'You don't have to lie to me, Dan, I'm not as innocent as I look,' I said and Dan said, 'No, I suppose you aren't. Sorry.'

'When the election comes,' roared the chinned wonder, drowning out other showground noises, 'you and I and all of us will have to make the main choice as to whether we want the next five years to be conducted as a free society or as perhaps a Socialist state . . .'

'Speak for yourself, mate,' said Dan far too loudly, causing several people to look round and frown. 'I've already made my choice.'

'. . . People are very apt to say that this is an argument to be used by intellectuals and clever people and doesn't really affect you and me . . .'

Dawn took a deep breath and roared, louder than the grand-ring loudspeaker, '*Speak for yourself, sunshine. Are you calling us stupid, or what?*'

An uneasiness rippled through the crowd, like chickens sensing the presence of a rat in their snug henhouse. Sir Edward's eyes glinted and darted like a gamekeeper's; rats, in his book, were vermin to be disposed of. Those standing at the front had to crane their necks to see who was being so rude, and some eyes rested momentarily on my direction. I looked down at my shoes and blushed furiously so they'd know it wasn't me. Rupert's parents and Major Smedley, Mr Allcock, Lady Potter-Smith, Lady Margetson, in fact most people looked daggers, and one woman went 'Shhhhh'. But one or two people – bottom-drawer, by the looks of them – smiled and nodded at Dawn. Dan and the Wild Ones, needless to say, were grinning from ear to ear.

Dawn said quietly to me, 'There's no need to look embarrassed, Sarah. MPs expect to be heckled. It's part of the job.'

Sir Edward curled one half of his lip into a half smile. If he was trying to imitate Elvis Presley he was failing dismally; Charles Laughton at his most sneering would be nearer the mark.

'Very well, I'd better rephrase that. An argument to be used by intellectuals and clever people like the young lady in the red suit with the er, elaborate hair-do.'

Then another voice, a horribly familiar close-to-home one, shouted. 'And the woman in the black and white dress and the sun-glasses, *if* you don't mind. Patronising so-and-so.'

How could she! Aunt Lynette, who drank sherry with Sir Edward in his drawing room and played croquet on his lawn and was paid good money to paint his hairy rodents. How could she turn against her own kind like that! Dan would be next, I just knew it.

'I say, do pipe down and let Sir Edward have his say,' said a small man smoking a large cigar near the front, and several people clapped.

'The outlook under the Socialists is indeed bleak. Do you think you want a change just for the sake of change? *You must not change this Government,* which has given you such great prosperity in the last twelve years . . .'

Beside me I felt Dan muster his strength the way Snap Dragon had before bolting, and surely this couldn't be the purple hearts at work already? Surely they were like aspirin and took at least half an hour? '*What about the two million unemployed, eh?*' he yelled, confirming once and for all that the Hillingtons had turned into complete and utter traitors.

I stood four square like a Suffolk Punch, bracing myself for a torrent of, if not bad eggs exactly, at least abuse. But it wasn't forthcoming. In fact, several people nodded their heads at Dan and one man in a cap gave him the thumbs-up sign and said, 'That's right, sonny. You tell him.'

Sir Edward, his cheeks now the colour of medium rare steaks, decided on a new tack. 'If the Socialists came into power they would abolish the nuclear deterrent. But I want my country to be a *first-class power* . . .'

'Do mean you'd like to see your country blown to smithereens? What about Hiroshima?' screamed Aunt Lynette.

'Yeah, better Red than dead,' squealed Dawn just for the fun of it. 'You toffs are so paranoid about Reds under the beds I'm surprised you get any kip at all.'

And then all hell let loose, some people laughing and agreeing and others saying let Sir Edward get on with it.

So Sir Edward, his cheeks now very rare steaks, tried one last tack; an unwise one, as it turned out. 'The moral fabric of this country is sadly crumbling . . .'

Dawn took a large, triumphant breath of air. '*Is it any wonder when you toffs set such a bad example,*' she screamed, and it really was a scream this time. '*What about the Profumo Affair, eh? Eh? It's bloody disgusting what you lot get up to, yet you expect* us *to behave ourselves. You're all bloody hypocrites.*'

'Yeah, hypocrite,' yelled Dan and Ronnie Bone and Rick Benton and Greg Hannant raising their fists, and several other people joined in, and I mouthed 'Yeah, hypocrite' very quietly for my ears only, and Sir Edward raised his arms and said, 'Ladies and gentlemen, please . . .' and a great fat woman in a yellow headscarf bellowed. 'I came here to see them flowers, not get involved in a lot of political argy-bargy rubbish.' She got the most applause of all, and when order was restored Sir Edward announced that the Flower Tent was now open.

351

'See, what did I tell you about people round here?' Dawn said to me, her eyes brighter and blacker than ever. 'They're more interested in flower arrangements than their futures.'

I gave a non-committal shrug; like the good Liberal that I was, I could see all points of view.

CHAPTER TWENTY-SIX

In the cool calm hush of the Members' Tent, Hattie and I sat at a trestle table covered in a thick white cloth and toyed with ham and chicken salad.

Like a peaceful library in an old country house, the Members' hadn't changed: its smell of warm grass tinged with alcohol, the way the light gently filtered through the canvas, the soft background noise of top-drawer people on their best behaviour ...

What a mercy Dawn was meeting Albert for a hot dog in the beer tent.

I was hoping to overhear people say 'Look at those poor neglected children eating alone', but no one had even noticed us. Further down the table, Lady Thoroughgood was drinking brandy and smoking a small cigar. She looked younger without the horsehead scarf; her hair was surprisingly fair and curly. She was talking to Major Smedley and laughing. Perhaps she had already started dining out on Dawn. I wondered if Mrs Smedley, selling potpourris on the WI stall, knew about her husband's lunchtime companion.

A fat, squabbling, greedy family sat down at the next table, all talking at once in broad Norfolk accents. If they'd been birds, they'd have been seagulls.

Let's pretend we're grown-ups,' said Hattie, dabbing at the corner of her mouth with her napkin. 'I say, would you care for a glass of wine, Priscilla, my dear? Or a sherry, perhaps? And how about some mustard on your ham? My daughter Esmeralda won the hunter class hands down, don't you know?'

'That's not being grown up, that's just being posh,' I said and told her, the way I would tell Mr Richards, about the heckling.

'That oon't dew, Shirley, yew nearla hit your ole hid, just sit yew still,' shrieked the mother next door, and Shirley whined that she wanted to go to the toilet and the father said, 'Tha's a funna thing. Git her in a car or a tent ... Yew've bin about twenta times already today, wha's wrong with yew, gal?'

'Honestly. This time last year they would never have been allowed anywhere near the Members' Tent,' said Hattie, and I said, 'It seems to me that everyone round here is either rough and rude or posh and polite. That's why I'm a Liberal, and I think that's what you should be, too.'

'Why can't we just be us?' said Hattie. 'By the way, Aunt Daphne didn't come anywhere because Boxer shied at the brush three times. She's in a filthy bate, and I don't blame her. He's never shied before in his life.'

'Perhaps he saw Dawn out of the corner of his eye,' I said and told her about the Yellow Dog, though not about the watch. 'I think it's because she's wearing red. Animals hate red. Let's hope there aren't any bulls on the loose.'

'Let's hope there are, you mean. She might get gored.'

'Hattie!'

'Well, honestly. I'm convinced she's a witch casting spells on our family,' she said, pushing lettuce to the side of her plate. 'In fact I thought that from the moment I saw her. Granny didn't get anywhere with her roses and according to Mrs Allcock Great Aunt Beth's flower arrangement only got Highly Commended. Normally, they both come at least second.'

'Jack didn't get anywhere with Mildred, either, because her teats belong to the days of hand-milking,' I said. 'Never mind, I bet we win the Fancy Dress.'

'Bet we don't,' said Hattie. 'I think we should have played safe and been Captain Pugwash and Cut-throat Jake.'

'Today isn't the day to play safe,' I said, tossing my head.

Sir Edward strolled to the bar with Mr Allcock and Sir Eustace, Rupert and Fiona's father. From their conversation it soon became apparent that if these three highly respected pillars of the community were newspapers, they would be the *News of the World* wrapped in the outside pages of *The Times*.

Assuming that in the Members' he was among like-minded people, Sir Edward talked loudly without first looking round to see who might be listening.

'You should have seen her, Eustace. Peroxide hair, false eyelashes, false this, false that. Cockney accent you could cut with a knife. Looked – and sounded – as though she'd stepped straight off the streets of Soho ... Three double Scotches, please, dear.'

'She's Winifred Hillington's char,' said Mr Allcock. 'Can't think what possessed her to employ a cheap tart like that. Wouldn't be surprised if senility isn't setting in. Her granddaughter's got it into her head she's going to murder Win for her money. I told her you need brains to plan a murder, ha, ha, ha!'

'So *that's* what you were talking to him about in the churchyard,' hissed Hattie. 'You could have told me.'

'Shhh,' I said, my face purple. 'Let's listen.'

'They've turned into a bunch of hotheads, that family. First Lynette and now the grandson. Pity. Anyway, when I started banging on about moral standards she had the damn cheek to bring up the ruddy Profumo Affair. She, who probably has the morals of a guttersnipe! Mind you I wanted to laugh when she started on about Reds under the bed. She was wearing a bright red costume, you see, and I was tempted to say ...' never mind *under* the bed, sweetie ...' and he lowered his voice so I couldn't hear.

If only I had had Grandpa's gun, I would have aimed it right between Sir Edward's eyes. And maybe Mr Allcock deserved one over the left eyebrow for betraying me. Would a bullet pass through a spectacle frame? I wondered.

I'd simply have to channel my fury into my only weapon: my tongue.

'Watch,' I said to Hattie. 'I'm going to do the bravest thing I've ever done.'

If I pretended I was Black Champion who had taken a purple heart, I could do anything. I got up and, with legs wobbling like a person who's spent three weeks in bed, walked over to the three pillars.

'Excuse me,' I said to Sir Edward, my voice as shrill as Aunt Lynette's. 'I hope I'm not being rude, but I don't think you should talk about such things in front of children. As you know, Winifred Hillington is my grandmother, and once you get to know Dawn Potts, she is er, a very nice person indeed, and not at all how she looks. Her morals are far from a guttersnipe's, I can assure you. You can't judge a book by its cover, you know,' and I glared at him so he'd realise I was talking about him, too. How tempting to call him a hypocrite. But I didn't want to overdo it.

'Oh, er, I do beg your pardon,' spluttered Sir Edward, his cheeks returning to a pleasing very rare. 'I didn't see you ... of course, you're Sarah, aren't you. I say, what a big grown-up girl you've become.'

'Yes,' I said. 'I'm eleven now. And by the way, Mr Allcock, I feel most affronted that you betrayed me. I spoke to you in the utmost confidence and, if I might remind you, you swore to secrecy on Jeremiah Lambert's gravestone. What is the world coming to if one's secret isn't safe with a family solicitor?' And I turned on my heel and strode back to the table.

'Honestly, Sarah, you were brilliant,' whispered Hattie. 'You've become a different person this summer. Mummy and Daddy aren't going to recognise you.'

355

'Good,' I said, pushing my salad to the side of the plate and putting down my knife and fork.

Dawn was supposed to be helping us change into our fancy-dress costumes, but she spent most of the time painting her nails and regluing her false eyelashes.

I was a gamekeeper and Hattie a snared rabbit. In the cold light of Show day it didn't seem quite such a good idea.

Hattie wore the white rabbit outfit, shortened and taken in by Dawn. We had considered starting again with brown fur but decided the 'blood' would show up better on white. The snare was a long bow. I wore my deerstalker, an old tweed riding jacket and green trousers tucked into Wellington boots. Wound twice round my waist was Grandpa's cartridge belt. Over one shoulder I carried a giblet as Dawn called it though I was sure that wasn't the right word, from which hung a toy fur mouse, a toy owl and the yellow Christmas-tree bird. On the other shoulder I brandished Grandpa's 12-bore shotgun, made in 1931 to his own specifications.

'I'm sweltering already,' said Hattie in a muffled voice, and Dawn said now she knew how she'd felt in the play. She drew a moustache on my upper lip with her eyebrow pencil. 'There. You two look terrific. Blimey, Sarah, I wouldn't fancy meeting you down a dark alley. The giblet looks bloody brilliant. Shame they aren't real dead animals, but you can't win 'em all.'

'You keep saying that.'

'Well, you can't can you. Mind you, if you don't win this the judges'll want their heads examining.'

I had my doubts. As Dan had said, it smacked of biting the hand that fed you because the judges, and indeed most of the people at the Show, were bound to be pro-gamekeeper, and we were definitely being anti.

The three of us must have looked a rum old sight as we made our way to the Grand Ring. We were just sloshing red paint over Hattie's leg when we heard a familiar, heart-sinking yell.

'Goodness gracious, Sarah. What in heaven's name are you doing with that gun?'

'It's all right, Aunt Daphne, it isn't loaded.'

'My dear, I don't care two hoots whether or not it's loaded, we simply can't have children wandering round showgrounds with real guns. Whatever next!'

'But I'm a gamekeeper. I've got to have a gun.' (And I'm not a child, either.)

'Yeah, it would be like, er, you not having an 'orse,' said Dawn.

Aunt Daphne gave Dawn a long, cold, prison-warder's stare and said through gritted teeth, 'I will not allow a child for whom I'm responsible to walk around a showground with a real gun. And that's final.'

Dawn gave her a cold, black-eyed stare and said, 'Your mum said it would be all right. Anyway, according to her, *I'm* responsible for her.'

'*You*? You aren't capable of looking after yourself, let alone two vulnerable little girls,' hissed aunt Daphne. 'Just look at you.'

The devil had been brought out in Dawn yet again because she said, 'Have you taken a look at *yourself* lately. Those leather boots and that whip. Looks dead kinky to me.'

'I *beg* your pardon ...' said Aunt Daphne turning crimson beneath the powder and I quickly said 'Honestly, it's not loaded, Aunt Daphne, so it can't hurt a fly. I mean, you wouldn't mind if I carried a knife if I was a pirate, would you, and that's far more dangerous.'

'How dare you speak to me like that, Sarah.' (And how dare you speak to *me* like that so everyone all round can hear.) 'When I say no I mean no. And incidentally, may I also add that I find your choice of fancy dress morbid in the extreme.'

'That's the whole flaming point,' said Dawn. 'They want to show the blood and guts side of the countryside; make people think twice before going out and killing innocent animals. You know, prick a few consciences. Or should I say, prick a few *pricks*' consciences, ha, ha, ha!'

Aunt Daphne, pretending Dawn didn't exist, said, 'I've just had a splendid idea, Sarah. Why don't you borrow Henry instead? All gamekeepers have a dog.' I wanted to say I didn't want a smelly old flea-bitten Labrador, I wanted a gun, and what right had she to tell me what to do, why she was only my aunt. But I decided to save my fighting strength for things that really mattered.

'Oh, all right,' I snarled, snatching the lead from her and giving the gun to Dawn, only to have it snatched away from her by Aunt Daphne.

'Now be a good boy, Henry,' said Aunt Daphne. 'You've got to catch that white rabbit.'

'Thanks very much,' mumbled Hattie.

'Don't say "thanks", Harriet, there's a good girl,' said Aunt Daphne and Hattie muttered through her fur, 'All right, ta, then.'

Hattie got down on her hands and knees and we reluctantly joined the procession of Little Miss Muffet and Mary Mary Quite Contrary, Robinson Crusoe on horseback with a boot-polished

Man Friday running behind with a spear, Maid Marian and Robin Hood, Sooty and Sweep, Pinky and Perky, Humpty-Dumpty on a pony dressed as a wall, a Dutch girl, the Lone Ranger and Tonto, a knight in shining cardboard, and Little Bo Peep who was none other than that Samantha Croft girl whom Michael had picked to be his wife.

Both the spectators and the judges – the new manager of Barclays Bank, a corn merchant and Lady Potter-Smith – averted their eyes when they saw us. Why should they look at something that made them feel uncomfortable on a nice sunny day when they could feast their eyes on harmless play-safe characters from nursery rhymes and television programmes?

Of course the judges chose the pretty, golden-curled Bo Peep as the winner. She put her hand to her mouth and gave a little-girl squeal the way she had when she had been chosen to be the farmer's wife. Boy, it had certainly been Samantha Croft's summer. Maybe she had some deadly bone-marrow disease or leukaemia even, and would be dead within a year.

It was the first time we'd never got a rosette – not even Highly Commended. Hillingtons *always* came somewhere. It was traditional. Perhaps the judges hadn't recognised us. It was so humiliating. And with hundreds of people watching. They watched, too, as Hattie accidentally crawled over a horse's mess, and Henry broke free and chased Little Bo Peep's sheep – a wolf-in-sheep's-clothing white woolly snarler of a dog – causing Little Bo Peep's mummy to scream, 'Keep that labrador under control, *if* you'd be so kind,' and I longed to roar at her, 'Watch who you're speaking to, mate! My grandfather started this Show and if it wasn't for him you wouldn't ruddy, bloody well be here today.'

'See,' hissed Hattie in tears, ripping off her rabbit's outfit before we were barely out of the ring. 'You and your wanting something "relevant".'

'You were streets better than the rest – cor, what a bunch of boring, run-of-the-mill pansies,' announced Dawn to the whole showground. 'I was just thinking. If you'd been a poacher instead of a rabbit, Hat, you'd have won.'

'Why?'

'Because people don't feel uncomfortable about humans being caught the way they do about animals,' I said.

'Never mind, dears. Better luck next time,' said Aunt Daphne, striding up in her dead kinky boots and taking Henry's lead. 'I'm off to the flower tent if anyone would care to join me.'

'We've already seen it, thanks,' Hattie lied.

We changed out of our outfits and Dawn, proudly consulting her watch, said blimey, only forty minutes to go; she was getting ever so nervous and us not winning didn't bode well for her, did it; she'd better go to the lav and get rid of some of that beer or she'd have a pot belly and wouldn't stand an earthly.

She wiggled her way through the crowds, causing a horse to shy and a group of men to stop and watch her. My heart began to race. The men were American, they just had to be, it stood out a mile! They wore smart jeans with creases down the middle, and some wore cowboy boots and one wore smart tinted glasses that weren't National Health ones, no, siree. Their hair was short and neat as though they'd just stepped out of a barber's. And the way they stood, thumbs hooked in the loops of their belts, so casual, so *cool* ... Talk about somethin' else! Talk about making every other man on the showground look namby-pamby and fuddy-duddy!

The black one who had been laughing in the pink car was there, and the crew-cut one. And even though I couldn't quite see his face, I knew the one standing slightly apart from the rest, the tallest and strongest of them all, was the driver of the pink Cadillac. My heart leapt like a young salmon.

'Hattie, which of those Americans do you think is the most handsome?'

'Oh, blimey, not again.'

'No, for Aunt Lynette.'

'Oh.' Hattie studied them. 'That dark-haired one. But don't you think he's a bit *too* handsome for her?'

'We might as well aim high to start with,' I said. 'Foreigners seem to like, er, plainer English women. Miriam Poole's sister is as plain as a pikestaff and she had that handsome Greek boyfriend.' I didn't feel very convinced, though. Americans didn't somehow seem foreign the way Greeks did.

For a moment I wavered. Why couldn't Aunt Lynette find her own husband? On the other side of the sheep ring between a farm machinery stand and the St John's Ambulance caravan I could see her standing at her CND stall. Perhaps I could say she was just helping out a friend and didn't really believe all that ban the bomb rubbish.

All in all, things didn't look promising. But the thought of her having a mongrel, or spending the rest of her life crying into her gin, spurred me on. At least she was looking quite pretty today, in her black and white dress with the full skirt; at least she was wearing lipstick. At least if all else failed it would make an interesting anecdote for my diary.

'Watch. I'm about to do the bravest thing in my whole life,' I said to Hattie.

'I thought you just had, talking to Sir Edward.'

'This is even braver.'

'But you can't ... Sarah, come back,' and she tugged at my arm. But thanks to the pretend purple heart whirring my legs into action, there was no stopping me. No, siree!

My heart thundered like a big bass drum as I walked up to him. Out of the corner of your eye he could easily be mistaken for Elvis Presley.

'Er – excuse me, Sir,' I said in a voice that sounded as though it belonged to my shadow.

He looked round and down at me and smiled and said, 'Hi, kid.'

Boy, how thrilling! This was the first time I'd ever spoken to a real live American! I felt like an actress in *Oklahoma*! or *Dr Kildare*, and the 64,000 dollar question was: should I reply in American or English?

He squatted down so we were at eye level, and gee whizz, what eyes they were! A beautiful twinkly hazel-brown kind like a tawny owl's, that looked right into the heart of my soul, and the way they smiled at you your whole body wanted to smile back. His skin was as tanned as a nut and perhaps he had Italian blood in him (and I hoped he had, because then he was bound to be interested in art; how could he not be, with Michelangelo and Leonardo da Vinci as fellow countrymen?). One thing was sure, to be sure; you'd never find that sort of colouring in an Englishman, and what a beautiful baby my cousin was going to be! I wouldn't write this in my diary in case Mr Richards felt jealous, but he was without doubt the most handsome man I'd ever seen, and what a mercy we weren't living in Victorian times because I would have swooned, I know I would, and smelling salts would have had to be fetched at the double. The way Dawn was with her lover, I knew if he touched me it would feel as if my whole body was on fire. If only I was ten years older! Never mind Aunt Lynette, I'd have him for myself!

He was so close I could smell his chewing gum. Chiclets. Suddenly it had replaced both Aslan's warm breath and horse as my favourite number one smell. For the rest of my life, whenever I smelt Chiclets I would be reminded of him.

'Er, well, I know this is a bit of a cheek but you see I have an aunt who's a very good artist – brilliant, in fact, and fairly famous in art circles – and is very funny and interesting and you'd like her enormously. And she drinks Martini sometimes and likes Frank Sinatra so you'd have some things in common. Er, I was wondering whether, in fact, you'd like to meet her. It could easily be arranged. It would be no trouble at all. That's her over there in the black and white dress. She's got a nice physique and drives a big red sports car, so you'd have a love of fast cars in common too. Er, perhaps you could have races . . .?'

The American's beautiful brown eyes travelled across the sheep ring to Aunt Lynette, and how unfortunate – how typical! – she was standing right beside the YANKS GO HOME poster.

'Hey, fellers, I think this young lady's trying to fix me a date,' he said to the others though not in a mocking way, still chewing his gum, and oh, crikey, would they be jealous I hadn't picked any of them?' It looks to me as though your aunt and I wouldn't quite see eye to eye on certain matters.'

If his voice had been a horse's colouring, it would have been a beautiful, rich, deep bay.

'Oh, that,' I said, pretending I'd only just noticed the poster. 'It's only a phase she's going through. She doesn't mean anything personally.'

'It's a kind thought, kid, but it would be kinda like playing with fire, don't you think? I mighty appreciate the offer, but I think on balance I'd rather get me a warm beer. Care for some gum?' And he offered me a piece from his yellow Chiclets packet the way he might have done a cigarette.

I almost said, 'Gee, thanks, mister', the way Ricky would. But I didn't want him to think I was 'taking the mickey' so I said 'Thanks very much' instead. I would keep the Chiclet under my pillow for ever more to remind me of him.

Then he put his hand on my shoulder – it didn't feel like electricity as such, but it still felt very, very pleasant, like the cool soothing hand of a doctor when your skin is smothered in an angry red rash – and casually stood up.

'See you around, kid,' he said, and smiling his Chiclet at me strolled off with the others, who were smiling, too. He walked just like Uncle Sandy, though he moved his hips more than Uncle Sandy did.

He said something to the others and scratched his head but I don't think it was about me because they didn't look round and laugh. And maybe that was the difference between Americans and Englishmen; that Americans didn't make you feel a fool.

Hattie came hurrying up and I started to tell her what had happened but she said, 'Did you know you've still got your moustache on?' and doubled over into fits of giggles.

'You could have told me,' I said, hot tears trickling down the backs of my eyes, and Hattie said she had tried to but there was no stopping me.

I scrubbed at my upper lip with my hanky, stuck my tongue out at her and ran off to Aunt Lynette's stall.

'Hello, darling,' she said, bending to take leaflets out of a cardboard box and arranging them on the trestle table. 'Bad luck not winning. That's the price one has to pay for being controversial. It was most brave of you. I felt fearfully proud. Lummy, it's not the Hillingtons' day, is it. God knows how Dawn's going to fare in that ruddy Beauty Contest, and I've been abused by pro-Americans all day. Talking of Americans, what on earth what were you saying to that Yank, and don't tell me you were "chatting him up" or I'll simply die. Childhood's short enough as it is.'

'Actually, I was talking to him about you.'

'*Me?*'

'Yes. You see, Aunt Lynette, Dawn told me about you being desperate to have a baby, so I thought with his handsome colouring he might be a suitable husband for you,' I said and burst into tears.

'Darling, darling,' cried Aunt Lynette, hurrying round the table and hugging me and stroking my hair. 'How simply sweet of you to care. Honestly, talk about misconstruing ... I may have said to Dawn after a drink that I quite fancied having a baby, but certainly not enough to be saddled with a husband. Can you honestly see me washing shirts and cooking meals and leading an orderly life and having a great snoring hairy body beside me night after night? Pah! No thanks. I'm a Free Spirit, darling. Always have been and always will be.'

'Oh,' I said, suddenly feeling a warm, unexpected surge of love for her. 'Oh, Aunt Lynette, I am pleased. Free Spirit sounds much more glamorous than wife and mother, doesn't it. Trust Dawn to get the wrong end of the stick.'

'Darling, you should know by now to take anything she says with a bucketful of salt. She has such preconceived ideas ... Despite what she thinks, a woman can lead a perfectly fulfilled life without either a husband or a baby.'

'Yes, I know but ...' I wanted to ask why she got so unhappy, but a man with yellow rabbit's teeth was tapping on her shoulder.

'You let them old Americans be,' he said, waving a finger skinnier than the chicken bone in Hansel and Gretel. 'They're all right, they are, and so are them petrol-guzzling motors of theirs. If it han't bin for them I'd have lost me house, me garrige, everything. We'd have lost the war too and ended up in a right old muddle.'

'That's right,' said his wife, whose teeth were similar to her

362

husband's, and maybe that's why they fell in love, because they had rabbit's teeth in common. 'We depend on 'em for our livelihood. Without 'em we'd be back to square one with three little uns to feed.'

'But surely you want your, er, little uns to have a future?' said Aunt Lynette.

I left her to it. I had heard it all before and besides, Dawn would be needing help getting ready for the Beauty Contest.

CHAPTER TWENTY-SEVEN

'*Six faults*,' announced the loudspeaker as a dejected horse and rider cantered out of the ring. '*And talking of faults, folks, you won't find many in the Dog Ring. And no, it won't be our four-legged friends you'll be feasting your eyes on but booties on two legs ... a bevy of English roses and, no, I'm not talking about the sort found in the flower tent, ha, ha. So leave the missus behind, gents, and hurry along for an eyeful of the loveliest lovelies, the peachiest peaches for miles, one of whom will become the very first Miss Shotestead. The judging of the Show's newest, hottest contest is about to commence!*'

Six peaches and an ugli fruit catwalked into the Dog Ring.

The Beauty Contest was the nearest humans and animals had got to merging into one so far that day. It was a wonder the judges – Major Smedley (had he remembered the 'grass down me drawers' incident?), Lady Margetson and, just Dawn's luck, Sir Edward – didn't run their hands down their legs and feel their udders.

Sir Edward's eyes travelled up and down each contestant's body, starting at the hair and ending at the toes. He didn't allow them to halt momentarily at any particular spot in case he lost votes, though that was what they would have done given half the chance.

The spectators, however, didn't have to worry about losing votes, and their eyes were having a field day, roaming like gypsies wherever they pleased. The more unruly ones wolf-whistled and shouted, but most just watched silently, like greedy men at a cattle market eyeing each cow in turn. A few hypocrites like Mr English and Brian Pike pretended they weren't really interested and carried on a conversation while watching out of the corner of their eye.

Every suspect on my list had come out of the woodwork. Jeremy the estate agent, uncharacteristically smoking a pipe, one hand in his green cords jangling change; Rupert and his Young Farmer friends, talking in loud voices about harvest, their eyes never leaving the middle of the ring; the Wild Ones, silently smoking cigarettes, their eyes darting willy-nilly behind their black sun-glasses; Mr Fox, in a red open-necked shirt and grey slacks, the brown animals replaced by fidgeting Chelsea boots, the glint in his eye not unlike the one he had when talking about his stiff brushes; Brian the library man, chewing on a piece of grass, his programme covering his lap; Adam Faith sitting on a straw bale, his legs wide apart and making coarse comments to his friends; Johnnie the tractor driver showing the gap in his teeth. Even the Americans had strolled over from the beer tent and were watching and smiling and sipping beer and chewing gum. The handsome one stood slightly apart from the others. Casually, he lit a cigarette with a gold lighter, his eyes never leaving the 'Lovelies'. Boy, how I'd have liked to have been a fly on the wall of his mind at that moment! Or, even better, to be the Lovely he had chosen to look at!

Aunt Lynette was tut-tutting to Albert about him allowing Dawn to go in for something as crass as a beauty contest. 'Talk about exploitation. It's in such poor taste. Can't think what possessed the committee to vote for it. Look at them. Like cattle, or a row of dolls,' and Albert said, 'I'm not too chuffed about it, either, Miss Hillington. All them men ogling my fiancée.'

'Aunt Lynette, what's the word that means the complete opposite?' I asked and Aunt Lynette said did I mean antithesis?

The English Roses are healthy, wholesome, rosey-cheeked, brown-limbed, country-bred-looking girls, with au naturel eyes and mouths and hair, and wearing sensible bathing costumes they have purchased from Marks and Spencer, I would write. *Dawn is the complete antithesis of all these things. She looks like a white poodle in the middle of a row of gentle spaniels and retrievers. Even though her bakeeni (so brief even the most unimaginative person can picture what she looks like without clothes) is the colour of grass, it doesn't disguise the fact (or hardly anything else, come to that!!!) that this white, painted creature is a Townie – a foreigner, some might think – through and through. The English Roses look shy and demure and lower their eyes as they answer the judges' questions in quiet voices you can't hear, their arms meakly hanging by their sides. I have consentrated all my powers on Dawn to make her behave the same. But I've failed. For with her hands on her hips like an American, she looks straight at the juges in difiance, and I bet it's the purple hearts' doing, normally she would have given them her eye-lash fluttering, powting look. Her loud, coarse laughter crackles through the air like a fishwive's at a garden party. Really, it is all very sad.*

'Talk about a thorn between roses. She doesn't stand an earthly,' said Hattie. 'I bet you ten bob Melanie Pratt wins.'

'It means so much to Dawn. Winning, I mean. I feel really sorry for her,' I said and Hattie said she only had herself to blame.

As soon as Melanie Pratt was given not a rosette but a smart red sash, Dawn flounced from the ring, wiggling her green and white bottom like mad and it wasn't clear whether the crowd were wolf-whistling at her or at Miss Shotestead 1963, and a male voice, I wasn't sure which, shouted, 'You're the winner in my book Dawn.'

Behind my tiger sun-glasses, my eyes swivelled like an American security man's as every lover suspect stared jealously at Albert draping a coat followed by a sympathetic arm round Dawn's shoulders.

'Okey-dokey, folks, here we have the pick of the crop, la crème de la crème,' crackled the loudspeaker man who, I'd just noticed, was none other than the Knick-Knack shop man, and what did he know about agricultural shows? Honestly, what was the world coming to! *'As Mrs Hillington, the Honourable Show Director, is sadly unable to be with us today Mrs English, the wife of this year's President, has kindly agreed to step into her shoes and present the cups.'*

Mrs English, in red, sling-back high-heeled shoes nothing like Granny's stepped down from the cart where all the important people sat and stood smiling beside the trestle table full of cups.

Dawn and I sat fidgeting on the top row of the straw-bale stand in the Members' Enclosure watching champion horses, riders, pigs, ponies, sheep, dogs, cows, bulls, the bowler-hatted donkey man, a Suffolk Punch, Little Bo Peep and a beauty queen sitting in a trailer decked out with flowers line up for the Grand Parade.

Way down below in the front row I could see Hattie's wavy, freshly washed hair sandwiched between two Panamas. The great aunts' eyes, like most other people's, kept straying like uneasy magnets towards Dawn. They were all giving her a 'what's a nasty girl like her doing in a nice place like this' sort of look, and Dawn and I gave them that sort of look back.

Michael English, in a smark dark suit because his father was President, looked round and up and said, 'None of us lot have done much good this year, then', and Dawn said, 'Too right, mate.'

'He fancies you, I reckon,' she said far too loudly, and I whispered, 'Don't be daft. He's only thirteen.'

Her sun-glasses disguised the fact she'd been crying. She had told me through tears that that was that then, all her hopes and dreams out the window. I said it was the same for me not winning the Fancy Dress and she said no it wasn't, I wasn't relying on it to change my life, was I.

'The crowd were obviously on your side,' I said, doubtfully. 'And Sir Edward's so ancient his idea of beauty is probably a flat-chested Flapper girl.' I had decided not to tell her about the incident in the Members' Tent.

366

'Just my luck he should be a judge,' she said. 'See, that's what happens when you voice your principles. Maybe you were right, maybe I *should* have worn a one-piece.'

'That would have been playing safe and today isn't the day for that. By the way, was your lover watching you?'

'How should I know,' said Dawn. 'I was so busy holding me stomach in and making eyes at the judges I didn't have a chance to look. Honestly, I feel such a bloody fool.'

'We've still got the dance to look forward to.'

'Yeah, but you don't get your mush in the paper for dancing,' she said. 'Gawd, why can't I find something I'm good at? Everything I've done today so far I've cocked up. 'Ere, do look at that pony,' she screeched. 'It's having a pee in the middle of the bleeding ring.'

'That's something you're good at. Attracting attention.'

I felt strangely restless, and soon got bored with the prize-giving – the only funny thing that happened was the Champion Arab tried to eat Mrs English's floppy hat. Dawn said seeing Miss Shotestead 1963 looking like Lady Muck made her want to spit, and I said same here with Little Bo Peep.

Leaving Hattie with the great aunts, we looked round the Flower Tent and the Police Exhibition of Crime Prevention and the Barclays Bank stand, where Dawn interrupted the man telling us about deposit accounts to ask about stopping a cheque.

We watched a sheep-dipping demonstration and strolled past the *Encyclopaedia Britannica* stand and a windscreen stand and a trailer stand and the Protestant Truth Society, and I was just wondering why the Show seemed so dull and tired and stale this year when my body stiffened with excitement. For over in a quiet corner behind the Ladies, I spotted a blue handwritten sign that said *TIP THE LADY OUT OF BED*! In smaller letters underneath it said *Bryants for your lingerie.*

'Come on, Dawn, let's have a butchers,' I said, pointing.

'Roll up, roll up,' shouted Hilda of underwear fame', her spectacles winking playfully in the sun. 'Try and tip the lady out of bed. All in a good cause.'

The 'lady' in question was none other than Fiona Margetson! Her audience consisted of a small noisy, top-drawer group of friends.

'Honestly, I've never felt such a fool in my *entire* life,' screeched Fiona, sitting up and smoothing down the pink eiderdown. She was wearing a striped nightshirt with the price tag hanging from the neck. 'God, I'm never going to live this down. Ju-Ju, don't you dare, I'll simply never forgive you!'

'So 'Ju-Ju', who looked rather like Mr Ed, half-heartedly threw a ball that didn't even get close to the target.

'What am I meant to be *doing*, anyway?' cried Fiona.

'Look alluring, sister dear,' said Rupert.

'What, like this?' and she put her head on the pillow and fluttered her eyelids and sucked in her plump rosy cheeks and pouted her lips, causing a man in a cap to look away grinning and shaking his head and saying to his friend, 'Oh dear, oh, lor.'

'Perhaps it's the nightcap that's a bit off-putting,' neighed Ju-Ju. 'I mean, people aren't exactly flocking to tip you out of bed, are they?'

'Don't embarrass me,' shrieked Fiona like a shrill version of Lenny the Lion.

'Ya, I mean can't you wear something slightly more revealing? It doesn't give a chap a frightful amount of motivation, ha, ha, ha!' said a sandy-haired boy called Charles.

'Oh, Charles, don't be beastly to poor Fee,' cried a girl in a tweed suit, called Amanda. 'I think she's a frightfully good sport doing it at all.'

'Ya, *and* I'm missing the Grand Parade,' said Fiona. 'Come on, someone, I can't just lie here like a complete and utter burk. *Someone* have another go.'

''Fraid the old shekels are getting a bit thin on the ground. Going to need some to get slaughtered at the dance tonight, what!'

The men in caps walked past, one muttering 'Don't reckon it's worth hanging about. Me missus falling outer bed would be more of a thrill.'

'Dawn,' I whispered, clutching her arm, my voice quivering with excitement. 'Are you thinking what I'm thinking? Why don't you have a go?'

'You're kidding. What would I want to tip an old cow like her out of bed for?'

'No. Being the lady *in* bed. You'd be brilliant. It would be your forte, I just know it would, all your skills – your personality and your humour and your, er, sexiness – in one fell swoop.'

Dawn looked at me and shrugged. 'I suppose I couldn't do any worse than her.'

'You'd be a million times better.'

'Know something, kid? You could just be right.'

'Now leave everything to me,' I said.

I hurried up to Hilda and when I told her the plan her chubby face lit up. 'She'd be a right improvement. This one's about as alluring as a sack of potatoes. Tell her I've got loads of sexy gear to choose from round the back.'

368

I then went up to Rupert. 'Hi,' I said.

'Hi. I say, Sarah, what *has* happened to old Dan this summer? He cut me dead just now and ...'

'It's only a phase,' I said, suddenly remembering I never did write him that letter. 'Look, when Fiona gets tired of being a tip the lady out of bed, er, lady, I've got just the person.' And I nodded at Dawn.

'Oh, *ya*, see what you mean,' said Rupert, looking round and grinning, at the same time that 'Ju-ju' said, 'I say, isn't that that blonde tart in the bikini?'

'Come on, you guys, this is getting frightfully tedious,' said Fee.

'Fear not, sister dear, a replacement is at hand,' said Rupert.

'I was just beginning to get comfortable,' said Fiona. She glared at Dawn. For a moment their eyes met and challenged each other: blue and innocent and aloof versus black and hard and cunning.

Then Fiona sighed and said, 'I suppose I don't have much choice. I mean, this is hardly *me*, is it – thank the Lord. She certainly looks more the type.'

'Get changed into some sexy gear round the back while I go and round up some men,' I said to Dawn, my voice as light as a powerful fairy's (this was without doubt the best wheeze I'd had all summer!) 'We're going to turn this Tip the Lady out of Bed caper into the star attraction, right?' and I ran off as fast as my legs would carry me.

I was like a character in *Rawhide* rounding up cattle who put their heads willingly in my lasso. Normally when you asked grown-ups to do something they'd think of reasons not to. But not in this case. Oh, boy no! This was just the sort of excitement they had been looking for. I braved the beer tent to tell the Americans and even climbed the rickety-rackety stairs to inform the Knick-knack Pad-dywack man who winked his bright mouse eye which was half-covered by his Beatles' fringe and said, 'Okey-dokey. I'll *tip* folks the wink.'

I found the photographer from the *Eastern Daily Press* and promised he'd get the best pictures of the day, and he nodded and hurried off.

I found Dan coming out of the Gents doing up his flies. 'You might get some inspiration for your tip the lady out of bed song,' I said, pulling him along by his hand, and he followed as willingly as a lamb.

To Fiona's chagrin, the crowd round the Tip the Lady out of Bed stand was swelling like the chest of a puff-adder. She flounced off with Annabel, leaving Rupert, Charles and 'Ju-Ju' to spend their thin-on-the-ground shekels. Obviously, tipping the new lady out of bed had suddenly become more important to them than getting 'slaughtered'.

The lady lay on her back, staring seductively at her audience preparing themselves for action, a come-hither, come-to-bed look in her eyes. She had the pink eiderdown pulled up to her chin so there were no clues as to what was underneath. Her loose hair spilled like white gentle seaweed over the pillow, her lips were parted and slightly pouting. What a perfect opportunity to be Brigitte Bardot and Marilyn Monroe, to be the vulgar, flirty, funny Dawn we all knew and perhaps even loved! This was so completely and utterly her forte it made me want to cry. She winked at me, and I was about to tell her she looked terrific when Hilda shouted, 'Sarah? Would you mind being in charge for a mo while I go to the lav?' and I said, 'Sure. Okay.'

'*We'd make a great double act*,' Dawn had said after our fight, and now her prediction was about to come true.

'Roll up, gentlemen, roll up,' I shouted, my voice soaring like a strong bird's, more powerful, less shy than I had ever known it. 'Try to tip the lady out of bed. You won't be disappointed. Roll up, roll up, we have some brilliant surprises in store,' and Dawn winked at me again and the 'gentlemen' swarmed round me like inflamed bees waving half-crowns, all wanting to be the first to tip the lady out of bed.

Balls began to fly thick and fast.

'Steady on, lads, one at a time. There's plenty for everyone,' she teased, and languidly turned on to her side.

It was Brian Pike's turn. The blue veins stood out on his neck as he took aim. He was taking this very seriously indeed. So was the Yellow Dog. His ears were pricked forward and body a-tremble like when he had found the right rabbit hole. You could tell he was really looking forward to seeing a lady being tipped out of bed. But his master missed every time.

'Not such a good shot without your gun, eh, mate?' said Dawn. 'And talking of guns, is that one I can see in your pocket, or are you just pleased to see me?'

For a second there was a stunned silence. No one had ever heard such a thing mentioned on a family showground, Norfolk, England, Europe, World, before. And then as one, the crowd roared and cheered and wolf-whistled. And even Brian Pike, after scratching his head, laughed too and said, 'You've got the cheek of the devil, you have!'

It was now Adam Faith's turn. His strong brown bare arm took

aim and threw. And missed. 'Dunno what I'm doing this for. I've
been trying to get you *into* bed all summer, not out of it,' he shouted
and Dawn smiled and fluttered her eyelashes and said, 'Yeah, but
don't you want to see the goods first? That'd be like buying a
pig in a poke, yeah?' and grinned at me because she'd used my
expression.

A ripple of frenzied excitement shivered through the crowd. Did
that mean that under the pink eiderdown the lady was . . . *naked*?

I ran round collecting up balls, taking half-crowns (I had to
restrict it to six throws per person), and organising the competitors
in an orderly queue. I had never organised grown men before but
these were no ordinary men; why, if I'd asked them to take down
their trousers and sing *God Save the Queen* they would have done,
just so long as they were allowed to try to tip the lady out of bed!

Arms drew back, one after another and another, and balls flew
fast and furious. Ju-Ju, his Mr Ed eyes narrowed in concentration,
Charles, sweat collecting on his sandy brow, Rupert, whose spot
had vanished and who said bugger twice, Keith the wrestling
librarian, the Wild Ones, cool, calm and collected behind their sun-
glasses. But none of them hit the target.

'Blimey,' said Dawn, stretching out one white naked arm, putting
her hand to her mouth and pretending to yawn. 'If you fellers don't
hurry up, I'm going to have a kip. I dunno. All ready and waiting,
I am, and none of you can manage it.'

Talk about red rag to a bull! Talk about almost inciting a riot!
It was as if their skill at aiming the ball was connected in some
strange way to their wedding tackle! It was the most exciting thing
ever, far more exciting than winning fancy dress competitions or
getting clear rounds on Black Champion.

Shirt sleeves were feverishly rolled up and beads of frustration
appeared on brows. The gay banter subsided. This was becoming
more like a matter of life and death. It was as if the one who could
tip her *out* of bed was the one who'd tip her *into* bed later.

The photographer kept snapping, and the competitors kept
missing. I was dying to have a go myself, but this was strictly men
only. It would upset the whole balance of things if a *girl* tipped her
out of bed.

It was now the Americans' turn. First the stocky one with the
grizzled crewcut, then the tall black one whose arms gleamed like
Black Champion's satin coat, then the one in the nice, non-Nation-
al-Health glasses and another older one who looked like a character
from *Laramie* without his hat.

The way you knew the golden-curled Bo Peep would win the

371

Fancy Dress and *au naturel* Melanie Pratt the Beauty Contest, so you knew that the tall dark American with hazel eyes was going to tip the lady out of bed.

He circled the ball in his brown smooth hands and stared not at the spot where the ball was supposed to go but at Dawn who, with parted lips and a look of longing in her eyes, altered the position of her legs under the eiderdown. If Aunt Daphne or Mummy had been there she would never have let me watch in a hundred years. But they weren't, so who cared!

The American conducted himself in a very cool, calm manner, perhaps the way Elvis Presley or Uncle Sandy would have done in the circumstances, and even though you couldn't see the outline of his wedding tackle through his jeans as such, you could sense its presence very strongly. He seemed like the only true man among a group of boys, the Aslan in a pride of lions.

'Bloody yanks. "Over-sexed, over-paid and over here" is still as true today,' muttered Ju-Ju and then all went as quiet as a mouse and everyone held their breath and stared at Dawn as slowly the American lifted back his arm, as strong and sleek and muscular as a steeplechaser's haunch, and took aim.

Clonk.

'Aaaaaaah,' cried Dawn and slowly, tantalisingly, the bed began to tip.

And then, just as all was about to be revealed, something happened that if the spectators had been only a fraction less civilised, would have made them smash up the whole showground.

For out of the blue, out of the green, crashing through the crowd like a rampaging bull in a thunderstorm, like a whirling dervish, like the great long red-legg'd scissorman himself, came Albert in his boater and apron.

'I'll give you Tip the Lady out of Bed,' he spluttered, his eyes burning, his cheeks in danger of bursting like over-ripe plums. 'Get you out of that there thing this instant', and he scooped up Dawn and the eiderdown in mid-fall so cunningly that nothing more than a milk-white calf was revealed.

'Steady on, Albert,' said Brian Pike.

'Time to split, you guys,' said the handsome American, shrugging his broad shoulders.

''Ere, leave off, will yer?' said Dawn, kicking and struggling like the rabbit tangled up in Brian Pike's net. 'It's a free country, innit?'

'I put up with that Beauty Contest but I'm not going to stand for this. What the hell do you think you're playing at?'

'Oy. What the hell do you think *you're* playing at, bor,' shouted

Adam Faith. 'There was no harm in it. It were only a bit of fun.'

'Yes, Albert, it's all in a good cause,' I said. 'We were doing a roaring trade. Just think, an old person might ...'

'I think we jolly well ought to have our money back,' said Ju-Ju.

'Stuff your money up your arse,' snarled Albert. 'And go and get your kicks off someone else's fiancée. You're kinky, the lot of you.'

'You're a killjoy, you know that, Albert Thirtle,' said Dawn, tears in her voice. She had given up struggling as she was carried away, her white bare legs hanging limply from the eiderdown like a dead person's.

The men shook their heads, and gradually dispersed.

'That's all very fine,' said Hilda. 'But who's going to be my Tip the Lady out of Bed lady now?'

'Don't look at me,' I said and laughed, though I'd rather have cried. Poor Dawn. Her moment of glory had been so short-lived though at least, I supposed, she had had one. Now all she had ahead of her, apart from the dance, was marriage to the tempestuous Albert.

'*Ladies and gents*,' said the loudspeaker. '*A dicky bird's just told me that in the north corner there's a Tip the Lady out of Bed stand. And my spies tell me the lady in question is a real* dream. *So* spring *over there, gents, and see whether you can get her into – whoops, I mean out of – bed, otherwise you'll never know whether or not the Sleeping Booty's wearing pyjamas, a nightdress or, like Marilyn Monroe, nothing more than Chanel Number Five ...!*'

CHAPTER TWENTY-EIGHT

Sipping tea and munching fig rolls in the still, long-shadowed peace of Granny's garden, the showground was another country. If you stretched your ears past the wood pigeon's coo-cooo-coo-coo-coo you could just hear the loudspeaker, but that was all.

Hattie was having a doze so that she would last the evening. I should have been having one, too, but my heart was far too wide awake. Besides, I wanted to be Granny's eyes and ears on what had happened so far.

We had stayed to watch the gymkhana events, half of me aching to be taking part (several events were for under-twelves which meant next year I'd be over the hill), and the Young Farmers' Obstacle Race, where not only had Dan's drainpipes slowed him up (how magnificent he'd been last year running like the wind in loose cords), but he'd also stood with his hands on his hips when he should have been loading straw bales. It was thanks mainly to him that the Shotestead Young Farmers came last.

We took part in Motor Musical Chairs, me as runner and Hattie sitting in the back. Fiona had wanted to be Dan's passenger, but he had said 'Sorry, already booked!' and nodded at us. (Poor Fiona. Her summer was turning out to be the antithesis of Samantha Croft's.)

Roaring round the edge of the grand ring was the usual affray of muddy Land Rovers, nippy Ford Anglias, dare-devil Austin-Healeys, cumbersome Zodiacs, Consuls and Victors, battered old Morris and Ford vans and Mazda trucks. Ju-Ju's great long red-nosed E-type jag would have stolen the show good and proper if it hadn't been for the American and his pink Cadillac. His passenger was Melanie Pratt and visually they belonged to another world. Boy, were they somethin' else. They were on a different plane to the rest of us mortals, and there can't have been one woman – or man – on the showground who didn't feel at least a shiver of jealousy. Even I did, sitting beside Dan slouched casually at the wheel of Aunt Lynette's MGB, and as for Dawn, sulking in the green Triumph Herald beside her killjoy fiancée . . .

When the music stopped I ran twice as fast as the other girls to the chairs in the middle, and we would have probably won if later some foul woman hadn't elbowed me roughly out of the way. Even though Dawn removed her stilettos and hitched up her skirt to run she was still out first but she didn't seem to mind.

Granny looked quite sprightly and sparkly under her last straw hat. Clearly, a day's peace on her own had done her the world of good.

'Tell me everything, darling,' she said, and her eyes looked as though they meant it.

'For a start, it wasn't the same without you,' I said. 'Simply everyone asked where you were and how you were. Mrs English made a real hash of dishing out the cups. An Arab tried to eat her hat.'

'Darling, I think the term's "presenting", not "dishing",' and she sighed. '"I fear Dawn hasn't been a good influence on you. I don't know what your mother's going to say.'

'She's been an influence on me but not a bad one,' I said. 'One has to move with the times. And talking of moving with the times, you should have heard the loudspeaker man. He was the man from that Knick-Knacks shop and kept saying okey-dokey and making appalling puns. Everyone in the Members was complaining.'

'Perhaps the younger generation liked him,' said Granny. 'The committee decided to try someone new this year in order to be more with-it – do I mean with-it, darling?'

I munched my fifth fig roll and Granny said, 'I daresay I should have put in an appearance, but . . . quite frankly, it becomes more of an ordeal each year. All those people, all that polite conversation . . . Your grandfather would be turning in his grave if he knew I hadn't gone, but I feel quite liberated, I think is the modern word. I've always found it so wearing.'

'Coo, you'd have found it really wearing today with Dawn,' I said and gave her a cunningly censored version of events so far. The only event I didn't censor was the tale of the handsome American and Aunt Lynette while wearing my moustache, and Granny's half-old half-new eyes twinkled.

'Darling,' she said, reaching over and touching my hand. 'I really can't approve of you getting involved in such grown-up concerns. I do wish you'd go back to being a child. It's so much more fun.'

'Granny, can I ask you something, please?' I said, deciding to make the most of having her to myself while she was in a good, non-gaga mood. 'If Aunt Lynette isn't hankering after a husband and baby, why does she get so morose sometimes? What I was wondering was whether during the war she didn't fall madly in love with someone, an American fighter pilot, for example, and he got killed and she decided she could never love another man again, and that's why she cries sometimes, because she's thinking of him.'

Granny smiled and said, 'Darling, there doesn't always have to be a reason why we do things. Human beings are rather irrational creatures, you know. One can burst into tears sometimes without there being any reason for it.'

This was news to me. I thought about it, then said, 'Granny, the great aunts said Dan was going the same way as his grandfather. What did they mean, exactly? Surely Grandpa didn't have long hair and sing in a pop group?'

Granny laughed half-heartedly and trained her eyes on a shrub in a far-away, long-forgotten corner of the garden. 'Of course not, darling. Perhaps they simply meant he went through a slightly rebellious stage, too. It did happen sometimes, even then.'

I couldn't let the opportunity go by. Not today. Not on I go where others fear to tread day. Not on strike while the iron's hot day. 'Er, Granny,' I said. 'You know that photograph Dawn found? The cut-out servant wasn't really a groom killed in the trenches, was he?'

Granny brushed an imaginary crumb off the table. 'What on earth makes you think that, darling? Really, I haven't the faintest idea who it was. It was all so long ago ...' For the first time I noticed her eyes were slightly hooded, like a bird of prey's.

'Well, I'm pretty sure – in fact, I know – that it was a woman.'

Granny stared at me then, and was there just the faintest trace of fear in her strange old blue eyes? 'Darling, how can you possibly ...?'

'Because someone had cut the shape out very carefully with nail scissors, round the hair and shoulders. And the person was definitely wearing a long skirt. If it had been a man you would have seen the shape of his legs.'

She took a gnat's sip of tea. Her brown spotted hand was shaking very slightly, like a startled toad. 'Darling, it was fifty years ago.'

Accusing one's grandmother of lying wasn't the done thing at all, and normally I'd have left it at that. But today wasn't normal. No, siree! If I could tick off an MP and talk to an American airman wearing a moustache and run a Tip the Lady out of Bed stand single-handed, I could somehow coax the truth out of Granny.

I held her soft, shy, warm-blooded hand and said, 'Granny, please tell me. I know your memory's good – tons better than mine. I know it's none of my business but I hate not knowing things. It must be the detective in me. You see, I noticed that there was something about that photograph that upset you; you went into er, a slight decline after that, if you don't mind me saying. I know Austin and Clifford didn't help, but ... You see, if I don't know I'll imagine all sorts of things and worry myself to death.'

For either ten seconds or ten minutes Granny gazed through the lengthening hoods at the shrub in the far-away corner. If she didn't speak after three more pigeon coos I would have to play my trump card. She didn't, so I did. 'You see, Granny, our new teacher, Mr Richards, set us a task this summer: to open up our minds by asking er, older people about their pasts. And so far I haven't got anything much apart from Jack rambling on about farm life before the advent of machines.'

Granny shifted in her seat and gave a small sigh. Then she smiled faintly and said, 'You're making it very hard for me, darling,' and then there was another long pause.

Like the most ruthless policeman in South America, I continued my interrogation. 'Granny, if it's something well, a bit upsetting, perhaps it might be good for you to talk about it. Dawn's always saying a trouble shared is a trouble halved.'

Granny smiled thinly and, still looking at the shrub, said that I'd certainly inherited my father's powers of persuasion. Then she said, 'Very well, I suppose it won't do you any harm knowing. It's all such past history now and you've become such a grown-up girl. No one else knows, though. It'll be our secret. Do I make myself clear?'

'Perfectly,' I said and let go of her hand. I shifted in my seat, and braced myself. The wood pigeon had stopped cooing so he could listen, too.

But still she didn't say anything. Had she forgotten the question? After what seemed like an age, I said, 'Shall I tell you who *I* think the mystery figure is? What I thought was that perhaps Grandpa had a brief love affair with the maid – before he met you, of course – and it all had to be hushed up to avoid a scandal, which was why she was cut out of the photograph.'

'Darling, how clever. You're absolutely right,' said Granny, still not looking me in the eye. 'There's only one thing to add: the missing person in the photograph was me.'

There was a frenzied fluttering in the trees. Perhaps the wood pigeon was so surprised he had fallen off his perch.

I didn't show anything on the outside but inside I was gasping, and my heart beat so fast it prevented me from finishing my fig roll. This was better than even I could have dreamed of! My grandmother a servant!

'Are you fearfully shocked, darling?'

377

'Er, no, not at all,' I said. 'Except ... I didn't think parsons' daughters became servants.'

'They don't as a rule ... I'm afraid the parson's daughter story was conjured up by my parents-in-law.'

I felt a tiny stab of disappointment. So my literary talent didn't stem from her side of the family after all. But if she wasn't a Yorkshire parson's daughter, whose was she?

'My family, like Dawn's, were cockneys,' said Granny and this time my mouth did drop open. 'I was even born within the sound of Bow Bells. My father was a builder and my mother worked at the Bryant and May match factory. She was, in fact, one of the first women in the country to go on strike.'

(Even though my brain was on tenterhooks, it still couldn't help registering the joke about matches and going on strike for the diary.)

'In 1912 my father was buried alive while demolishing slum houses in Shoreditch and so my mother, tired of sooty, grimy, noisy, dangerous city life and thinking the country air would do us good – tuberculosis was very prevalent then, and my younger brother James was hellbent on becoming a gardener – moved us lock, stock and barrel to her widowed sister's in Norfolk – Cawton, to be precise, in that little thatched cottage on the heath (the one where you found an adder nearby, do you remember, and the woman came rushing out with an axe). My elder brother George became an apprentice to a blacksmith, and James an under-gardener at the Margetsons – later, of course, they were called up by Lord Kitchener. I had the choice of agricultural work – stone-picking, gleaning at harvest time, fruit picking, that sort of thing – or going into service. So I picked the latter and ended up here at Gressenham Hall as a housemaid.

'It was hard work – all that grate blacking and water carrying and step scrubbing – but it was infinitely preferable to working in an East End sweat shop. What a different world it was to the one I knew! Oh, you should have seen it all then, before the Great War – the shooting parties and picnics and cricket matches ... I remember when they had tea on the lawn we weren't allowed to put the hot water jug on the grass in case it left a brown scorch mark. And how the gardener couldn't trundle past with a barrow of weeds in case it upset the dignity and repose of the tea party!'

Granny's eyes had travelled back fifty years in time, and so had mine. Boy! I hadn't been so agog since being in Mr Richards' presence.

'Gradually the young master, your grandfather, began to take a

378

fancy to me. At first it was nothing very serious. Just a quick cuddle when no one else was about. Even though I thought him quite divine – he was so handsome, so witty – I kept my feet firmly on the ground. How could there be any future for us, him a dashing young gentleman and me a cockney housemaid? And then, one day – oh, darling, I'm sure you're too young for all this – he seduced me.'

'I'm not too young, honestly, Granny,' I said, taking an ant's nibble at the fig roll. 'Did the er, seducing happen in the black summerhouse, by any chance?'

'Darling, how clever. It was all very secret, and very exciting. We were so very much in love. And then needless to say I er, found that I was expecting a baby. What an uproar! His parents were all for sweeping me under the carpet by sending me away to some sort of ghastly home, but your grandfather stood by me and insisted on marrying me, which was most honourable of him. Not many men would have done such a thing then ... He was so *eligible*, you see. The Hillingtons were really quite powerful then with all that land, and of course he was frightfully handsome. Several well-bred young ladies had their eye on him.

'Almost the day after we married the Great War began. Most of the menfolk went off to fight, and your great-grandmother spent the next four years teaching me how to speak 'proper' and generally behave like a lady, and bring up my son – your father – in a manner accustomed to a young gentleman. My brothers died in the trenches – Dawn was quite right when she said the bottom-drawer were cannon fodder; the Hillingtons came back virtually unscathed – and soon after that my mother died of a broken heart as it was called then and my aunt of pneumonia. All evidence of my dubious origins had been wiped out, and a new era had begun. Dear Jack is aware of my origins but he is so loyal he'd never tell a soul. So you see, darling, I'm afraid your Hillington blood isn't quite as pure as you thought it was.'

'Oh, I don't mind at all, Granny. As Dawn says, it all comes out in the wash. In fact I feel tremendously proud.'

And I did. I had servant blood inside me! The jigsaw pieces were fitting into place thick and fast! Now I understood why the great aunts were hostile towards Granny; because while they made do with a cluttered cottage Granny, a mere servant, lived in style at Gressenham Hall – and all because their brother had an eye for a pretty face! Now I understood their dismay when they spotted Dan and Dawn together, because they thought they were seeing history repeating itself. It explained, too, why Granny wore the last straw hat and fluffy pink slippers and used the foul tea cosy in West Ham colours – because after spending her life pretending to be top-drawer, she was now turning a bit gaga and sliding back through the drawers to being bottom again! It explained why she hadn't got crosser with Dan and Aunt Lynette during their political rantings; because with a striking mother and brothers killed at war, in her heart of hearts she felt the same as they did! It explained why she didn't mind Dawn singing *Fings Ain't What They Used to Be* at table. And most important of all, it explained why she had employed Dawn in the first place: because Dawn reminded her of herself in her youth!

And what drawer did all this make us? If Daddy was half top and half bottom, and Mummy was middle, that made us middle. But just say Mummy was more bottom than middle that would make us bottom, too. Wow! Did that mean we could be rude when we liked and wear unsuitable clothes and do everything we wanted to apart from stepping on blue suede shoes!

Say Mr Richards chose this extract to read out in class. But so what if he did? It was something to be proud of in this day and age to have a Granny who was a servant – why, according to Aunt Lynette the working class was all the rage, the new aristocracy! – and if people looked down their noses at me I would just accuse them of being toffee-nosed snobs and never talk to them again.

'It must have been quite lonely at first,' I said. 'And was it a strain pretending to be, er, a different drawer to your real one?'

Granny said it was extraordinary how quickly one adapted; the only time she lapsed back into her cockney accent was once in 1922 after drinking a drop too much sherry, which was why she hadn't touched alcohol to this day.

'Didn't you resent having to go against your grain?' I asked and Granny said it was a very small price to pay for being allowed to marry the man you loved.

'Did you swear, Granny, and have yellow hair and black eyes like Dawn?'

Granny laughed. 'Oh, heavens no. I was very quiet and demure. Things were so much stricter then. So now you can see why I chose Dawn for the job. She evoked so strongly the memory of my youth – the accent, the humour. And when you reach my dotty old age you want someone around who makes you laugh. I think at heart once a cockney, always a cockney.'

'It was very brave of Grandpa, wasn't it, to disobey his parents and marry you?'

'Extremely. But there always seemed to be a tradition – a tendency among Hillington men to allow their hearts to rule their heads. There was a cousin, I believe, who eloped with a seamstress from Battersea, and your great-grandfather kept a mistress for years.'

'So he was a real hypocrite, wasn't he, wanting you swept under the carpet.'

'Not really, darling. You see, it was one thing – and quite an accepted thing – to have a mistress, quite another to marry her. Which was why your grandfather was such an unusual man.'

'And why you were such an unusual woman,' I said tactfully. 'You were obviously very special – and still are, of course. Er, has Daddy got this Hillington Tendency, do you think?'

Granny said good heavens no, all that died out years ago. 'Times have changed so,' she said vaguely.

'Even so, when you employed Dawn weren't you a teeny bit worried the Hillington Tendency would raise its head and Dan would fall in love with her?'

'I thought it so unlikely it wasn't even worth considering,' she said. 'For a start she's engaged to Albert, and that ghastly hair and all that paint on her face ... I personally find it most unattractive, and I'm sure Dan does, too. Besides, as it's turned out he has more than enough on his plate with his, er, pop group.'

'And Hilary Wentworth-Smith,' I said.

The Pinky and Perkies' horsebox crunched up the drive. 'Oh, no,' I said. 'There's so much more I want to ask you. Does Aunt Daphne know about this? Or Daddy or Aunt Lynette?'

'No, darling. They might suspect, but I've never actually told them. I promised my mother-in-law faithfully I would never reveal my source, as a journalist would say, so I've kept to my Yorkshire parson story throughout. So you see, all this talk about hypocrites ... I must be the biggest one of all, pretending to be something I'm not.'

'No, you're not, Granny. You're just keeping your promise.' And that was an interesting point: which was worse, to break a promise or spend your life pretending to be someone you're not? And if the person to whom you've done the promising is dead, would you still be breaking your promise? I would have liked to have discussed this with Granny, along with a hundred and one other things, but Aunt Daphne and Susan were rounding the corner.

'Now not a word to a soul,' said Granny and I said that my lips were sealed. 'And Granny, thank you for telling me. It's been the greatest of privileges.'

The last thing I felt like doing was talking to the Pinky and Perkies. I just wanted to sit quietly and ponder about this latest bombshell. But chance would be a fine thing as Dawn – and maybe Granny! – would say.

'Mind if we drop in for a cup of tea, Mummy? We're parched,' boomed Aunt Daphne. 'Goodness, what a day. We've all done disastrously. This Show certainly won't go down in Hillington as our finest hour.'

'We'll just have to put all our trust in Dan's performance tonight,' I said.

Aunt Daphne looked down the length of her nose at me. 'That brother of yours isn't fit to be let out in public, let alone on stage in front of all our friends. Great Aunt Beth and Gertie were almost in tears about him. Talk about a hooligan. He's wearing ghastly drainpipe things, Mummy, and extraordinary shoes and sunglasses. He's completely let the side down.'

'I bet he'll let the side *up* tonight,' I said and wanted to add that she had nothing to be hoity-toity about, why, her mother was only a cockney housemaid. I didn't say it with my mouth but I did with my eyes; I made them steely and cold. 'You're a good one to talk. You're as common as muck,' they said.

But Aunt Daphne just showed me her nostrils and said, 'Don't give me one of your Miss Madam looks, Sarah. I blame it all on that despicable Dawn Potts. Honestly, have you seen her today, Mummy? She looks like nothing on earth, causing havoc wherever she goes, and she was so unbelievably rude to me ... I've said it once and I'll say it again: I can't think what *possessed* you to employ her.'

I smiled. I knew and Granny knew. I wondered if Dawn knew, too.

CHAPTER TWENTY-NINE

'*I can't stop lov-ing you. It's useless to say,*' wafted woefully across the dusk-coloured showground.

'Dig that swinging sound,' laughed Dawn, slamming the car door.

'Now then, there's nothing wrong with a good old romantic song,' said Albert, putting his good old romantic arm round her bare shoulders.

'Yes, I thought you liked sentimental songs, Dawn.'

'Not when I've got me dancing shoes on. Get off, you soppy date, you'll mess up me barnet!'

'*So I'll just live my life in dreams of yesterday . . .*'

We'd been picked up in the Triumph Herald, and how grown-up to be taken to a dance by a *boy*, even if it was only Old-Spiced, spruced-up Albert!

He had changed into his shiny light blue suit, plus surprisingly pointed shoes which were almost but not quite winklepickers. You had to adjust your eyes when you looked at those shoes; it was like looking down expecting to see friendly hippos, say, and seeing crafty crocodiles instead. His swept-back hair glistened like moist marmalade and he wore at his throat a bootlace tie. I remarked on it and he touched it as if it were a sleeping tarantula and said, 'You don't think it makes me look a bit of a prat? It's my one gesture to this rock 'n' roll lark, and people can like it or lump it.'

He had obviously tipped the Tip the Lady out of Bed incident out of his mind and was back to his cheery old self, making jokes about being a thorn amongst roses and how he must be the luckiest fellow in East Anglia to be escorted by three beautiful girls.

And we *did* look beautiful: Hattie minus her spectacles in her pink swishing party frock and matching Alice band; she'd brushed and brushed her hair till it shone like Black Champion's coat; Dawn, with tumbling, all-fall-down Brigitte Bardot locks and a magnificent, all-fall-down-if-it-isn't-careful strapless white dress with large flame-coloured flowers (and flame lipstick to match), the waist clinched in with a white belt, its skirt stiff with the rustle of petticoats; and me in my kingfisher dress with its thin-as-a-whistle straps and matching knickers, my fresh-out-of-rollers hair bouncing and bob-curtseying, a sprinkle of powder on my face, a splash of Dawn's scent behind my ears, a dash of lipstick and mascara purely for 'definition' ... For the first time in my life I felt pretty, oh so pretty!

'Darling,' Granny had said touching my bare shoulder, and there were almost tears in her eyes. 'My little grown-up granddaughter. Be a young lady for the dance but do go back to being a girl tomorrow.'

Hattie hadn't been so polite. 'Blimey, it's a good thing Mummy can't see you in that dress, she'd have a hundred fits. And is that make-up I can see? It's the thin end of the wedge, you know. In two years' time you're going to look and *smell* just like Dawn.'

And meanwhile, just for tonight, I was going to be Cinderella, the belle of the ball!

Rustling and jangling and chattering, we picked our way through litter and cowpats to the Members' Tent.

The sun was going down and people were coming from miles around to see Dan being the 'leader of a big old band', just like in *Johnny B. Goode*.

'The nights are drawing in,' remarked Hattie. 'Summer will soon be over.'

At the entrance to the marquee, 'Ju-Ju' and Charles sat at a trestle table collecting the entrance money in a beer mug. You could tell by their dull-eyed looks they were already beginning to get 'slaughtered'.

I say,' Ju-Ju said to Dawn, 'I almost didn't recognise you out of bed, ha, ha, ha!'

'How much do I owe you?' said Albert hotly and roughly and drew a brisk circle over our heads to indicate he'd like to pay for us all. I began to protest but Dawn whispered to let him or his male pride would take a bashing.

'Thanks very much, Albert,' I said. Tomorrow I'd ask Granny to put in an extra-large meat order.

A wave of warmth greeted you when you went inside. Boy, it was like walking into an inferno! An inferno that smelt of bodies and soap and beer and aftershave and canvas and grass and gin and cigarettes.

People of every age, shape and drawer sat at trestle tables or stood at the bar, the women huge in stiff-petticoated dresses, the men dapper in suits and with hair as neat as hats. They drank and smoked and talked and looked at the dance floor and the stage, where twinkling fairy lights formed a multi-coloured picture frame

384

round the edge of James Wilkes and the Shotestead Shoe-Shufflers.

All three musicians wore dinner jackets and black bow ties, their hair as polished as their shoes. The drummer was Albert's father. For drumsticks he used what looked like paint brushes with splayed wire bristles. 'Tsch-tsch-tsch' they went. He had his head on one side and was looking over to his left. Mr Finch the barber and tobacconist was on double bass and James Wilkes – or James Whelks as we called him – from the fish and chip shop played guitar.

As he sang, he stared misty-eyed on to the dance floor at the older generation. Aunt Daphne was among them, wearing fierce blue eyeshadow and a black dress with thin-as-knicker-elastic straps, almost as thin as mine, in fact, her bosoms skimming against Sir Edward who glided her round the dance floor like Jack be nimble (or Jack the Lad, as Dawn muttered); the large, galumphing Rev. Rackham side-stepping on Mrs Smedley's beige-suede shoes; fluffy-haired Jack, in a baggy-trousered, turned-up, fly-buttoned suit dancing stiffly and straight-backed with Aunt Lynette who looked radiant in sunshine yellow; Mrs Rackham, her petticoat showing, military two-stepping with the galloping Major Smedley; pretty Mrs English and handsome Mr English looking quite turtle-dovey; Mrs Bone, teetering in high heels like an amateur stilt walker in a tight, purple spangly dress, bending and kicking and quick-stepping and tango-ing and rumba-ing with Mr Bone who still wore his mustard waistcoat plus an old brown suit and a skew-whiff tie; Uncle William doing the turned-out-toe shuffle with Sir Edward's wife, turned-in-toed, twin-bosomed and pearled.

My eyes swivelled like searchlights through the gloom and the smoke for the American. Disappointingly, he was nowhere to be seen, Michael English was, though, complete with a rough and tumble Beatles' fringe.

'Gee, I hardly recognised you, Sarah,' he said, jangling the pockets of his sports jacket like a grown-up. 'You haven't forgotten that dance later?' and I smiled and shook my head. 'Just got to see a man about a dog,' he said winking and for some reason I felt pleased as Punch.

'I was right about him,' said Dawn. 'I know the face of a smitten geezer when I see one.'

'Keep your flaming mouth shut – i.e. your lipstick colour,' I said and added that we were never going to have the nerve to do with-it dancing, it wasn't the right sort of place, and Dawn said, 'Just you wait. When your bro comes on the atmosphere will change just like that,' and she snapped her fingers.

She went to the bar to help Albert carry the drinks and Hattie and I stood on our own near the entrance, feeling rather small and, like Jack and Albert at my birthday tea, unsure what to do with our hands.

'I feel so nervous stroke excited,' I said. 'Do you think Dan's going to be a wild success or a complete embarrassment?'

Hattie said he'd been a complete embarrassment all summer so she didn't see why tonight should be any different. 'And he'd better not use any rude words,' she added. 'The Hillington name will become muddier than it already is. Isn't it funny seeing all these people in headscarves and jodhpurs all day and now done up to the nines. You wouldn't recognise some of them. Look at Aunt Daphne. She looks almost pretty, or is that because I'm not wearing my glasses?'

'I wonder if she fancies Sir Edward,' I said. 'Look how close they're dancing.'

'Sarah, honestly! You sound just like Dawn! They're both married to other people and anyway, those sorts of people don't behave like that.'

'Oh, no?' I said. 'Everyone's the same underneath.'

James Wilkes finished his song about chains and hearts and being set free and gave a brief bow. There was a smattering of applause loud enough, say, to wake a blackbird and two rooks dozing a couple of fields away. 'And now, ladies and gentlemen, our last number . . .'

'Thank gawd for that,' said Dawn, far too loudly considering her future father-in-law was the drummer, coming up with a tray of drinks. 'Don't Albert's dad fancy himself on the drums! Here's something to wet the old whistles.'

Hattie's was a Pepsi and mine was a shandy. 'Albert and I thought I'd give you a bit of Dutch courage for whom we hog the limelight, Sarah,' she said winking. (That was another thing to note for the diary; that people didn't half wink at you when you were all dolled up.)

My first alcoholic drink all to myself, in a half-pint beer mug! I sniffed its bouquet and took a sip. It tasted a bit on the beery side but I was going to drink every drop, no fear! If I ended up talking about politics and smoking cigarettes and either laughing or crying, who cared? Today was anything-can-happen day!

Aunt Daphne glanced our way and I said, 'What's the betting she tells me off about a) my dress, b) my lipstick and c) my shandy,' but to our amazement she simply smiled and waved and walked to the bar on the arm of Sir Edward.

'I'll tell you something for nothing. If that ain't a woman with a crush my name ain't Dawn Potts. Blimey, there's no accounting for taste.'

'Talking about you and me?' laughed Albert with a beer-foam moustache, and she laughed too and kissed his cheek. Perhaps she had at last come to terms with marrying him and was starting to make the best of it.

James Wilkes sang of catching a falling star and putting it in your pocket, while trying to look like an innocent young boy in love though he must have been all of forty-five. 'Tsch, tsch, tsch,' went Mr Thirtle, his head still on one side.

'What stupid words,' said Hattie. 'How can you put a star in your pocket?'

Still only the older generation danced, plus Albert wobbling his mother round and round like a laughing jelly, his wild pointed toes narrowly missing her stout ankles. Dawn watched with a tender smile on her face.

How sad for James Wilkes and the Shotestead Shoe-Shufflers. Their last song and no one young dancing. Couldn't they sense they were way out of date and play something like *Rock Around the Clock*? I suggested to Hattie that we danced just to lower the age ratio and she said no thanks, not for all the ponies in the New Forest. So I smiled at the Shoe-Shufflers and tapped my foot so at least they'd know one young person was enjoying their music.

When the song finally faded away, the Knick-Knack man, who had changed into a natty white suit and even nattier red and white spotted bow tie, jack-in-a-boxed on to the stage and said into the mike, 'Let's give a big hand to the pride of our alley, the stupendous James Wilkes and the Shoestead Shoe-Shufflers,' and we all clapped, including Dawn because Albert's father was looking her way. 'Okey-dokey, folks. There will now be a twenty-minute interval. But don't go away. Put on your dancing shoes and get those feet-a-tapping in readiness for The Wild Ones,' and a group of excitable Honourables, square in dress and round in limb, clapped and cheered and squealed like pink-faced piglets.

'If they think Dan's going to be a blond version of Cliff Richard, they're in for a big surprise,' I said.

'Too right,' said Dawn. 'Uh-oh. Talk of the devil.'

'Hi,' he said, unshaven, sweaty-browed, wearing Grandpa's grubby old mac with the collar up, jeans and Chelsea boots. 'Gee whizz, is this my pretty, hip sister I see before me? Man, you look far-out!'

A warm glow filled my tummy, or perhaps it was the shandy beginning to work.

'*You* don't, Dan,' said Hattie, perhaps because she was jealous he hadn't said she looked far-out. ('Your turn will come,' I'd tell her later. 'You wait till you're eleven. Boys will be queueing up to give you a compliment.')

'You can't please all of the people all of the time,' said Dan, shrugging.

'But you're *on* any minute, and you haven't changed into your suit.'

Dan shrugged again and grinned in a so-what sort of fashion. Perhaps it was the purple hearts at work, but for a man about to make his grand début he seemed extraordinarily relaxed.

I was about to ask him whether there was anything we could do to help when the Honourable Gang, led by Fiona, circled round him squealing 'Can we have your autograph now or later,' and 'God, what a hoot! You're so fearfully brave doing this, Dan,' and 'Dan. God, your hair!' (*They treated him like a purple heart-throb!!!* I would tell Mr Richards.)

'Is any of them that Hilary woman?' asked Dawn. 'All them horsy girls look the same to me.'

I said it didn't look as though she was coming and hoped Dan wasn't too disappointed. Then, as Hattie turned to talk to Mrs Rackham, I said, 'Have you said hello to *your* lover yet, by the way?'

'What makes you think he's here?' said Dawn, putting her hand on her hip and sticking out her chest like a pigeon. 'Talking of lovers, look at the way your Uncle William is ogling Sir what's-his-name wife's knockers ... Bloody nora! Look what the cat's just brought in.'

It was Brian Pike, complete with quiffed oily hair, long red velvet-collared jacket, bootlace tie, frilly shirt, drainpipe trousers and thick-soled shoes. Talk about a swell! Talk about a swagger! Talk about a turn-up for the books!

Hattie put her hand over her mouth to laugh and Dawn, wearing her wicked-lady look, sidling, flirting, bosoming up to him, said, 'Blimey! You didn't tell us you was a closet Ted.'

'You gotta keep one or two secrets tucked up yer sleeve, han't yer,' he grinned. 'I borrowed it for the evening. What d'yer think?' and holding his lapels, stuck out his frilly chest and wiggled it from side to side.

'Beats the Mr Gamekeeper outfit any day, eh, Sarah?' Dawn said and I said, 'Yeah. Definitely,' and just for a second allowed my eyes to glance briefly at his trousers to see if there was a gun in his pocket; but there seemed barely room for a rat's tail, let alone a set of man-sized wedding tackle. I trusted it hadn't throttled itself; I trusted it had room to *breathe*.

At midnight, I wondered, would Brian Pike and Aunt Daphne and all the others turn back into their real selves? Or was *this* their real selves?

Cousin Susan came over in a really square dress that looked like a village-hall curtain and said surely Dan was leaving it a bit late to change and I said, 'Actually, rock 'n' roll singers are meant to look scruffy. The scruffier the better, in actual fact.'

On stage, someone with untidy-haystack hair twiddled knobs on what could have been brown suitcases, and ear-piercing whines came from two thin wardrobe-looking things. Whines came from the audience, too, when the twenty minutes had come and gone, and I overheard one woman say, 'We might as well wait and see what that Hillington boy's like.'

The brewing excitement was beginning to stew in its own juice; people kept looking at the stage to see if anything was happening, and Young Farmers glanced at their watches mumbling, 'I wish they'd get a ruddy move-on. Ruddy amateurs.'

At last the whines from the amplifier ceased, the toy-coloured electric guitars were tuned, the microphones were at the right height, the stage was empty bar the grinning Knick-Knack man.

'Okey-dokey, folks, can we have a bit of hush,' he said, his gold tooth winking in the limelight. 'We have now come to the act you've all been waiting for, and you'd better lock up them daughters of yours, gents. Because they're hunky! They're brand new! They're with it! And most of all they're WILD! Ladies and gents, will you please give a wild welcome to ... THE WILD ONES!'

I felt sick in my throat but not in my stomach.

Encouraged by the Honourable Gang (who only needed skating dresses and they'd pass as chubby American cheer leaders), Mr Bone, Dawn, Hattie, Albert and me, everyone clapped and Dawn whistled vulgarly through her fingers like a boy.

The Wild Ones made their grand début.

I felt sick in my throat *and* in my stomach.

They slouched and scowled and swaggered and slopped and beer-swilled on to the stage in sullen sun-glasses, rough and ready denim, bully-boy leather, walking-on-the-wild-side footwear, rumpled shirts revealing surly truck-driver chests ... And their hair! Talk about harum-scare'em, hair-raising, haywire, wire hay, raggle-taggle gypsy, black, brown and blond rags to a bull!

389

They put on or sat at their instruments, not one of them smiling at, let alone acknowledging the existence of, their audience.

Was this what Dawn meant by mean, moody and magnificent? Mean and moody they might be, but magnificent was an extremely debatable point.

And yet, and yet ... How casual they looked, how *far out*, how brave for being not bow-tied, mother-loving, kind-to-animals, non-nose-picking all-round entertainers!

'Dear oh deary me,' sighed a man behind me. 'Is this what we won the war for?'

I whisked round. 'The singer's only doing this as a hobby to fill in time. He's going to Cambridge next term to study law.'

The man looked bashful and his wife said, 'See, Cecil. I'm always telling you shouldn't judge a cover by its book.'

Dan – or rather Pete O'Flame – didn't introduce himself or say good evening ladies and gentlemen, or look even remotely grateful he'd been given star billing. He just swigged at his beer and said, 'Testing, testing,' into the mike in a dead-pan pop singer's voice. Then he looked at Rick Benton, said, 'One, two, three, four,' and crashed into action.

What a din! What pure and utter hell! There wasn't a trace of a tune, just loud, ugly noises, If it had been food on a plate it would have been corned-beef hash with brown sauce and gooseberries.

Hattie and I looked at each other with sinking faces; so did Mr and Mrs Bone. 'Oh, lor,' Mr Bone's mouth went and he shook his head and sighed. The waistcoat buttons sighed, too; they were still all present and correct, just, which was more than could be said for the squares in the audience, who were dropping out like flies. 'Come back,' I wanted to cry. 'It can only get better.'

Aunt Daphne looked as though she'd just developed a chronic migraine, Uncle William and Sir Edward knocked back large whis-kies, Susan, the traitor, put her hands over her ears and Hattie kept shouting, 'Isn't it *awful*. I think I'm about to die of shame.' The Honourable Gang pretended they were enjoying it by clapping their hands, though they would have done that if the song had been *The Teddy Bears' Picnic*. And when Dan started singing, the words were as far removed from *The Teddy Bears' Picnic* as, say, a child's red-button shoe from a sanitary towel. For it was the Tip the Lady out of Bed song, and why, oh, why had he picked that to go first?

'*With your rich-bitch free-milk thighs*,' he snarled and spat into the mike like an outraged tiger being forced against his wishes to perform in public. '*And lure me under your snug, smug sheets with your Tory-blue come-to-bed eyes*,' rang out as clear as a ring in a

390

bell. Every word acted like a wasp sting on my nervous system, and if only the generator would pack up, if only a fuse would blow, if only I had the nerve to get up on stage and say into the mike, 'My brother is simply going through a somewhat unfortunate phase, ladies and gentlemen. He's not like this really, I do apologise.'

People's mouths swung open in amazement; they'd never heard anything like this before – and the singer a so-called *gentleman*.

The name Hillington had gone to the dogs once and for all.

Aunt Daphne started talking earnestly to cover up the words, the Honourables talked to some Young Farmers and Dawn looked round at me, winked, gave the thumbs-up sign and yelled over the din, 'Shall we kick off the dancing then?'

I glanced at the empty, canvas-covered floor. 'No fear,' I said. 'I can't dance to this rubbish in a million years.'

'Rubbish?' screeched Dawn. 'It's bloody brilliant. Look at the toffs. They're all about to have heart attacks. Dan's created exactly the impression he set out to. He's split the tent in two: the squares and the swingers.'

I looked at my brother trembling his knees and wiggling his hips and pretending to be hip and cool and rude and all the other things rock 'n' roll people are meant to be. As far as I was concerned, all this was fine if you were Elvis Presley performing in Memphis, Tennessee, but not if you were an English ex-public schoolboy on stage at an agricultural-show family dance. If being a swinger meant liking this sort of thing, then there was no getting away from it: I was a square through and through.

'*For the times they are a-changing, tip the lady out of bed, oh yeah . . .*'

Despite my red cringing face, despite being drenched in shame, I noticed that my foot had begun to tap and, by the time the song ended, I was even swaying my hips very, very slightly. The tune wasn't bad. It kind of grew on you, like poison ivy.

A few people clapped, and two whistled. But several booed, one man shouted 'What a load of rubbish' and most people made about-to-go-home noises. I clapped softly against my beer glass, for when all was said and done he was still my brother.

Dan ran his sleeve across his nose like a slum child, gulped at his beer and said in his flat-as-a-pancake voice, 'Thank you, thank you.' (At least it wasn't thanks or ta.) He ran his fingers through his hair, then took off his sun-glasses, revealing not only his true identify but yet another horror. From where I was standing it looked suspiciously as though he had some of Dawn's black stuff

391

round his eyes. But he *couldn't* have. *Surely*. I put it down to my shandy beginning to work.

'Are you having a good time?' he asked in a half-American, half-cockney accent and how *could* he when it was so obvious no one was?

A small smattering of swinging people said 'Yeah,' and a few in-between people said 'Yes,' and one square person shouted, 'We would be if you shut your trap.'

'I said *are you having a good time?*' (Oh, don't, Dan, *please*, and if this wasn't the purple hearts affecting his brain I didn't know what was.) This time a few more people, maybe out of fear, ventured a 'Yeah'. 'Well, I want you to prove it by getting on that floor and dancing – all right? I said *all right?*' and how *could* my gentle, kind, fun-loving brother be so humourless and cool and bossy?

The music crashed into action again. '*Well, the joint was rocking. Going round and round. Yeah, reelin' and a-rockin'. What a crazy sound. And I never stopped rocking. Till the moo-oon went down,*' he snarled, bear-baiting his audience, leaping and thrusting round the stage like a man possessed.

Dawn looked at me and nodded at the dance floor. 'Come on, let's get the ball rolling – or should it be rocking!' she yelled. 'It's a Chuck Berry, right? You like him.'

I wanted to dance, quite badly. I could hardly keep still, in fact. But a wave of shyness plummeted to my feet and glued them to the ground. And anyway, if I danced, it would be like giving the music my seal of approval. 'Oh, Dawn, I can't. Not in front of everyone. I've forgotten it all.'

'Course you ain't. Dancing's like riding a bicycle. Just let the beat take over. Come on, it's your chance to be a star,' and she snatched my shandy, grabbed my unwilling hand and dragged me onto the empty dance floor, right under the noses of the Wild Ones.

'*Start moving your feet. Yeah, clapping your hands . . .*'

We began to dance, in front of all those hundreds of people, in front of anyone who was anyone.

One thing was sure; dancing was nothing like riding a bicycle.

Beside Dawn, who swung and snapped and swayed as gracefully as a swan, as sexily as Marily Monroe or Christine Keeler, I felt as stiff and awkward as a new-born cardboard foal. My feet felt like frozen roots, my body a rigid tree trunk, my arms branches stiff with frost. It was as if the old bugger of a winter had reared its ugly head one last time and I bet Dan was praying people wouldn't realise I was his sister, the way I'd been praying people wouldn't realise he was my brother.

When the song at last ground to a halt I slunk, red-faced and hot, back to Hattie standing in the shadows. I asked her if I looked awful and she said as she wasn't wearing her glasses she could only see my outline, which she had to admit did look a bit stiff, like a puppet; like Muffin the Mule, in fact.

'Come on, kid, let's try again,' said Dawn. 'And for Gawd's sake loosen up. You're Cinders at the ball, remember, not one of the ugly sisters. We'll jive this time. 'Ere, listen, it's Elvis. We've *gotta* dance to this.'

'I suppose I can't make more of a fool of myself than I have already,' I said though if it hadn't been the *Jailhouse Rock* I would have never set foot near a grown-up dance for the rest of my life.

So once again, Dawn and I swung into action.

Maybe it was because jiving involves two of you, or because the tune was familiar, but this time I didn't feel as conspicuous.

'*Let's rock. Everybody let's rock,*' snarled Dan, as we turned and twisted and pulled and swung in perfect harmony.

Gradually, an extraordinary and unexpected feeling came over me. Maybe it was my pretty dress, or my brother's riproaring voice, or because I was eleven, or the shandy, or because I wasn't as top-drawer as I thought I was, or a combination of all these things, or none of them, but it was as if something inside me had broken loose; it was as if my heart had suddenly been tuned into Dan's electric guitar socket and was beating time to the music! Spinning, twisting, whirling, I felt wild and exciting and excited and *alive*!

'*Do the jail-house rock with me let's rock. Everybody, let's rock . . .*'

It was as if I had been set on fire! It was as if the chains had been taken from my heart and set me free! It was as if the music was oil lubricating my joints, four-star petrol pouring into my tank! It was as if me and Dan and Dawn and Elvis Presley were one person! And who cared if people were staring. Cats can look at a king! All that mattered was moving to the music, which had awakened something deep inside me, something that would always be with me for ever more.

The audience spun round and round in a haze like a circus audience, smiling, frowing, swaying, clapping, stamping, shrugging, admiring, muttering, disapproving, nodding at me spinning and flickering, swinging my legs high round Dawn's waist like the daring young man on the flying trapeze, then straight out backwards, then swooshing through her legs, my flashing thighs and matching knickers on show for the world and his wife to see.

393

'You're looking good, kiddo,' yelled Dawn. 'You're a natural-born dancer, d'yer know that?'

'So are you – kiddo!' I laughed feeling the happiest I'd ever felt in my whole life.

'*Let's rock. Everybody, let's rock*,' rasped Dan, wriggling his tightly-clad snake's hips behind his guitar.

It was as if Dan, Dawn and I, the three Fire Signs, the three Kindled Spirits, were a smouldering human magnet. For out of the crowd, out of the woodwork, out of the black of the night, out of the mod-con bungalows and no-mod-con cottages and public houses, out of the steamed-up coffee bars and dusty harvest fields and spick-and-span canning factories and fly-filled cowsheds, out of necks of woods and nooks and crannies came other rock 'n' rollers: Teddy Boy Pike and Hilda of underwear fame in a brilliant orange dress and maybe, who knew, a black bra, Adam Faith and his friends and the pale girls in the Top Spot, the churchyard boys in leather jackets doing a strange, hunched, war-cry dance round their full-skirt-swinging girlfriends, the long and the short and the tall, the long-haired, the Beatle-haired, the greasy-haired, the bouffant-haired, the bobbing-greasy-coxcomb-haired. And all their experience of rock 'n' roll up till now had been via crackly wireless and Dansette record-players but never right under their noses, in the raw, confronting them head on like this. It was as if, like Aslan and the statues, Dan had breathed life into them. Apart from Hattie, all the other squares in the marquee could go to hell as far as I was concerned, and it didn't matter in the slightest if people couldn't jive properly like Dawn and me, just so long as the music had taken them over, too, that was all that mattered.

'*Twistin' the night away*,' sang Dan and that's just what we all did, and people like Aunt Lynette and Albert and the Bones joined in. Then he sang *Somethin' Else* by Eddie Cochran and quite a rude one called *He Would, Wouldn't He* about the Profumo Scandal and hypocrisy and being really rude about the Government and I swung my hips like mad and waved my arms in the air like Dawn, and threw in a bit of Locomotion for good measure without a care in the world. Then came *Shakin' All Over* (boy, that's just what I was doing!) then a very moody rendition of *Heartbreak Hotel* in an aching, quivering, arousing voice, and then *Good Golly, Miss Molly*, wildly, madly, and boy, I wished my name was Molly, though it could have been the way I was dancing, and if only Mr Richards or the handsome American could see me now! I made do with Michael English and some of the other boys instead, and Michael said 'I'd never have guessed you were such a good little mover, Sarah,' and

394

I said, 'You're not so bad yourself.'

When *Good Golly, Miss Molly* came to an end, Dan said into the mike, flatly, sweat waterfalling off him, 'The next number, *Sweet Little Sixteen* by Chuck Berry, is dedicated to my sister Sarah who has surprised us all by revealing that she's a closet rock 'n' roller like the rest of us – and a really hip dancer to boot,' and everyone looked round and smiled and clapped and Dawn shouted, 'Hear, hear.'

Oh, *Dan*! Talk about one's finest hour. Talk about swelling with pride! Talk about the happiest moment of your entire life! As the music started and I, a 'really hip dancer to boot' began to move with even more gay abandon than before, I hoped people would mistake my tears of joy for beads of perspiration.

'*All over St Louis, way down in New Orleans. All the cats wanna dance with Sweet Little Sixteen,*' went the song dedicated to me.

Oh, Mr Richards, I planned in my head, for when you're dancing your brain can encompass the world. *If only you could have been here to see me. I don't want to sound big-headed but I feel so pretty and well, sexy and grown-up! It's as if dancing in this hot sweaty smokey marquee to my brother's rock 'n' roll band, I can see the light. Everything sort of suddenly makes sense. I feel as one with Dan and Dawn and every non-square person here. At last I feel I belong somewhere – here, on the dance floor, with all these happy rything people! Everything that Dawn and Dan and Aunt Lynette have been saying all summer have suddenly clicked like a jigsaw into place. I'm a rebel, too! I'm a Labour ban-the-bomb person through and through and if I was old enough I would vote for Mr Wilson tomorrow! I want to be an angry young girl and have love affairs like Christine Keeler when I'm older, and end up marrying whoever I fancy no matter which draw he comes from, or maybe I won't marry at all! Maybe I'll be a Free Spirit like Aunt Lynette! One thing is for sure, to be sure; never in a million years will I end up a prissy hypocrite like my cousin Susan.*

'Sweet Little Sixteen, she's got the grown-up blues. Tight dresses and lipstick, she's sporting high-heel shoes,' *sings my brother, rotating his hips beind his guitar in a most sugestive manner. Greg and Rick doing likewise, Ronnie learing behind his drum set.* 'Oh but tomorrow morning, she'll have to change her trim, and be sweet sixteen and back in class again.' *And though I am only 11, though I am not sporting high-heel shoes the song is about me to a T. Why, I'll be back in class again in the future, and talking of the future, Mr Richards, I can see it all stretching ahead as clearly as if the music has become my crystal ball.*

Granny will marry Jack and, because they are both the same drawer, Granny won't mind about his table manners. Dawn will have her baby and Aunt Lynette will adopt it. Because Mother and Father will be getting divorsed and won't care about me, I will run way with Dawn to America where we will drive all over St Louis and down in New Orleans with a Tip the Lady out of Bed stand! The double act we'll make! The sensation we'll cause! The laughs we'll have! The boys we'll meet! And all of them handsome dark ones who call you honey and laugh with their eyes. This has to be the most brillyant plan I've ever had in my whole life. It has, has to happen; I know it will; I can feel it in my bones. I can't wait to tell Dawn but now isn't the time as we whirl and twerl and wiggle with all eyes on us; tomorrow – judgement day – I'll tell her and her eyes will light up and she'll say, 'You're a bloody genias, what are you?'

But meanwhile, do you know, Mr Richards? It is just like 'all the cats wanna dance with Sweet little Sixteen' in the song, because I have danced with almost every single 'cat' in the whole tent! Dawn and me have them practicly queueing up! And the whole time I am in danger of bursting with pride, a little bit for myself but most of all for Dan. He is the true star, followed by me and then Dawn. Never mind Elvis Prezly, Dan is going to be the greatest rock 'n' roll singer the world will ever know. He is brillyant. *His animal magnetisam is to be seen to be believed! All the anger and rage and frustrations that have been building up inside him over the years have exploded like a time-bomb – right here on the stage. And people understand. They recognise the same thing in themselves, and Boy, have we all gone wild! Boy, if our parents could see us now! 'Rock 'n' roll for ever!' Dan roars, half-man, half-beast, taking off his guitar then his jacket, swinging it round and round, then undoing his final shirt button so you can see his glisening bare chest and tummy, too, and, like Dawn being tipped out of bed, almost insiting a riot. 'Yeah,' we all scream. 'And bolaks to the rest of you stuffy lot,' shouts Dawn towards what is left of the squares and we all scream 'Yeah' again. And now Dan is singing 'Blue Swade shoes', broodily, moodily, powerfully, rithing and leaping and wipping everyone into a frenzy, and the words I'M A FREE SPIRIT! roar through my brain, and my jeoi de vive runneth over and I want to cry and scream and leap and go wild with happiness, and as long as the music keeps playing I will have this lovely feeling inside, the first really truly free, happy feeling I have ever had in my whole life.*

Brightly shone the moon that night as Hattie and Jack and Aunt Lynette walked arm in arm along Cow Parsley Lane. I danced ahead, my ears and heart and head and soul still spinning from the music, '*Let's rock. Everybody, let's rock.*'

'I don't know where all that energy be coming from,' laughed Jack.

'No. I've never seen you like this before, Sarah,' said Hattie. 'It's as if someone's put a tiger in your tank.'

'Dan's put rock 'n' roll in my tank,' I said.

'Rock and roll, my eye,' said square old Jack. 'People don't go in for a good old tune these days.'

'I don't see how music can give you energy,' said Hattie. 'I can see how Lucozade does but not music.'

'I think Sarah's had her first taste of ... freedom,' slurred Aunt Lynette. 'Heady stuff, eh, darling?'

'You bet,' I said. 'From now on I'm going to be a Free Spirit like you, Aunt Lynette. Honestly, I could dance all night, and all tomorrow, and the next day and the next', and I leapt and whirled and hop-skip-jumped. 'I'm far too excited to sleep.'

But I did, a deep, black, bottomless-pit sleep, as soon as my head touched the pillow.

CHAPTER THIRTY

It could have been five seconds, five minutes or five hours later that Sir Edward began to loom out of the harum-scarum, now-you-see-it-now-you-don't landscape. He was standing on a bed. 'Tip the hypocrite out of bed!' Splat! An egg landed on his cheek. Crack! Another landed on his head. The white spread like a lawyer's wig and began to fry in the sun. He didn't seem to mind, in fact he was smiling, perhaps because of the Red in his bed. The Red was Dawn. 'Tip the whore out of bed!' The eggs turned into blue cough sweets. Thwack! Smack! They sounded as though they were hitting not soft flesh but a hard surface. Perhaps Dawn was really a doll. 'Get you out of bed!' Albert shouted and then all hell was let loose; some people agreeing with him, others not, some on Sir Edward's side, others on Dawn's, voices coming at you from all sides, sides you did and didn't want to join, you couldn't decide seeing as how you were only eleven so you put your hands over your ears but the confusions wouldn't go away.

There was only one thing for it; like a strongman prising open the lids of two awkward boiled-sweet tins, I opened my eyes.

The bedroom was in bitter disappointing blackness with not a whisker of early-morning light showing through the curtains. But Free Spirits weren't afraid of the dark – no, siree!

'Sarah! Sarah!' I heard, followed by a splatter of stones. But ... if I was awake, how come I was still dreaming?

Gradually it dawned on me that the shouts and stone splatterings were for real, and how come Albert had known which window was mine? Was it just guesswork, or had Dawn told him our room was below hers?

Hattie slept soundly as I stumbled bleary-eyed and heavy-hearted to the window.

By the light of the full moon I saw Albert standing in the drive. Although it was a still and cloudless night, he was swaying like a branch in a storm. His pointy shoes turned outwards to act as roots. His hair looked as though he'd just been tipped out of bed by ruffians. He had removed his 'one token to the rock 'n' roll lark', and his top three shirt buttons were undone.

'Sarah, do us a favour,' he whispered hoarsely, urgently, over the night-time rustlings of the copper beech, and what was it Dawn had once said about men and full moons? 'Get you up to Dawn's room and see if she's there. I gotta ruddy well see her, yeah?'

For a moment I wavered. Surely a Free Spirit would say 'Bugger off and let me get back to sleep'? But he looked so forlorn.

I crept on to the landing and up the twisty, creaky stairs. I could feel in my bones that the only things on Dawn's bed would be the leopard-skin rug and the red-tongued toy.

My bones were right.

I crept back down and shook my head like a maid's feather duster through the window. Albert looked at his shoes and ran his fingers through his hair. When he looked up he resembled the amiable guinea-pig. Under different circumstances I would have roared.

'Sarah,' he said and this time he forgot to whisper. 'Come you down for a minute, will you? I want to ask you something ... It won't take long.'

'Can't it wait until tomorrow?' I hissed and Albert shook his head and said, 'That it can't.'

The night was too warm for a dressing gown. I felt around in the dark for my rabbit slippers. They felt surprisingly tight. Did dancing make one's feet grow? This time next year would I be wearing pink furry flip-flops like Dawn and Granny? A wave of sadness scuttled through me like a frightened mouse.

I crept along the pitch-black landing, my Free Spirit sinking dejectedly. I'd had my fill of adults and their problems for one summer.

I stood on the squeaky floorboard in the hope Granny would hear and come to her door and say 'Darling, where are you going at this God-forsaken hour?' I'd tell her and she'd say 'Albert has no business to be calling at this time of night. I'll see to him.' But her door stayed as still and silent as a tombstone.

I drew back the bolt on the front door and peered into the moonlit gloom. Albert had vanished. Perhaps he'd changed his mind! I was just going back inside when he shouted 'Oy!' roughly and rudely and appeared from behind the copper beech doing up his flies! What a cheek, the old me would have thought, a butcher going to the lavatory on Granny's lawn. The new me tried not to mind at all. It probaly did the grass good and besides, no one had seen.

'Listen, kiddo,' he said, lumbering towards me like a grizzly bear. 'You've gotta help me find that blasted fiancée of mine, yeah?'

His diction was as thick as a bowl of soup. Just because alcohol had addled *his* brain ...

'Why?' I said briskly. 'She's probably still in the marquee.'

'If she was I wouldn't be here now, would I?' he said and if I'd been Mother I'd have said 'I don't like your attitude, young man.'

By the light of the moon his dull, ditchwater eyes looked glazed, like two small French apple tarts. They tried to focus on my eyes but only made it as far as my chin.

'There's no need to be rude,' I said. 'Do you think I relish being woken up and dragged out of bed? I've had a very tiring day.'

'Shorry, kid,' he said, his words sounding like snowshoes ploughing through slush. 'The thing is I've gotta find out ... Gotta see her, see?' and he shrugged and slapped his thighs once with his large hands.

'Why?' I said again. 'Why can't it wait till morning?'

'I want to make sure she's okay, see. Yeah? I've looked round here and there and through windows and that, but I could be done for trespassing. But I wouldn't be if you were with me, would I?'

'Why do you think she's here? She could be in Norwich or Yarmouth for all I know.'

Albert tapped the side of his head with an unsteady finger. 'Male intuition, yeah?'

'I suppose we could look in the coach house,' I said gruffly. 'It seems highly unlikely. I mean, what would she be doing in there at this time of night?'

'What *wouldn't* she be doing in there at this time of night, more likely,' growled Albert. 'I just want to check she's all right, right? Not much to ask. I am supposed to be her bloody fiancé, yeah?'

I quick-marched like an efficient Army officer round the side of the house. The drunk and disorderly private ambled and shambled along behind me.

'Bet you ten bob she's not in there,' I said.

'I'll have a look for myself, if you don't mind,' he said, pushing me to one side. The rumbling door would have woken Rip Van Winkle. 'Are you here, gal?' he said wandering into the blackness and brash-bang-walloped over the bicycles. 'Blast ...' he said and I doubled over with silent, helpless, Bertha-Mason-mad laughter.

'What have I done with that torch of mine?' he said to himself, and suddenly the coach house was filled with a moving finger of white light.

'She isn't there and that's a fact,' he said stumbling out and rubbing his shin. 'Where d'yer reckon next?'

I shrugged. 'Haven't the foggiest.'

He pointed the torch at Aunt Lynette's studio then at the back of the house like a German searchlight. All was in darkness.

'If she was in the house she'd be in bed at this hour,' I said. 'And talking of bed, I think I'll go back to mine.'

Albert groped for my arm and gripped it the way he had in White Lion Street. In the owl-hooting, lonely darkness it felt even more sinister. I wondered again what it was men were supposed to do during full moons, or was I thinking of mad March hares?

I shook it free. He grabbed hold of it again. Tighter.

'You've got to bloody well help me. You're the only bugger who can.' Through my pyjama sleeve, I felt his fingers tremble like fury.

'Why should I?' I said, yanking my arm free again and stepping backwards.

'Because . . .' His glazed eyes searched wildly among the cobblestones. 'Because I've gotta know, that's why. For my own peace of mind. And don't say what. You bloody well know what.'

'Don't say bloody to me,' I said. He'd got off lightly. Mother would have added, 'And don't expect to see me in your shop ever again.'

He squatted down so our eyes were at the same level; his face was very close to mine. The aftershave had been replaced by a sweet and sour beery smell. It made me want to rear my head away like a horse.

'Look, Sarah, how would you like to be tortured day after day after flaming day, huh? I've just gotta know, see. Yeah?'

Spit landed on my chin. Even though I was a Free Spirit I was still too polite to brush it away. The torchlight showed up fresh wrinkles on his face. He looked haggard – a hag – a male witch.

'But how *can* I help you, Albert, if I don't know where she is?'

'Ah, because I'm bloody well sure you do know,' he said swaying, and I wished he'd sway too far and fall over and pass out and then I could go back to bed. Say I pushed him? He was so drunk he'd never remember. Say he cracked his head on a cobblestone and died? Would I be charged with murder? 'Well you see, ladies and gentlemen of the jury . . .'

'All I want is to know for sure whether she's playing silly buggers. If she is, I'll just have to try and get over her as best as I can; if she isn't, then I'll marry her tomorrow if that's what she'd like.'

'What if it isn't as black and white as that,' I said. 'What if, for example, it's say half and half – what would you do then, just out of interest?'

'What do you mean, half and half?' he said, his eyes narrowing, his face moving close to mine.

'Well, er, if – and I'm positive this isn't the case – she loves you

401

very dearly and wants to marry you but is just er, making hay while the sun shines, sort of thing.'

'Well, the sun'll just have to stop shining, won't it,' he said. 'Now where is she?'

I shrugged and he said, 'Oh, come on, Sarah.' He released his grip on my arm, got clumsily to his knees and looked at me. Silent streams of tears were trickling from his pond eyes. 'Don't kick a man when he's down. I've not had a wink of sleep for weeks. For my own peace of mind you've gotta help me. *Please*.'

What a quandary I was in: protecting Dawn versus putting an end to Albert's torturing; Albert, who had paid for us to go to the dance, who'd bought my shandy which maybe contributed to me becoming a Free Spirit, who always gave Granny the choice cuts of meat, whose family did so much for charity . . . He had to know, sooner or later, about Dawn's lover, didn't he? 'Let's get the Show out of the way first.' That's what Dawn and I had decided. And now it *was* over, and past midnight, and she'd said Sunday was judgement day. Besides, now I was sure I knew who her lover was I was all for it. Why, he was far more suitable for her than Albert would ever be. And anyway, it was easy to say no to a man when he was angry and gripped your arm; but kneeling at your feet in floods of tears was a very different matter.

'Don't be upset, Albert,' I said. I didn't have a hanky to lend him. 'I can think of one more place we could look. But if we do find her – and I'm sure we won't – do you promise you won't be cross? Do you promise you'll be kind?'

'Sure,' he sniffed and tottered to his feet.

'Say you promise.'

'I promise. And thanks, kid, you're a real pal,' and he biffed his bear-like paw against my shoulder.

By the light of his unsteady torch, I led the way across the courtyard towards the shadowy ghost of a kitchen garden wall. A rabbit, caught munching in our path, stared for a moment through frightened torchlit eyes before lipperty-bobbiting off into the night.

'Actually, Albert, I'm leading you up the garden path!' I said in an attempt to put some cheer into the proceedings.

'You'd better not be, kid.'

The tone of his voice made me look round sharply, and my blood ran cold at the sight of his face all twisted with hatred in the torchlight, at his red eyes burning and blistering and fierce as a cornered rat's, and I knew then that I was in the presence of a madman.

402

I knew, too, that leading him to Dawn would be the worst mistake of my life.

'Albert,' I said and tried to block his path. 'You promised you wouldn't be cross.' But he brushed roughly past me as if I was a bush. 'Albert,' I cried, pulling his arm. 'I really am leading you up the garden path. There's nothing at the end of it except tangly wood and some undergrowth and an old shed and a railway line, honestly.'

But he must have already spotted way ahead the dim, dull glow in the window of the black summerhouse.

'Tip the lady out of bed!' barked Albert. 'I'll ruddy well tip the lady out of bed. Lady! Pah! Bloody whore, more like.'

'Albert – stop,' I shouted and threw my arms round his waist and tried to drag him backwards. 'You *promised* you wouldn't be cross.'

He spun round, grabbed my wrists and bent so his savage sandy-whiskered fox's face was on a level with mine. 'Listen, kid, you've done your bit,' he spat, his face as ugly as a fairy-story witch. 'Get you back to bed before you get hurt,' he snarled before crashing and thrashing on.

'Hurt! No one's going to get hurt,' I screamed, tugging at his arm.

'Just fuck off, will you, kid.'

From the summerhouse came the gentle murmur of carefree, happy voices; it reminded you of rabbits snug and safe in their burrow, blissfully unaware of a ferret wending his wicked way towards them.

'Albert,' I cried. 'You've gone bonkers, honestly. You're like a bull in a ...'

My words froze like china statues. For like a scene from a Hammer horror film unfolding before my very eyes, Albert had drawn out from his jacket a butcher's knife.

I felt the same chilling stab of fear, personified a thousand times, that I had felt years – aeons – ago on learning that Little Red Riding Hood's granny was, in fact, the wolf.

Taking a deep breath, my dumbfounded mouth managed to shout '*Look out! Albert's coming and he's got a knife!*'

I then did the bravest thing I'd ever done, for Albert could so easily turn on me and plunge the knife deep into my heart. I did it not so much to stop him – he was far too strong – but to prove I wasn't part of the plot.

'You *promised* you wouldn't be cross, Albert,' I yelled, and divebombed at his legs. 'Dawn loves you and wants to marry you, honestly.'

He teetered but didn't fall, twisted one leg free and kicked my

403

shoulder so hard with his pointed shoe it brought tears to my eyes.

Cursing, he shook his other leg free and continued to stalk his prey. They had come to the doorway huddled naked behind the patchwork quilt, blind mice blinking in the torch beam, Jews stepping out of their cattle truck and being confronted by the bewildering bright-light horrors of a death camp.

I barely recognised Dawn. Her hair spilled softly round her shoulders and her face was completely *au naturel*; she looked about fifteen and beautiful; like Snow White, like Hayley Mills in fact. Dan, too, had gone back to looking like a young innocent schoolboy. They both seemed helpless and vulnerable and frightened, like Babes in the Wood; it was as if they were the children and I was the adult, and *If you can keep your head when all about you are losing theirs and blaming it on you . . .* flashed through my brain.

Behind them through the open doorway, the candles flickered snugly on either side of Snuff Mull. He had been blindfolded by Dawn's bra. It hung, a cup over each eye, a strap round each horn, like white sagging spectacles.

'Caught you cunts at it at last,' growled Albert through bared teeth, like Heathcliff or a jealous husband in a Noel Coward play. 'I knew it was you, you bastard, with your smooth-talking ways and your fancy rock 'n' roll crap,' and he wielded his knife as if it were a sword. The blade winked in the light of the silvery moon. Unless they leapt over the shoulder-high side of the veranda they were trapped.

'He's turned. I told yer he would,' cried Dawn, her pale young eyes as frightened as the rabbit's. 'Sarah, what on earth did you . . . Calm down, Albert love, you're pissed. Just put that bloody thing down.'

But her words didn't wash with Albert. Oh, boy, no. If anything, they acted as a red rag.

Dan moved in front of Dawn behind the patchwork quilt to shield her and implored Albert to be reasonable, and Dawn shrieked in a voice I hadn't heard before, '*Go and get help, Sarah. Quickly. For fuck's sake.*'

From then I wasn't me but a girl in a film or a dream.

The girl turned and ran like the wind, like a hare, like a windy hare, like a mad March wind, the inside of her head screaming, 'Yes, but who shall I get help from?' Her grandmother was too old and her sister was too young; neither had a telephone. Her aunt was too drunk. The cowman was too slow. The farmer was too far away. There was only one person: the gamekeeper, the girl's arch enemy all summer. And now the burning question of the night was: *Did he have a telehone?*

Suddenly, her galloping heart jumped high enough to clear a five-bar gate: for out of the blue, like a gift falling from heaven itself, she remembered the afternoon she was on the back of a pony near the gamekeeper's cottage and the American plane screaming overhead and narrowly missing – *telephone wires*!

By the light of the moon she turned right and flew like a bat out of hell up the red brick road. Was the matter serious enough to dial 999 and if so should she ask for the police or an ambulance? The butcher was only threatening her brother and grandmother's maid with the knife ... Was that against the law? Say he didn't actually use it? Say all those policemen and ambulance men were disturbed from their night's sleep for nothing? Then right on cue she got her answer: searing through the night like the devil himself came a blood-curdling scream.

Go, go, go Sarah go, go, go. Sarah be good, roared through her head in a torrent ... Except she *hadn't* been good. Question: why is Sarah Hillington the wickedest girl in the world? Well, would *you* lead a vicious murderer straight to your brother and your best friend?

Her rabbit slippers were slowing her down. She kicked them off and left them where they lay in Cow Parsley Lane. Who cared if she stepped on five dead hedgehogs and caught tetanus or ten broken bottles which cut her feet to ribbons so had to wear built-up orthopaedic shoes for ever more? It was no more than she deserved.

Black Beauty had had to gallop eight miles by moonlight to fetch the doctor to save his mistress's life. The girl knew the words by heart and reciting them in her head spurred her on.

John said to me, 'Now, Beauty, do your best,' so I did: I wanted no whip nor spur, and for two miles I galloped as fast as I could lay my feet to the ground; I don't believe that my old grandfather who won the race at Newmarket could have gone faster ...

Like a bolting pony, the girl crossed the main road without looking right nor left, then galloped down the grassy loke as fast as her legs would carry her.

Dimly shone a light that night ... The gamekeeper was at home!

Now wasn't the time to imagine savage, yellow-eyed night creatures and ghouls gloating in the black of the Wild Wood, from which came rustlings and stirrings that could turn the imagination crazy if it had the time and the inclination.

With fumble-fisted fingers she lifted the latch on the gate and ran up the rough and ready path. Panting, perspiring, she pounded on the wooden door.

'Mr Pike,' the girl yelled, as soon as she could muster the breath. 'It's a dire emergency. Come quickly.'

From the other side of the door the Yellow Dog woofed to hear such fun, and the gamekeeper said, 'Quiet, Juliet.' Was it only in the privacy of his own home that he called his dog by its Christian name, the girl wondered, and how strange; all summer she had assumed the dog was male.

The gamekeeper opened the door while tying the cord of his dressing gown. Its rich-tea-biscuit colour was the same as the hair of Hilary Wentworth-Smith, her brother's 'true-love' known from now on as 'The Red Herring'. The gamekeeper's hair resembled a wild black gorsebush and if there weren't so many other things going on, the evening could go down in history as the Night of the Funny Hair-dos.

Behind the gamekeeper, down the narrow twisty brown stairs, waddled a pair of plump bare legs followed by a plump, green-coated body followed by the no-spectacled face of the lingerie assistant who sold white bras but not black ones. Her hair, too, resembled a backwards hedge.

'What's up, love?' asked the gamekeeper kindly, putting his arm round the girl, seemingly not at all put out that she'd interrupted him from playing hide the sausage, and how she'd misjudged him, the way she'd misjudged so many things that summer.

'It's Albert,' she gasped, and if her heart could survive this it could survive anything. 'He's gone stark staring mad. He's found Dan and Dawn in the black summerhouse and he's got a knife. He's stabbed one of them already. Can you come? I must dial 999.'

'Oh dear, oh lor. I thought trouble was brewing,' and he glanced wrinkle-browed at the lingerie assistant. 'Righto, pet, the phone's right here. I'll get dressed at the double.'

The front door opened straight on to the wooden-beamed sitting room. With its armchairs covered in faded roses and a wood burner with turned-out toes and some dried flowers in a vase and a Norfolk church in water colours on the wall and not a sniff of a stuffed fox in a glass cage, it was more like a schoolteacher's or a market gardener's sitting room than a gamekeeper's.

The girl's hands trembled so severely, her heart beat so fast, she had a job aiming her finger into the 'nine' hole.

How come no one was answering? This was an emergency.

Time seemed to stand still, which was more than could be said for the Yellow Dog who prowled and yowled round the girl while

406

upstairs, floorboards creaked as a gamekeeper pulled on socks and trousers and a lingerie assistant hooked up a black bra which made her feel wicked and probably made the gamekeeper feel wicked, too.

How come no one was answering?

On the wall hung a *Shooting Times* calendar of a brace of dead pheasants, a gun and a springer spaniel. Beside the 18th of August Brian Pike had written 'Mum's b'day'. Oh, the antics your brain gets up to in an emergency! For if you said 'Mum's b'day' out loud it sounded like 'Mum's bidet'! She would have to remember to tell her sister the joke as soon as the nightmare was over.

How come no one was . . .

A weary man's voice asked whether she required the police, ambulance or fire service.

For a second, the girl hesitated. Someone had been stabbed, so certainly ambulance. And police, because you couldn't just go round stabbing people without being arrested, could you? As for fire, those candles could easily get knocked over in a struggle and the black summerhouse would go up like a tinderbox. Instinctively, she looked through the window and far far away. Sure enough, above Lion's Mouth Wood huffs and puffs of belching white breath billowed and bellowed towards the moon. Would Snuff Mull survive, she wondered? Was all this in fact his doing to avenge those who made him wear brassiere spectacles?

'All three, please,' the girl gasped, secretly vowing that if he said he didn't take orders from children she would emigrate to New Zealand and never speak to another Englishman for the rest of her life, but he seemed to know an urgent tone when he heard one. 'There's been a stabbing and the summerhouse has caught fire.' She gave the man her name, address and detailed instructions on how to get to the scene of the crime.

'Please tell them to go like the wind,' she added. 'It's very, very serious. I think it may be a matter of life or death.'

She trembled down the receiver and the gamekeeper hurtled downstairs doing up his top fly button and how extraordinary, the girl thought; two sets of undone flies in one evening.

He picked up his gun and torch and, followed by the girl and the dog, hurried off into the dark and flickering night (and what a mercy, the girl thought, that he was wearing not his cunning city-slicker shoes or brothel creepers but stout, sensible, down-to-earth lace-ups).

'I'll catch you up,' shouted the lingerie assistant, puffing like a grampus, her bosoms bouncing wild like beach balls under her coat.

'Don't you wait. I'll follow that there smoke.'

The Yellow Dog bounded on ahead, then the girl, then the gamekeeper. The girl, slowing to a spanking trot, told the game-keeper that the butcher had promised her he wouldn't be cross. If she'd known he had a knife she wouldn't have taken him anywhere near the black summerhouse.

The gamekeeper told her not to blame herself, Albert would have stumbled upon them sooner or later. Tension had been mounting all day, why, she had seen the way he behaved at the Tip the Lady out of Bed stall. A right old hothead and demented with jealousy, that one was, and by the sound of things not without good reason.

'Even so,' said the girl, 'being consumed with jealousy is no excuse to attack people with knives, is it?'

'Blast, no,' puffed the gamekeeper. 'Though if people play with fire they must expect to get your fingers a bit burnt. I'm a good one to talk, mind. I asked her for a date meself though thank the Lord she turned me down fair and square.'

'Was that what your letter was about roughly, Mr Pike, asking her for a date?' and he said that it was, and unless he stopped talking he was going to run out of puff.

The girl pondered all these things in her pounding heart, and for a moment she felt a rush of compassion for the butcher. Every other grown-up involved with this hazy, crazy night had funny hair because they were hiding sausages; he had funny hair because he was demented with jealousy. He, a 'simple, straight-forward, down-to-earth bloke', as he had described himself, driven half-crazy by that bugger of a thing they call love.

'Oh, please, Snuff Mull if you're alive or if not, God, could all not be as it seems,' the girl prayed as they swerved at the double into red brick road. 'Please could the smoke be because Dan didn't put out his Woodbine properly, please could the scream be because Dawn stood on a spider in bare feet or spied a wayfaring rat in the shadows. Please could only the firemen be needed. To the police and ambulance men I'll say, 'I've made the most ghastly mistake. I saw the knife, you see, and when I heard the scream what else could I suppose? I'm frightfully sorry to have wasted your time,' and I'll smile sweetly and tomorrow I'll ask Granny to send a contribution to their benevolent fund. Or if this isn't possible, please could Albert have slit his own throat as he said he would, not seriously enough to die or anything, just enough to make Dawn scream. Or if it *has* to be either Dawn or Dan could it be Dawn, just a teeny scratch, but please, please don't let it be my handsome, talented brother who's in his prime and is the last of the Hillington line; the rock 'n' roll lark and being rough and rude and political and scruffy and having affairs with maids is only a phase; honestly, it's not his fault, he's just been cursed with the Hillington Tendency. He doesn't deserve to be punished.'

Panting like carthorses, steaming like pots on the fire, the game-keeper, the girl and the Yellow Dog at last arrived at the scene of the crime.

The girl glanced at the gamekeeper. The look of horror on his firelight-flickering face confirmed that it was all for real, and how many more shocks could one's heart and soul and teeth bear?

The black summerhouse's bristly roof blazed and crackled and sparked like wildfire. The camp bed, the rocking chair, the Pat Smythe and Royal Family posters were already charred remains. The only evidence of Snuff Mull was one silver horn dying in the embers.

The knife lay snug as a bug out of harm's way. It had done its dastardly deed and was now having a rest. It was feeling very satisfied with its performance, and was winking to itself in the firelight.

In the flickering undergrowth the maid, a white furless animal, was being kicked by a pointed shoe that was almost but not quite a winklepicker. 'Oh, God, oh, God,' she sobbed. 'Fucking bitch. Cunt. Bitch,' snarled the butcher like a schoolboy in a swear-word contest. The maid's head was buried in her hands and the insides of her legs were smeared with something black that in daylight would be red. Perhaps amongst it was the beginnings of a baby – the girl's nephew or niece and the next in the Hillington line.

The last of the Hillington line lay to the left in the shadows. He too was white-as-a-ghost naked. He lay curled up on his side in a sleeping position with his eyes open. He was groaning softly like a wounded bullock. Blood ran from a gash in his arm. His hands, covering part of his chest, were covered in blood, too. The girl told herself the knife couldn't possibly have pierced his heart. Why, the wound was slightly on the right and the heart was on the left ... wasn't it? At least he had had the strength to crawl away from the burning inferno and thus avoid being roasted alive.

Thwack went the shoe. Snap, crackle, pop went the fire. Pop, crackle, snap. Pop, snap, crackle. The girl felt a sudden urge to take a running jump into the flames. That would really give the fire something to crackle about; that would stop people blaming her for the tragedy.

If you can keep your head when all about you . . .

'This is no place for a young un,' gasped the gamekeeper, slipping off his jacket. 'Get you back to your bed. We don't want no one else getting hurt.'

'Stuff and nonsense,' said the girl loudly like Alice and rushed to her brother's side, while the gamekeeper lolloped towards the butcher shouting 'If you don't stop that carrying-on right here and now I'll blast out them brains of yours,' and raising his gun like a cowboy. The butcher looked as though he would have liked to have set about the gamekeeper. But he didn't fancy having his brains blasted out. Nor did he fancy being ravaged by the Yellow Dog. Reluctantly, he stepped backwards. Like a modern-day Sir Walter Raleigh, the gamekeeper covered the maid's nakedness with his jacket while keeping his gun trained on the butcher. The Yellow Dog yelped and whined. The brother moaned. The sister put her arm round his clammy cold shoulders. She knew there was no point in asking if he was all right, so she said, 'Hello, Dan, it's me, Sarah' instead; she knew she should show no fear the way you shouldn't with a horse, because fear was contagious; she knew, from watching *Dixon of Dock Green*, you shouldn't move the patient; she knew she could perhaps do the kiss of life at a push; but that was all she did know.

Perhaps she should try to halt the flow of blood. She took off her pyjama top, laid it across his chest and put her hands gently over the wound. The gash on his arm would have to sort itself out. If the worst came to the worst a man could survive without an arm but not without a chest. In her gentlest nurse's voice she told her brother that Brian Pike was taking care of Dawn and an ambulance and a fire engine and a police car were on their way. 'And, Dan, I had no idea Albert had a knife,' she added. 'Please don't be cross with me.'

'I'm not,' whispered the brother through pale, dry lips. 'You're only a kid, how were you to know?'

His breathing rasped like an old man's and blimey O'Reilly, she thought then, has a lung been pierced? But lungs were lower down – weren't they? In the heat of the moment she forgot all she'd ever learnt in biology; hearts, lungs, livers, pancreases, kidneys, spleens floated in front of her eyes like a badly organised meat counter. If the worst came to the worst a man could survive without a lung . . . couldn't he?

Already her hands were damp and sticky from the blood that was seeping through the pyjama top. She started to cry warm, silent tears then, because when you can feel something with your own flesh you know without even a shadow of a doubt that it's not a film or a dream but for real.

How many pints had he lost? Two, say. That still left him with six or was it seven to contend with. Blood was thicker than water. Her brother's blood was her blood. If need be she could have a transfusion and give him all hers, bar, say, one pint. Then they'd be blood brothers for life.

Where was the ambulance? Bowling down black country lanes with its siren on full blast and its blue light flashing? What if the driver had been on the lavatory at the time of the phone call? What if he still was on the lavatory because he was very, very constipated? What was that rhyme about a battle being lost because a horse needed a nail in its shoe? What if her brother were to die simply because the ambulance driver hadn't eaten up his cabbage? Or what if the hospital gates were locked and no one could find the key? What if the ambulance's battery was flat? What if a tyre was flat? What if the man on the phone hadn't taken down directions properly? What if, say, he had written right instead of left? What if she had *said* right instead of left?

'Sorry you've got involved in all this mess. Sorry about, you know, Dawn and ... lying to you,' rasped the brother, taking in mouthfuls of air like a fish. 'I don't expect you to understand. I love ... We were made – for each other. Kindred spirits and all that.'

'I know,' said the girl. 'And you needn't have kept quiet about it. I wouldn't have been at all upset.' She could feel the fire warming her cheek. She could feel the blood ooze through her fingers. She could smell singed earth and burnt wood and stale beer and fresh ash. She could taste the salt in her tears. She could hear her teeth chatter like ninepins. She could hear the voice babble on and on, the words cascading into her brother's ear like a never-ending brook.

'Shall I tell you when I knew for absolute certain it was you? When you gave me that look on the showground after Dawn told you I'd given her the watch. Because you knew then I liked – loved – her, didn't you, and honestly, I nearly wanted to cry with happiness because I never dreamt my opinion of her mattered so much to you.

'At first I dreaded you having anything to do with her – she was so coarse and common and rude and such an invasion of our privacy – and I prayed like mad it wasn't you who was her lover, though in my heart of hearts I always knew. I deceived myself on purpose the way Mr Macmillan did with Mr Profumo. I pretended not to be able to smell the Woodbines in the summerhouse, I pretended you laughed at her jokes and got on so well with her not because you liked her but because of your social conscience ... But now I'm really, really glad it's you. You're kindled spirits, and did you know her whole body feels inflamed when you look at her, let alone touch her ... Your souls are like fire and fire, aren't they. You're like Cathy and Heathcliff, and you'll never in a million years guess who else you're like and this is deadly, deadly secret, me and Jack are the only two who know; you're like Granny and Grandpa because – are you bracing your hooves for this? – once upon a time Granny was a cockney housemaid just like Dawn and Grandpa fell in love with her and seduced her in the black summerhouse and when she got up the spout Grandpa did the honourable thing and married her. So you see there's nothing to be ashamed of in the slightest, it's just history repeating itself, you're following a Hillington tradition. And did you know Dawn's expecting your baby so like Grandpa you must be honourable and marry her. Just so long as you promise to let her and me go round America with a Tip the Lady out of Bed stand. We can do that while you become a rock 'n' roll star and Aunt Lynette looks after the baby. And then when we've all had our adventures we can settle down here at Gressenham Hall and live happily ever after for ever and ever.'

The girl's tongue was having a final fling before holding its peace for ever more. It was like a crazy machine-gun. Rat-a-tat-tat-a-tat-tat-ta-a-tat.

'And Dan, I was so proud of you this evening. I wasn't at first but I soon was. It was your finest hour. You were fantastic. A hundred – million – times better than Elvis Presley or Cliff Richard, and I can't tell you how much it meant to me you dedicating that song to me; honestly, it was the proudest moment of my whole life. I was crying with happiness, did you notice? Honestly, the music and the dancing and everything made me feel as one with everyone there sort of thing. It sort of turned me into a Free Spirit, too, like you and Aunt Lynette. It made me understand everything you've been saying all summer, and I promise that I won't grow up to be square, I promise I'll vote for Mr Wilson, too, when I'm old enough. And honestly, Dan, I know – I can feel it in my bones – that you're going to be the greatest rock 'n' roll star the world has ever known. So you'd better jolly well hurry up and get better at the double.'

The brother didn't respond. The sister knew he wasn't dead because dead men's eyes don't blink. So she said, 'It's a shame the great aunts aren't here. They'd have found you some smelling salts at the double!'

The brother didn't laugh. His eyes were focused a long way away

412

on the butcher's shoes. The butcher, angry and clumsy and noisy, was trying to justify his behaviour to the gamekeeper, whose gun was now pointed to the full moon. The Yellow Dog licked the sobbing maid's tears. The maid turned her head and peered through white strands of seaweed hair towards the brother and sister. 'Dan!' she groaned. 'Is Dan okay?' The girl nodded and gave her the thumbs-up sign. She didn't trust herself to speak. The brother raised his head, too, and for a second their eyes met across the flames in a burning, yearning, passionate embrace.

The fire crackled and sparked and chuckled into its embers; it was the only thing enjoying itself at that moment. It was as if it was celebrating both VE Day and its twenty-first birthday. The girl hoped it wouldn't go out too soon; the firemen wouldn't be pleased. Red sky at night, fireman's delight, she thought absurdly. Red ground at night, ambulance man's delight; silver knife at night, policeman's delight.

'Sarah,' the brother rasped. He raised his head but it flopped back like a badly stuffed toy. 'I was proud of you, too. My kid sis ... I want you to promise me three things.' His mouth sounded as dry as the girl's during her fight with the maid, days – years – ago; dry mouths obviously run in families. She had spent nine months in the same womb as her brother; unless you were a twin you couldn't get closer to someone than that.

'One is that you take care of Dawn. Two is that you tell the parents how sorry I am I've made a pig's ear of things. Make up some story. Tell them something they want to hear. Tell them I was good tonight. Tell them it was ... my finest hour. Tell the guys in the band to carry on without me.'

'Dan ...' said the girl sharply. He was talking as though he was going to ...

'Look, I said I was going to live dangerously and that's what I've done. It's been the best summer of my life. Better to have lived dangerously than... And lastly, that you bugger off out of here and look after Hattie. If she sees this little lot, she'll be scarred for life. I'm only sorry you've ... my brave, grown-up kid sister,' and he reached for her hand. 'Now go on – bugger off – please?'

A dying man's wishes have to be obeyed ... But what stuff and nonsense! Her brother wasn't going to die. People didn't die in their prime in this day and age. It wasn't even as if there was a war on.

'And I want you to promise me one thing, Dan. That you won't, er, you know – that you'll get well soon. I'll come and visit you in hospital first thing in the morning.'

'Course he's going to get well, lovey,' panted the kindly lingerie

413

assistant, bustling up like a plump partridge. She knelt down and examined the patient with not a trace of horror on her round face; she could have been looking at a smiling baby or a light-weight bra, even. 'I'll see he's all right. I belong to St John Ambulance.'

A small, warm ray of hope stabbed at the sister's heart. How strange, she thought, that a gamekeeper who killed animals and hung them up like washing and a fat girl who sold bras would be the ones to save the day.

'I want to stay and help,' she said. 'He is my brother, after all.'

'You heard what he said,' said the shop girl gently yet firmly like a hospital matron, removing the blood-soaked pyjama top and magically pulling from out of her handbag a mound of clean rags. 'now buzz off, lovey, do, and keep that little mite out of the way.'

The girl pictured her young sister appearing out of the gloom in her blue pyjamas clutching Teddy, her little face drained of colour, her eyes terrified behind her pink spectacles. She already had a withered leg, a squint and constipation to contend with.

'Oh, all right.'

The sister brushed away her tears and squeezed her brother's clammy hand and whispered in his ear, 'Dan, if you were a horse you'd be Champion No Wonder Horse. I wasn't sure for a while but I am now. You're Champion through and through and I love you very, very dearly – more than anyone else in the whole world, in actual fact,' and she kissed his cold, salty, unshaven cheek.

The brother's mouth twitched into a sort of smile, and he ran his tongue over his lips to moisten them. A tear began to trickle sideways down his cheek as he whispered, 'I love you, too, Sausage.'

Before the girl turned the corner, she looked back one last time. It was like looking at a tableau at Madame Tussaud's, or the final scene of a tragic play in an open-air theatre with Lion's Mouth Wood as the backdrop. Any minute now the curtain would descend out of the sky. When it rose the actors would be standing in a row holding hands and smiling and bowing. The audience would be in tears, but not unhappy ones that stemmed from the soul because it was, after all, only a play.

CHAPTER THIRTY-ONE

I crept across the black, snug, safe-as-houses hall and up the creaky stairs. Apart from the snip-snap-snip of my chatterbox teeth and the rat-a-ta-tat of my knocking heart, nothing was stirring.

Like an important biblical event, I went to the bathroom to wash away Dan's blood. I also washed my face and arms and chest so Hattie wouldn't smell smoke, and my feet which weren't as tender as my shoulder. Thanks to Albert and his new taste in footwear, it was coming up in a whopping great bruise. It made you wonder what Dawn would look like in the morning. I'd got off lightly. None of my blood had been shed. I poked my finger into the bruise until I winced.

My body kept twitching in unexpected places like a dying snake and boy, were my teeth chattering! I looked in the mirror and saw a stranger aged at least sixteen, with cheeks as white as classroom chalk and smudgy blackboard eyes; haunted ghoul's eyes that looked as though they'd just been told some terrible secret which would prevent them from ever going back to the way they were.

I noticed something else, too. Dawn had been right about this being the last summer I'd be able to run round topless. Did a family tragedy, I wondered, make one's bosoms grow?

I crept into the bedroom and listened for Hattie's deep breathing. How perfect if she had slept through it all. How perfect if we could wake up in the morning and go into Granny's room and tell her about the dance while downstairs Dawn crashed around preparing breakfast and Dan had one of his lie-ins.

Whoever said life was easy must have spent all of his asleep in a four-poster bed with the curtains closed. For out of the dark a small accusing voice said, 'Where have you been? You've been gone hours and hours. I was just about to come and find you.'

There was nothing else for it. I would have to put Plan B into operation.

'Oh, hello. You know I've been having bad dreams all summer? Well, I've just had the worst one yet,' I said. 'I must have slept-walked, too.' And I told her more or less what had happened.

415

'So when did you wake up and realise it was a dream?' asked Hattie suspiciously.

'Er – I'm not sure. When I came indoors, I think. But maybe I'm still in it. How can you tell?'

'Pinch yourself. That's what people do in Enid Blyton books.'

I did. Nothing altered.

'Come into my bed for a snuggle if you like,' said Hattie. 'I bet it was all that rocking roll that made you dream. Or the shandy. Yes, that must be it. You know what alcohol does to people. Your voice sounds really peculiar, by the way. All crackly, like Cousin James's.'

I found One-Eyed Lamb, and climbed into Hattie's warm bed.

We cuddled up. Whatever happened to other people, Hattie and I were all right, Jack; nothing could harm us. 'Look after Hattie, darling. She's only very little,' were Mummy's last words. 'Protect her from this little lot or she'll be scarred for life,' were Dan's, and that was what I was doing. From now on, that was all that mattered.

'You feel all funny and shivery and twitchy. And where's your jim-jam top?'

'I told you. I put it over Dan – in the dream. We'll probably find it in the morning covering something that I thought in my dream was him.'

'Wouldn't it be hilarious if we found it on the muck heap!' said Hattie. 'Or on the back of a bullock!'

'Mmmm.'

'I can smell bonfire on you. Are you *sure* it was a dream?'

'Come off it,' I said, fresh tears springing to my eyes, for I had turned into as big a liar as everyone else. 'This is England, you know, not America or the East End of London. People don't go round stabbing one other in these parts.'

'They might if they're con ... cons ... riddled with jealousy,' said Hattie. 'Anyway, I've just remembered *my* dream. It was hailing outside and you said you'd better get up and close the window. So that means it must have happened. We couldn't both have dreamt it, could we.'

'Er – course we could. Sisters often dream the same dream.'

Soon the 999 brigade would be arriving. I'd have to somehow cover up the noise of the sirens. Perhaps if I persuaded Hattie to sing, or burrow under the bedclothes ... (Please, God, I'll do anything in the world, become a nun even, just so long as Dan doesn't die.)

'Let's tell jokes,' I said, the words 'internal bleeding' dancing before my eyes; surely blood was *supposed* to be internal – wasn't

416

it? 'You know, to keep my mind off my nightmare.'

'I don't feel like telling jokes,' Hattie said. 'Anyway, you know all mine. They're all old hat.'

'Don't you mean old Hattie?' I said, astounded that even though inside I was a seething tin of worms, my smooth-as-a-cucumber veneer was capable of telling jokes and probably limericks too if I asked it nicely, and perhaps that's what I should be when I grew up: a con woman extraordinaire.

How I longed to cry out loud, to howl like a wolf, like Howlin' Wolf, to say I'd been lying and it was all for real and I was just pretending to be cheerful, the way Dan had pretended to be in love with Hilary Wentworth-Smith and Dawn had pretended not to be in love with Dan and Albert had pretended he just wanted to check Dawn was all right and Mummy and Daddy had pretended they still loved one another. When all the chaos died down, I'd make a pact with Hattie that we'd never fall in love. It caused far more trouble than it was worth.

'Let's sing something then.'

'It's the middle of the night! I'm not in the mood.'

'Oh, please, Hattie. I promise I'll never ask you to do anything ever again for ever more.'

'You always say that and you always do. Oh, all right.'

'Something jolly,' I said. 'How about *Summer Holiday*?'

'The words are all wrong. Our summer holiday's nearly over.'

'Don't think about the words. The way you don't when you sing a hymn.'

'Oh, all right.'

'*We're all going on a summer holiday,*' we sang in thin, reedy, mouse-squeak voices, and what a contrast to the time we sang it with such gusto in the car on our way to Granny's a hundred years – a lifetime – ago. '*No more working for a week or two ...*'

Over the hills and far away a siren gave a fleeting wail. If Hattie remarked on it I'd say there must have been a fight in the marquee between two drunk Teddy Boys. Perhaps that was the secret of lying; the more often you did it the better at it you became.

'*Fun and laughter on our summer holiday ...*'

The question that was to haunt me again and again, over and over for ever and ever, was: who was to blame for the tragedy?

Granny for giving in to us and not having the black summerhouse destroyed when she knew there was something fishy about it?

The wicked old bugger of a winter for killing off Mrs B, and for turning Granny slightly gaga? If she hadn't been maybe she wouldn't have felt the need to be reminded of her childhood and

417

thus wouldn't have employed Dawn when she was fully aware of the Hillington Tendency? (Perhaps very, very subconsciously she had *wanted* it all to end in tears of some sort, and that her employing Dawn was her final gesture to the Top Drawer in general and the Hillington family in particular, who had wanted to sweep her under the carpet and who got off scot-free in World Wars while her family were fed to cannons.)

The Government for not catching Mr Rachman earlier, for not doing more to house people properly? If Dawn had grown up in a nice home with her own room she wouldn't have felt the need to make a fresh start somewhere else.

Dawn's father? If Dawn had loved and respected her family she might not have felt the need to adopt another one.

Dawn's mother for firing Dawn's imagination with romantic stories of being swept off her feet by handsome Americans, thus implying that the only time a woman can ever know true happiness is when she's passionately in love?

The Profumo Affair and the newspapers for giving Dawn ideas above her station, for whetting her appetite for the glamorous high life?

The general mood and restlessness of the times?

National Service being abolished? If it hadn't been Dan would have spent the summer 'square-bashing' of a different kind.

The Hillington Tendency itself? If Dan hadn't allowed his heart to rule his head ...

Mummy and Daddy's marriage being on the rocks? It it hadn't been they wouldn't have had a Second Honeymoon and left us on our own in a place that was clearly unsuitable for children.

Mummy and Daddy and the public-school system and the fuddy-duddy Government and the square times we lived in generally for giving Dan something to rebel against, for making him want to play with fire and live dangerously and do things for kicks?

Drugs and rock 'n' roll?

Alcohol? If Aunt Lynette hadn't been drunk so often I might have confided in her ages ago. If Albert had been sober he wouldn't have got so jealous and behaved so badly.

But however much I tried to blame all and sundry, the finger always ended up pointing fairly and squarely back at me.

If I hadn't been such a Little Miss Prim and so disapproved of Dawn, she and Dan might not have felt the need to keep their love affair a secret.

If I hadn't written to Albert suggesting he change his aftershave, if I hadn't gone red when he asked whether Dawn had a 'fancyman', maybe he would have never suspected anything was afoot; the love affair would have ended naturally at the end of the summer and Dawn and Albert would have got married and had the baby that would have taken after Dawn.

If I hadn't dabbled in magic, perhaps the summer would have gone more or less according to plan. 'Mull', I discovered later, also meant 'mess, muddle'.

If I had accepted Aunt Daphne's offer and stayed with her, I wouldn't have been available to lead Albert up the garden path. And whatever anyone else said I knew, as sure as eggs were eggs, that on his own in his drunken state he would never have found the black summerhouse tucked quietly away in its secluded spot.

If I'd looked closer, I'd have recognised the madness reflected in Albert's pond eyes by the light of the full moon; if I'd thought I'd have realised the significance of him saying 'Well, the sun'll just have to stop shining then.'

And however many times I told sympathetic policemen and child psychiatrists and relatives and classmates that because I'd been brought up to do as I was told how could I possibly have said no to a grown man, a grown man on his knees *in tears,* what I didn't tell them was that I'd more or less decided to lead him up the garden path *before* he'd cried. Because a tiny part of me, the part that hadn't yet managed to turn into a Free Spirit, wanted to teach Dan and Dawn a lesson for telling me little white lies all summer; wanted Dan to be given a smart jolt so he'd revert to type and go to Cambridge and marry a blue stocking and have nicely brought-up well-spoken sons who would carry on the Hillington line.

But my deepest, guiltiest secret of all was that I'd led Albert up the garden path to feather my own nest. More than anything else in the world I wanted my diary to be the best in the class, for Mr Richards almost to faint with pleasure at its vivid imagery, at its drama and power and passion. And how could it possibly be dramatic and powerful and passionate if I wasn't there, in person, to witness the final showdown, the climax of the summer?

So numbed was I by the tragedy that when, three months later, President Kennedy was shot it simply confirmed what I already knew; that 1963 would go down in Hillington if not world history as the duffest year ever.

'*Everybody has a summer holiday, doing things they've always wanted to . . .*'

Our voices got warblier, and Hattie began to cry, too. But like two small sturdy fishing boats caught in the teeth of a night-time storm, we didn't give ourselves up for lost, no, siree.

Dan and Dawn were right about one thing: that this once-green and pleasant land *was* on the brink of a revolution. Not, as it turned out, a French or Russian type but a youth one. Suddenly it was good to be British. No longer were we regarded as America's shabby, fuddy-duddy elderly relation, and, while the Land of the Free became bogged down by race riots and a war in Vietnam, 'Swinging England', symbolised by the Beatles and its go-ahead prime minister Mr Harold Wilson, took on a new, dashing, fresh-as-paint lease of life. Beatlemania swept the country, then the world. Even girls at public schools went round bare-kneed with 'John, Paul, George and Ringo are fab' on their pencil boxes and 'Be ye mod or be ye rocker?' on their pale lips, and when they left school as long as they took the pill they were allowed to play hide the sausage without getting married first. Every boy worth his salt wanted to be in a pop group, and it didn't matter two hoots which drawer you came from as long as you were swinging. Like the Rolling Stones' long hair and rudeness and scruffiness and Dusty Springfield's black eye make-up, what shocked one day was par for the course the next. Dan and Dawn had simply been a year ahead of their time.

Like Albert's bootlace tie, you either liked or you lumped these brash, rash, tough, rough, bright and breezy, free and easy modern times. One thing was sure, to be sure: never again for the rest of your life would you see a kindly policeman with a blue budgerigar ladder sticking out of his back pocket, a bag of aniseed balls nestling snugly in his helmet shopping-basket.

So we're going on a summer holiday, to make our dr-eams come true-oo-oo, for-or me-ee and you.

'Please don't let's sing this beastly song,' sobbed Hattie, feeling for my hand to hold. 'Honestly, the words make me feel really depressed because they're such a lie. And talking of lies, I know it wasn't a dream you had. I'm not a complete fool. I can smell sort of cinders on your hair, and I heard the siren. I think we should go and see what's happening.'

'I think we're best off here,' I said firmly.

Her hand felt small and warm and comforting, the way it had when I'd used it as a brake in the car, the way it always did.

Like with Dan, whatever happened I mustn't show her I was afraid. 'Everything always seems much worse at night. Come morning what's the betting it'll all be back to normal.'

'God, I hope so,' said Hattie. 'And if we've got to sing something let's sing *Champion*. Bugger bloody Uncle Mac. If he can't play it for us we can play it for ourselves. Come on.'

It was the last thing I felt like singing. It reminded me of Dan and his blood and his one tear, but if it kept Hattie happy ... My voice croaked like a heartbroken frog.

'*Champion, no wonder horse! Champion, no wonder horse ...*'

Hattie was the only one to remain relatively unscarred by the tragedy. She hung her unfinished portrait of Dan over her bed with *Of Boyhood Changing into Man: the Unfinished Man and his Pain* (*Yeats*) written beneath it; apart from that she showed few other symptoms.

Granny died soon after from a broken heart like her mother, or maybe she never fully recovered from the old bugger of a winter; Daddy, Aunt Daphne and Aunt Lynette sold the Gressenham Estate to the Englishes/Barclays Bank who, according to Jack in a letter, *has stuffed the woods fair full to bursting with the vulgar, foreign-looking things. (You can't see the wood for the pheasants!) They peck at everything in sight, including my bedding-out plants and cabbages and sprouts ... During the shooting season, the place was taken over by businessmen from Essex and Antwerp and Birmingham. There's talk of building a heated swimming pool where your Granny's roses used to be, and turning the stables into 'holiday flatlets'. I sit here beside my nice warm fire of an evening thinking about the good old days ...*

Brian Pike moved into the farmhouse and 'lived in sin' with Hilda.

Daddy succumbed to the Hillington Tendency good and proper – not half-heartedly like he had by marrying Mummy – and moved into a flat in St John's Wood with his kiss-curled secretary Sally Anne. She too wore short skirts and black eye-stuff and called us kids but you never grew not to mind the way you had with Dawn.

Hattie and Mummy and I moved into quite a nice tall narrow terraced house that was built for artisans, whoever they were when they were at home, in St Alban's. It was the sort of house you would have felt embarrassed taking schoolfriends if your father was living there, but because it was just Mummy it didn't matter so much; women were expected to be poorer. It had a long skinny back garden that had no private places and wasn't big enough to set up a show ring and pretend you were in the Horse of the Year Show, though it didn't matter too much; my horsy phase had drawn to a close. In bed at night you could sometimes hear the neighbours play hide the sausage, but you just put your head under the covers and concentrated on England. Mummy, of all people, became a Women's Libber, though I never saw her burn her bra.

Aunt Lynette moved to a flat in Chelsea with a studio that faced north so the light was nearly as good as in Norfolk. She became quite a famous artist and later became active in a women's peace movement and appeared on *News at Ten*.

Lawrence the cat died of fox poison and so, with no men in their lives, the great aunts moved to a Retired Home for Gentlefolk on a breezy Sheringham clifftop. They strode daily round the golf links, clubs akimbo, and took up bridge at their ages. There were gentlemen as well as gentlewomen at the home and the great aunts seemed happier than they'd ever been. If was as if the tragedy had acted as a release, and now at least they could stop worrying about the Hillington Line and start enjoying themselves.

The tragedy was too tragic for the newspapers to have words like 'offal' and 'veal meat again' in their headlines; the tabloids said '*Butchered*!', the quality ones '*Tragedy on Norfolk estate*'.

Dawn lost her baby and suffered internal problems which meant she'd never be able to have another. She moved to London and got a job in a boutique in the King's Road selling clothes designed by Mary Quant. *I will never love anyone the way I loved your brother, Sarah, she wrote. You'll be pleased to hear I've got round to reading Wuthering Heights and I see exactly what you mean about us being like Cathy and Heathcliff. Except Cathy was sensible and married Edgar and didn't give in to temptation like what I did. Your brother was a really fab bloke, a one-off, but I don't need to tell you that. He's worth a million of these gits what strut down King's Road thinking they are Gods gift. Until I get over that summer – if I ever get over it – I don't want to see you. No offence, you would bring back too many memories, as I would for you. As soon as I clap eyes on you I would go into histerics. You're dead similar to him in so many ways. Maybe its the eyes. Honest, I only need to hear the first cord of Johnny B. Good or something and I'm in floods. One day, kid, I hope we will be the best of friends. You never know, we might even make it to the Land of the Free with a Tip the Lady out of Bed doodah one day! (I never did thank you for what you did with that; you were right about it being my forte, yeah? And I was right about us making a great double act!)*

Meanwhile, you know what they say about time being the greatest healer. So keep your pecker up, or keep cool as they say these days, and let's try and wash that flaming summer right out of our hair. It was the summer for going mad, as Dan was often saying. And for christs sake don't blame yourself for what happened. Just now and again, I have to admit, I think silly cow, she should have sussed Albert was off his bonce, but you're only a kid, how were you to know? I should never have got you involved in the first place. She signed it *Your loving friend.*

Albert spent the night in a police cell. In the cold light of day and cold sober, he was so full of remorse that he used his 'one gesture to this rock 'n' roll lark' to hang himself.

Dan broke his promise and died on the way to hospital.

According to Hilda it was ever so peaceful and he was even smiling slightly. He hadn't said anything, which meant that his last words on this earth were 'I love you, Sausage'.

I didn't dash my head against a knotted trunk; nor did I slit my throat; his death, like Cathy's for Heathcliff, was unutterably too much for flesh and blood to bear, and I went into a sort of numb, neither happy or unhappy trance.

Granny and Dan made the Hillington graveyard complete. It rested in peace under the speckledy yew trees.

Mummy started visiting a spiritualist and swore Dan spoke to her. She wouldn't let me go because I was too young, but what did I need a spiritualist for? As Heathcliff said about Cathy, the murdered *do* haunt their murderers. Dan often speaks to me, and so long as my imagination is firing on all cylinders, I can see and smell and feel him, too.

A pop singer called Sandie Shaw sang a song called *There's Always Something There to Remind Me*, and I knew just how she felt; a cricket bat, fishing tackle, a guitar, a Woodbine cigarette, a boy with his sleeves rolled up or in drainpipe trousers or untidy hair, a certain smile or slouch or shrug or look or laugh or expression or toss of the head ... Mick Jagger. Most of all Mick Jagger. The first time I saw the him being sullen and sexy and defiant on *Ready Steady Go,* scalding hot tears kept coming and coming. For it was like he *was* Pete O'Flame. (The Wild Ones came to nothing, of course; what good were wild ponies without their leader, their Champion?)

Mr Richards never did read my diary. The foxy-whiskered child psychologist tried to track him down because he was the only person in the world I would talk to, but he had vanished. According to Miss Sargent he had decided his vocation didn't lie in teaching, but no one believed her. Sheila Page reckoned he'd joined the Foreign Legion; eloping to Gretna Green with a beautiful girl from Thailand was mentioned, and going to America to raise funds for the IRA. His place was taken by an old frump of a woman called Mrs Cave, whose mind was as square as her jaw.

No one blamed me for the tragedy because I was 'only a child'. So I went back to behaving like one. I sulked and stamped and one day said 'bollocks' to the Cavewoman. She didn't give me a detention because she'd been told to be kind to me, so I told her to bugger off and she had to then. The class saw me in a new light. Veronica and I now had nothing in common, and Sheila Page became my best friend. While the others discussed their ponies and the Beatles, Sheila and I plotted to run away to London and change the world.

The Cavewoman showed no interest in our diaries, and even if she had I would never have shown her mine in a million years. It was for Mr Richards' eyes only. One day I'd find him, I knew it; I could feel it in my bones.

I wrote my final entry several months after the event, with red biro so it would stand out: *Well, my pradiction was right: it has all ended in tears. A tragedy has occured to end all tragedys: I have sent the last of the Hillington Line, the Champion of horses and the finest rocking role singer the world would ever have known if he had sirvived, to his death. There is only one crumb of comfort to be had from this: he will have met Presadent Kennedy in heaven. I bet they are getting along famosly.*

My Free Spirit has taken a very severe bashing. I will need to muster every ounce of my strength to sirvive this ordeal. But human nature being what it is, I'm sure I shall manage somehow.

'Like a mighty cannon ball he seems to fly ...'

It wasn't easy to put your heart and soul into galloping like the wind on Champion's sleek, powerful back with a distant blue light flashing through the orange and lemon curtains.

Hattie and I burrowed under the covers with Teddy and One-Eyed Lamb and entered our safe, black, warm, secret child's world. Our small muffled voices marched bravely onward like Christian soldiers: *'You'll hear about him everywhere you go the name of Champion, No Wonder Horse. Champion, No Wonder Horse ...'*

THE END